Test System Design
A Systematic Approach

Christine Tursky
Rodney Gordon
Scott Cowie

Prentice Hall PTR
Upper Saddle River, NJ 07458
www.phptr.com

ISBN 0-13-027260-4

90000

9 780130 272607

Library of Congress Cataloging-in-Publication Data

Tursky, Christine.
    Test system design : a systematic approach / by Christine Tursky, Rodney Gordon, and
Scott Cowie.
        p. cm.
    ISBN 0-13-027260-4
        1. Testing-machines--Design and construction. 2. Electronic apparatus and
appliances--Testing--Equipment and supplies. I. Gordon, Rodney. II. Cowie, Scott. III.
Title.

TA413 .T87 2000
658.5'77--dc21

00-061162

Editorial/production supervision: *Laura E. Burgess*
Acquisitions editor: *Jill Pisoni*
Marketing manager: *Julie Tiso*
Manufacturing manager: *Maura Zaldivar*
Editorial assistant: *Justin Somma*
Cover design director: *Jerry Votta*
Cover designer: *Talar Agasyan*
Interior illustrator: *Manfred Tursky*

© 2001 by Prentice Hall PTR
Prentice-Hall, Inc.
Upper Saddle River, NJ 07458

Prentice Hall books are widely used by corporations and government agencies
for training, marketing, and resale.

The publisher offers discounts on this book when ordered in bulk quantities.
For more information, contact: Corporate Sales Department, Phone: 800-382-3419;
Fax: 201-236-7141; E-mail: corpsales@prenhall.com; or write: Prentice Hall PTR,
Corp. Sales Dept., One Lake Street, Upper Saddle River, NJ 07458.

All products or services mentioned in this book are the trademarks or service marks of their
respective companies or organizations.

Printed in the United States of America
10 9 8 7 6 5 4 3 2 1

ISBN   0-13-027260-4

Prentice-Hall International (UK) Limited, *London*
Prentice-Hall of Australia Pty. Limited, *Sydney*
Prentice-Hall Canada Inc., *Toronto*
Prentice-Hall Hispanoamericana, S.A., *Mexico*
Prentice-Hall of India Private Limited, *New Delhi*
Prentice-Hall of Japan, Inc., *Tokyo*
Pearson Education Asia Pte. Ltd.
Editora Prentice-Hall do Brasil, Ltda., *Rio de Janeiro*

For Peter and Mitchell

Contents

Chapter 2   **Using COTS and Open Standards to Maximize Flexibility and Control Costs**   27

Chapter 3   **How Control Decisions Affect Hardware Architecture**   39

Part Three   **Racking Up**   **221**

Chapter 13 **Racking the System**   **223**

Chapter 14 **Documentation**   **247**

Preface

Test system design is a fascinating field. Leading or being involved with a test system design project is a start-to-finish process, going from design to integration and then deployment. It allows engineers and technical professionals to combine the technical and creative aspects of their profession in building tools of precision and power.

The aim of this book is to help engineers involved in designing and building custom test systems avoid common pitfalls as well as making the design and build processes easier. This book will help you improve your return on investment by helping you design and build a more efficient system up front, and also increase the useful lifespan of your system through planned, effective upgrades. We have gone through the whole test system lifecycle, from initial planning decisions to lifetime costs and future system upgrades.

You can also us, this book to manage your supplier more smoothly if you decide to contract out design and/or construction of your test system, or of any work packages from the test system project. Use the issues in each chapter as a guide to discuss how your contractor will manage these points, as you will still need to be able to check your contractor's approach to your satisfaction.

We have written this book for: manufacturing test engineers, especially in electronics manufacturing, who are implementing flexible, upgradable systems in order to improve results and lower costs as product margins continue to be squeezed; defense engineers, who are implementing more commercial off the shelf (COTS) systems as standardization and efficiency drives make this a more attractive option than full in-house development; R&D engineers, who need easily reconfigurable systems to meet their changing test requirements for each new project, and who also want to cut development costs; and anyone who wants to commission a third party to build a custom system, and needs to understand the issues involved.

Part 1, *Planning and Initial Design*, discusses ways of getting the most from your investment of time and money in the test system. It looks at ways of minimizing risks and costs though design techniques, choice of architecture, and the use of third party contractors.

Part 2, *Test System Design—Building a Completely New System*, looks at choosing and sourcing test equipment (including how to eliminate redundant equipment and tests). It also discusses aspects of system design such as interfacing to the device under test (DUT), cabling the rack, using switch panels and interface panels, and the electrical safety of the system. It also covers the design and implementation aspects of racking up the system, such as selecting racks and racking furniture, placement of equipment so that the system remains stable and is not awkward to use, and controlling temperature and power requirements.

Part 3, *Racking Up*, covers the physical racking process, documentation, training, and support.

Part 4, *Upgrading a Test System*, looks at getting more use out of an older test system. It covers dealing with obsolete items, ways in which you can protect against obsolescence, and the upgrade process itself.

Acknowledgments

There are a number of people who have contributed in the past two decades to making this book possible, whether through technical training, support and guidance during difficult system projects, or through demonstrating their confidence in the authors' work. To all these people who have supported us over the years, we say thank you!

Special thanks go to our families—without whom no writers could survive. We would also like to thank: Neil McCoy for his expert review of the book material; our patient and encouraging editor Jill Pisoni; the wonderful staff at Prentice Hall including Justin Somma and Laura Burgess; Manfred Tursky for his tireless work on the illustrations; Clare Rhoden and Marie Hansen for inspiration; Rod Just for his commitment to some particularly significant engineering projects; Roger Oblad and Grant Kreig for expert advice on software standards; Graedon Frazer for his tips on determining requirements; Sonya Oswald for working so many late nights; and all our colleagues at Hewlett Packard, Agilent Technologies, and SouthTech Systems for their ongoing support and encouragement.

Rodney Gordon and Scott Cowie also wish to note their great appreciation to Christine Tursky for establishing the project and keeping it in focus through a maelstrom of other distractions.

PLANNING AND INITIAL DESIGN

The one step that will make the greatest difference in the success of your test system design and build is the planning you carry out at the very start of the project. You need to consider not only the build, but also upgrades and supportability over at least three to five years. Your anticipation of possible future requirements for the system will help you plan features that will minimize the overall future cost of ownership, which is as important a part of the system costs as the initial cost of the equipment and components themselves.

Initial Planning

This first chapter explores the decisions that the test system designer needs to make at the start of the development process to avoid some of the pitfalls that the authors have seen or experienced first-hand. We discuss the system development process, the benefits of the initial planning we suggest you go through, considerations for many generic issues (many questions will be specific to your particular test situation and test environment), and some examples of what these decisions imply.

The aim of these initial decisions is to make a good investment in your system and to complete the system development process successfully. Your investment costs include not only money but also your time and other overhead such as staff time, assembly space, and support services. It is possible to minimize many costs and avoid possible pitfalls by making careful decisions about architecture and standards at the beginning of a project.

Test system design deals with economic, physical, environmental, ergonomic, organizational, and many other issues, as well as the technical design itself. A good system design will:

- Incorporate smoothly into your existing processes.
- Have a well-designed user-system interface.
- Have the right degree of automation for the task and your environment.
- Increase process quality.
- Add value to your organization.

Good system and test process design will also prevent rather than correct errors, which can be irritating, costly, or disastrous, depending on their degree and consequences. An exceptional design may also offer you or your organization opportunities to benefit from the intellectual property (IP) you have created in the system design, by selling copies of the system to other companies in similar industries or situations. Whether your test system is for in-house use only (such as a manufacturing test system for a cellular phone production line) or to be supplied to a number of customers (for example, a repair test system for cellular phones to be used in a number of service centers), a well-designed solution will add value to your processes and provide a good return on the resources invested in its development.

KEY POINTS:

- To start planning your test system, you need to know what constraints you face in five areas: time, technical specification, budget, the complexity of the device under test (DUT), and the population of components on the DUT.
- Three factors define the constraints you face in your test system project: time, technical specification, and budget. The factor that is most important to you will drive the other two; for example, if technical performance is the most important part of your project specification, then you will be willing to spend more money and take more time on the project to make sure that you achieve the best performance.
- Two factors drive the complexity of your tests and the number of tests: the complexity of the DUT and the population of components on the DUT.

1.1 Getting the Most from Your Investment

Test systems provide a way to analyze performance in a repeatable, credible, auditable, and reliable way. This may be in the form of a product prototyping process, a manufacturing test as part of a production line, confirmation that a repair has been carried out successfully, or an operations test to check that another system is working to specifications. Many people treat testing as a relatively simple part of an overall design or manufacturing process. However, the questions of what the system is being measured against and how the tests should be carried out are often complex, and can have a great impact on the effectiveness and the return on investment (ROI) of the test system.

Test instrumentation is only one component of the whole test system, but it forms the heart of your measurement solution. Test equipment needs to be selected in the context of other system factors such as the lifetime costs of running the test system, the software control you plan to use in a semi- or fully-automated test system, and what the test results will be used for. Accuracy is key. At a fundamental level, the test instrument compares a quantity against an internationally agreed-upon standard. Simply taking delivery of test equipment is not enough to assure ongoing accuracy of your measurement results. Even though test equipment is built to meet its published specifications, it must still be calibrated to ensure continued traceability to primary standards. Traceability is the ability to demonstrate that you can relate the measurements you take on your equipment to recognized international standards through an unbroken chain of comparisons. If this is not done, your test results are unreliable, and uncalibrated equipment will have a real impact on your quality programs. In particular, if you have a systematic error in your equipment, the only way to overcome this is by documented traceability to primary standards.

The test system as a whole includes everything from the cables to the operating software. The success of a test system is based not only on whether it performs technically, but also on whether it adds value to the overall product or processes with which it is involved. A test system on a manufacturing line, for example, will not give you an overall benefit if the test costs more to run than the manufactured product is worth.

Using a process and avoiding common pitfalls can help you end up with a system that is both suitable to the task and meets your overall goals.

1.1.1 An Overview of the System Design Process

Whether you follow the process described here or use a different one that suits your work style better, planning your approach to the system design process and the major decisions you will have to make will save you time, money, and effort. Our aim in describing the design process is for readers to have a good picture of this process and the major decisions ahead before starting a system design.

Your aim is to get through the test system design process with as few errors or as little rework as possible, and to have a system that performs tests to your required specifications in an efficient and effective manner. As with any project, the three factors that will drive your test system design process are time, specification, and budget. You will have to make trade-offs between these three factors, which will depend on how strongly each of them will affect your final result.

If you have limited time, you may need to spend more money on contractors or other resources to complete the project to schedule. If the success of your system rests on it meeting challenging technical specifications, you will also see value in purchasing the best test equipment for your specification. If the cost of the system is a more important driver than the time it takes to design, then you may have to complete most of the work yourself or with a small technical team, meaning that the project will take longer.

Understanding the major factors which will influence your choices, and where they fit into the system design process as a whole, will mean that you will be less likely to miss any key decision points or any of the major problems that can affect a system design. The likelihood of successfully completing a test system project to specifications and within time and cost constraints is increased by following a planned approach.

Figure 1.1 shows the main stages of the test system development process.

The process diagram shows the main stages you will go through in designing and implementing a test system, including where these stages are likely to overlap. For example, you will most likely scan the test equipment industry to update your evaluation of suppliers and available test equipment at the same time as you choose your list of possible test equipment for your system. You will save time and money if you have made at least some initial decisions before you start the test system design process on issues such as test methodology, project plan, hardware specification, software specification, interfacing (for example, mass interconnect to fixture to the

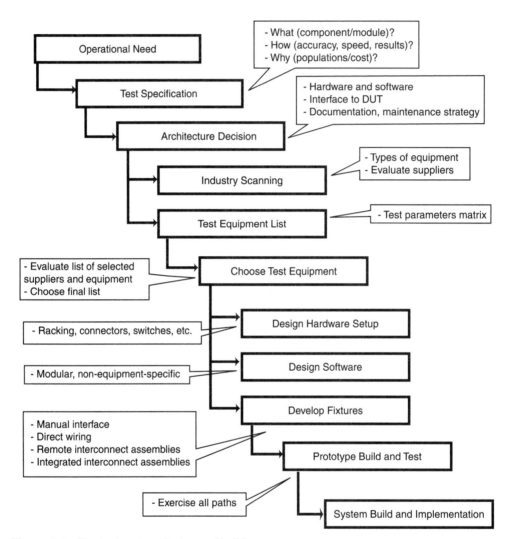

Figure 1.1   The test system design and build process.

DUT or harness to the DUT), the generic test solution, prototyping, vendor assessment, change management, obsolescence protection, etc. The degree of overlap between tasks, the order in which you execute these tasks, and the number of iterations you go through to tune your solution to its best effect will vary. The complexity of your test system design and build process will be dictated by the complexity of your application and system specifications. For example, a solution with a number of components such as test equipment, switch matrices, and so on will be more difficult to integrate than a simpler solution. Combining a number of different architectures will also take more work than a single-architecture solution, especially if a proprietary architecture is one of those used. By planning through some of the key issues before you start investing in system development, you can avoid backtracking through many of the major hurdles that the authors have encountered in the test system industry in the past two decades.

Using a structured process such as the one above also makes it easier to develop a work breakdown structure. Having a series of defined tasks within the overall project makes it easier to assign work within a team, or to contract out particular tasks to a third party. It will also help you estimate costs, resources, and time required for each stage, and highlight any problems under your goals. Monitoring progress against your project's cost and time constraints during the project lifecycle will give you early warning if you need to negotiate additional resources or time.

Having formal project management skills or experience within your team is a great advantage. It is rare for test system development projects to be completed smoothly, and even a project management handbook or Internet training course will provide you with tools, terminology, and skills which will increase your control over the project process. It will also help avoid problems by drawing attention to potential variances in your project plan as early as possible, allowing you to address them in a timely fashion.

Many test system issues will be specific to your application; for example, technology constraints. An overview of the more commonly faced generic issues is given below. Most of these issues are also discussed in greater detail later in this book.

1.1.2 Minimizing Risks and Costs through Good Design Techniques and/or Management of Third Parties

Allowing time at the start of your project for overall strategy and planning is a crucial step. The three major factors that drive any test system project are cost, time, and technical specification, and these may even change during the design or lifetime of the project. Today's test equipment makes it easy to jump in and start connecting equipment together – and for a simple system, this may work – however, your strategy should be to minimize risks and costs by doing some planning at the start of the project. By avoiding major pitfalls, you will save time and money, and you will achieve your required specifications with a minimum of rework. By setting your overall system strategy at the start of the project, you will also be able to plan for future upgrades, avoid obsolescence problems, and lower your overall cost of ownership of the system.

The three main areas which should be considered at the start of a test system project and which can create problems are:

- Technical and system aspects.
- Information and planning aspects.
- Organizational and project aspects.

The main factors to consider are discussed below (some are also covered in more detail in later chapters).

Technical and System Aspects

Test specification and accuracy.   Accuracy (in conjunction with the degree of complexity of your test requirements) will always be a cost driver for any test system. Greater accuracy involves dealing with or overcoming technical limitations of some sort; for example, the design of the test equipment, the test setup and methodology, or basic measurement physics. Deciding what you really need to test and to what degree can have great impact on the success of your system design. Deciding what you need to test sounds obvious; however, deciding on the right balance between "just enough test" and "complete surety" is an important step. Too much testing or too much accuracy will increase both your system costs and your time-to-test (which itself will increase your usage costs). The main issues are:

1. What measurements are needed?
2. What level of accuracy is needed?

Accuracy is a measure of how closely the measurement made will agree with primary standards. Calibration procedures and the capability of the equipment used are both key factors influencing this. Resolution is a measure of how small a change in signal can be observed.

You will generally know what tests are required from the system, either from the manufacturer's product specifications that need to be confirmed or from a test specification that you have received. You may even receive a test equipment list or the design of a generic test system as part of the package from the DUT manufacturer. For example, with a few pieces of test hardware, a user can measure many of the specified quantities of a RADAR. However, each RADAR manufacturer has built their product slightly differently, even though the block diagram is essentially the same.

Designing a generic test system requires technical expertise, as it has to apply to a range of slightly different situations. As you learn the nuances of the product or system you are testing, you will be able to add or expand certain tests to gather further information relevant to your specific application. For example, some manufacturers of communication receivers will only test the gain of amplifier filters at certain point frequencies. With modern test equipment, the full bandwidth of the filter/amplifier can be swept, which would provide accurate information on the shape of the filter's frequency response across its full range rather than results obtained from discrete frequencies. This provides a better manufacturing test for the producer, or more thorough acceptance testing for the purchaser.

You may not always have an explicit technical specification for your test system. In many cases, you may simply have an operational need which you must solve, and you will need to translate this into technical specifications that can be used to design a test system (see Figure 1.2).

One approach is to define the results required (for example, assurance that an amplifier has been manufactured to specification), and then define the parameters required to obtain these results. The test parameters matrix described in Chapter 4 uses the list of parameters to be tested

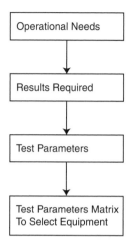

Figure 1.2 Translating operational need into technical specifications.

to build up a minimum list of test equipment required. This process involves some iteration to check for redundant tests and combine specifications where possible.

In an environment such as a multi-stage manufacturing process, for example PCB assembly (with a possible manufacturing process test stage) followed by product assembly and final test, you will also need to decide which tests to carry out at what stage of the process. Tests that can be *cost-effectively* moved to a functional test stage rather than the final assembly stage will lower scrap and rework costs and shorten final test time, as some faults will be identified earlier in the manufacturing process. They will also help increase the first-pass yield at the final test stage.

Test system specifications can frequently fall short with regard to accuracy requirements. Test results are never absolute. It is easy to read off a figure from an instrument, but it is also too easy to treat this as a completely accurate result. Relating this to a real-world result requires an understanding of the limitations of the system and the uncertainties that occur with any measurement, even the most precise. An application that does not require "leading edge" accuracy can be implemented at a lower cost than a much more complex system which pushes the limits of current measurement technology. Accuracy does cost money – it is the greatest contributor to the cost of high-end test equipment, where the last 10% of measuring accuracy can cost as much to design and manufacture as the first 90%. The question of how much accuracy at what cost is usually a major trade-off a system designer needs to make (see Figure 1.3).

Today there are many manufacturers of test equipment, and the authors believe that if an instrument exists that measures the quantity required, there would need to be compelling reasons not to purchase commercially available test equipment. Some people view the cost of test equipment as expensive, and suggest that it would be cheaper to build test equipment in-house. However, the costs involved in designing your own test equipment (as opposed to the test system)

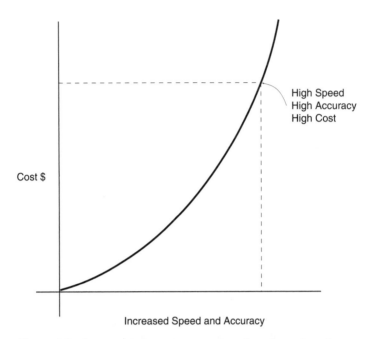

High Speed
High Accuracy
High Cost

Cost $

Increased Speed and Accuracy

Figure 1.3   Increased accuracy, speed, and equipment cost.

include staff and real-estate overhead, opportunity costs for the extra time spent, as well as the development costs of the test equipment itself. This is not a trivial or inexpensive task once the real cost to the organization is taken into account. Measurement equipment is a commercial reality and is available in a market-driven environment. Chapter 2 includes a further discussion on how market drivers affect factors such as the cost, availability, and post-sales support of commercially available equipment to the benefit of buyers. If you have underutilized resources in your organization, you may possibly find that developing a piece of test equipment is cost-effective; however, the experience of the authors is that this is rare. Applying your resources to an area within your organization's core business will provide a better return.

TIP:

Always heed a manufacturer's test literature, which will describe in detail the procedures necessary to repair/calibrate their equipment. Calibration and maintenance costs should be included in the life-time cost of your system and thus will affect its ROI.

Another important question concerning the overall specifications is how the results are to be treated. How long will you need to keep the results of tests? Some defense or government contracts can require storage of test results for up to 30 years. This impacts the cost of ownership of the system, as plans will need to be in place to store data in a usable fashion (paper copies rarely give much flexibility or easy access to large amounts of data for analysis). It will most likely also be necessary to update storage media as technology changes and to transfer existing stored data to more modern media; otherwise, you may need to maintain data storage beyond the manufacturer's supported lifetime for the existing storage media.

The use that test data will be put to also influences what information you need to store. It is possible to be left with junk data because something as simple as the timestamp was not stored as part of the results! Results are discussed in more detail in Section 1.1.3.

TIP:

When designing measurements, avoid using unusual or very specific measurements made by a box from a single manufacturer. If you ever have to upgrade the system and that measurement is not available in the same form, you may have to rewrite code or implement an alternative solution – both of which are expensive. Work out what you have to measure, then match it to a measurement technique before you select test equipment.

Level of test. The level of test you require is a consideration in drawing up your technical specifications. The results you require may involve component-level or module-level testing. The requirement to test to component level rather than to module level on the DUT may require more signals to be applied simultaneously and may require more analysis. The cost and complexity of both software and hardware increases with component-level testing.

Architecture. Architecture decisions also affect cost, integration time, and accuracy. You may choose an open standard architecture such as VXI, "rack & stack" instruments and a particular communication bus such as IEEE 488, or a combination of equipment and communication methods. You will have better long-term flexibility in selecting and updating equipment if you try to use open standards where possible. Try to avoid using proprietary standards unless there are considerable advantages in a particular proprietary solution. Open standards also give a much greater chance of success when integrating equipment from multiple vendors. Proprietary systems tend to tie you to a single vendor, which limits your choice and flexibility considerably. You may have a specific technical requirement that cannot be met by commercial, off-the-shelf (COTS) equipment, which means that you may have to design your own solution or contract out this task. You can develop your own devices, such as fixtures, based on particular needs. COTS and open standards are discussed further in Chapter 2, as they are important considerations in designing test systems. Steps to deciding on architecture are discussed later in this chapter.

In overall terms, make your design and major system decisions, then stick to them. If you need to make changes to the system, redo the design rather than trying to implement patchwork fixes – it is very difficult to plan for the implications of impromptu changes. Once the system is built in line with your overall design strategy, you have a solid working foundation to start from if a change or upgrade is needed.

Control. Test systems can be designed for manual, semi-automated, or fully-automated control. Manual systems cost less to implement, but cannot provide the throughput or repeatability of an automated system. Less automation also means that operators must be more skilled to run and troubleshoot the system appropriately. Your system environment and application will influence the degree of automation required; for example, a high-volume components manufacturer will require automated systems to increase throughput. Chapter 3, "How Control Decisions Affect Hardware Architecture," deals with this topic in more detail.

Interfacing to the DUT. The interface to the DUT will affect both cost and technical specifications. The interface to the DUT that you design may be less demanding than a contract customer's DUT if you are developing a test system for someone else. It is a valuable exercise to check against standards requirements to see what you need to cover over and above your own tests to ensure compliance. Whether you intend to interface using cable harnesses directly to the test equipment, to connect to a patch panel, or to use a fully automated, switch-controlled interface which would guarantee compliance, the interface method is an important design decision you need to make early in the design process. Interfacing to the DUT is discussed in detail in Chapter 6.

Documentation and training. Training, standard operating procedures (SOPs), work practices to enhance repeatability of testing, and thorough documentation are especially important. The documentation will include information such as the setup procedures, calibration procedures, the test methodology, any upgrades to procedures, routine tests to verify system operation before use, and any pre-measurement techniques (such as connector inspections). Generally, the higher in frequency you need to measure, the more precautions are required, both for correct measurement technique and for test safety. This will apply to any high-power tests or measurements that have the potential to cause injury or death to individuals.

Training operators also helps ensure that errors are reduced during the system's operation (the classes of errors that occur and their causes will be discussed in Chapter 15). When considering this aspect of your system, particular thought must be given to the level of competence of your staff. Trained technicians, general technical officers, production staff, non-technical operators, and research engineers will all have different levels and areas of knowledge and may make different assumptions about test procedures. Even highly technical people can be inexperienced in measurement theory and practices, and well-designed documentation and training will take this into account. Documentation is covered in more detail in Chapter 14. Operator training is covered in more detail in Chapter 15.

Safety. Safety deals with how to build an electrically and mechanically safe test system. Safety is a crucial issue for any engineer and is a key responsibility for anyone involved in system design. This topic is covered in more detail in Chapter 9, and it should always be carefully considered under any circumstances, with reference to appropriate safety training and other safety information. This book does not deal exhaustively with safety information and procedures. Any engineer or technician is responsible for the safety of their work, and should make use of other appropriate resources to make sure that system and user safety are integrated into the total project task.

Reliability.   The reliability of a test system depends on careful selection of components and equipment, as well as good design techniques. Selecting suppliers with a reputation for quality and with a worldwide support and maintenance network will help you achieve a high level of reliability for your system. One technique used by manufacturers, which also applies to system design, is to de-rate components of a system or a product. A plus or minus 1% resistor, for example, is used instead of a plus or minus 10% resistor, increasing the accuracy and measurement reliability of the product. It is also important to consider the degree of use of the system in your calibration and maintenance plans. Frequent or incorrect use can increase connector wear on cables, for example, requiring more frequent replacement of connectors. Although you will not need to purchase top-of-the-line equipment for a basic benchtop application, investing in appropriate quality and ruggedness (where required) will give you benefits in the future. In particular, accessories such as cables and connectors should always be the best you can afford.

Information and Planning Aspects

Planning for future performance.   Future performance and the lifetime of your system can be affected by your initial design decisions. It is becoming more common to evaluate a test system in both technical and economic terms. For your test system to make an overall contribution economically as well as technically, you can consider the possible ROI of your system over its planned lifetime. This is affected not only by the system's initial cost – in both equipment and development costs – but also the system's effectiveness and efficiency over time. If you can re-use the system or parts of the system for a later project, or if you can upgrade it later on to work more effectively or complete tests more quickly (if your application is in a high-throughput environment), then you can get a better ROI from your test system. A chip production facility testing three million parts per week, for example, will see a better bottom line even by shaving a few milliseconds off the time for a single test. Depending on the cost structure of your organization, different features will provide different benefits. Increased speed will be a benefit in a high-volume manufacturing or repair environment; but in a research lab, having the flexibility to vary your tests for different prototypes or the ability to get more accurate results may be more important and thus "worth" more. This will influence whether you get more benefit from and are thus willing to spend more on expandability (for example, when shopping for switch matrixes) or accuracy and future enhancements (for example, when evaluating vendors).

Getting the best information.   One of the aspects of an engineer's, technician's, or operator's skill is in sorting out the best information from the wide range available. Every engineering situation is different, and every test system solution will be different. Vendors, technical organizations, and professional networks are all excellent sources of information, especially when combined with an individual's professional experience. Chapter 5, "Sourcing Test Equipment," discusses equipment vendors and their role in providing test expertise. Section 1.4 of this chapter also discusses teams and other organizations as sources of expertise and value.

Management of third parties.   Making the most of your relationships with vendors or using contractors at particular stages of your project can sometimes simplify your overall design and implementation process. In some circumstances, vendors will be able to add value to your project by saving you time, money, or improving your performance to specifications. A vendor or third party can save you time, for example, by completing a particular task under contract more quickly than you could with in-house resources. They can save you money by managing their delivery times so that your project is up and running (and contributing to the bottom line) faster, or by lowering the cost of test by recommending improvements in test procedure. They can contribute to technical performance through advice on appropriate test equipment, cables, and so on or by consulting on the test specifications or test methodology itself.

Dealing with a smaller number of reliable vendors can give you better access to vendor advice and support than if you buy small amounts from a large number of vendors. You may see some initial cost savings by chasing the best prices for individual components, but building a relationship with a reliable vendor will pay dividends in terms of that vendor's involvement (if necessary) in your project and with ongoing support. Vendors understand their equipment and how it works, and it is much more straightforward to get product support when integrating equipment that is mostly from one company. If you purchase equipment from ten different vendors and have problems getting the system to work, it is too easy for one vendor to blame other vendors' equipment. When dealing with project costs, buying more of your equipment from one vendor can also put you in a stronger position to negotiate pricing, delivery, or payment terms as opposed to many quotes for individual pieces of equipment.

In addition to the cost of equipment, the reputation and resources of the vendor are also important. A higher cost may reflect on the quality of the support you receive. Part of the equipment cost may go toward maintaining a local repair and calibration center. Having to send mission-critical equipment overseas to be repaired or calibrated may mean that you need to have multiple spares on-hand – increasing your system support costs even though a single piece of equipment costs less than the alternative. You may also want to check the detail of the technical specifications available. One example is the MTBF (mean time between failures) information available and whether it is based on actual customer data – rather than projected MTBF figures based on data for individual components used in manufacturing the equipment. Having technical user support available in your own time zone may be important to help staff solve user problems quickly. The ability to trade in equipment when you upgrade the system may impact your projected cost of ownership for the system.

When you decide on a manufacturer, take the time to have a vendor representative visit you. Discussing your needs with a supplier representative will allow you to do two things. It will allow you to gauge the representative's test expertise and what level of expertise is available to you from that company. Not every company representative can be an expert in all areas, so the range of expertise in that company and your ability to gain access to it is important. Test equipment supplier representatives should be able to source the right information for you as well as have a good level of technical knowledge themselves. At the same time, the representative may be able to add value early in the design process by discussing alternatives with you, perhaps with an appropriate discussion of how other companies have succeeded in this test (although confidential information about another customer should *never* be shared by a vendor). The representative may even be able to help you future-proof your system by:

- Suggesting different options for equipment that will make it suitable for other test applications, or even new equipment that will be released soon (you may have to sign a non-disclosure agreement to receive information about future product releases).
- Suggesting higher performance equipment that will future-proof your system by planning for improvements in product performance for relatively low incremental cost.
- Recommending a flexible architecture based on your application requirements and the most suitable test equipment and software.

The objective in considering planned applications is to make the system as future-proof as possible without exceeding your budget.

Organizational and Project Aspects

Staff skills. It is a good idea to go through a resource planning step early in the project. This is an opportunity to identify staff competencies you will need for the design, procurement, and build teams, as appropriate. For a large project, there may be some staff overlap between teams. For a smaller project, you might only be working with a few other people. This chapter discusses in more detail the in-house resources and competencies required for a test system design project.

Project costs. The cost of hardware will include the instruments, racks, cables, connectors, numbered cable ties, and so on. However, there are a number of other costs which should be taken into account. Even if your organization does not assign overhead costs to particular projects, it is a crucial point to be aware of the real costs involved with a test system project. In-house resources and services are not "free"; they still cost the organization money – not only the costs of the resources and services themselves, but also the opportunity cost of not having them available for other projects that may have brought a greater return.

Major contributors to test system project costs are:

- Staff time. Methods for calculating loaded staff costs (or total cost of employment) can vary from company to company, but generally include allowances for annual leave, health insurance if provided, accrual of retirement benefits, any benefits such as company cars or stock purchase plans, and so on, as well as the staff member's actual salary.
- Space on company premises. Loaded real-estate costs generally include a proportion of building costs allocated according to the amount of floor space used. These may include a share of lighting, cooling, and heating costs, any rates or taxes applicable to the building, building and ground maintenance, cleaning and security, and building insurance.

- Tools and safety systems for assembly, acceptance testing, and in-use areas. These include assembly and electrical tools as well as electrical and mechanical safety systems.
- Storage of equipment and other inventory until it is required.
- Freight costs if the test system needs to be transported any distance; for example, for repair or calibration as a system, or to an alternative site. Access will be necessary, so equipment should have direct access to a loading dock, elevators, and so on – especially if the system is heavier than the weight limit for a two-person elevator (as most are).
- The in-use environment necessary for running the test system; for example, screened rooms, industrialized wiring for power requirements, air conditioning, floor loading, computer flooring and environmental control, and clean room for space- or weapons-qualified assembly.
- Any specialized equipment required for acceptance testing of the system; for example, an antenna range, screened room, or special chamber such as is required for EMC testing.
- Support contracts as applicable for both service/repair and calibration (although these are generally counted toward the running costs or costs of ownership for the system).

The cheapest bid for a component of a project (whether it is a product such as test equipment or services such as contracting out a particular task) will not always give you the cheapest system in the long term. This is an area where familiarity with the real costs involved in a project is crucial to making sound business decisions. A company may gather quotations for a particular product or service and consider them in isolation from the real costs of the project or from other factors which should be part of the selection criteria. The authors have seen organizations spend more than $100,000 on test hardware and then try to control it with a low-cost software product. As the software selection was driven primarily by price and without fully considering the technical specifications of the project, the purchaser did not realize until too late that the software did not include the correct drivers to control the hardware. Hence, the company had to buy the appropriate software product or write their own drivers. Either way, both money and time were wasted.

Version control for software and hardware.   Changes in hardware and software over the lifetime of the system require careful version control, including updating all documentation and also updating any identical systems as appropriate. Maintaining multiple versions of test systems will increase an organization's support and maintenance costs, so an investment in maintaining system standardization will benefit the organization in the long run. Chapter 2 includes additional notes on software standards and version control. Chapter 14, "Documentation," discusses the importance of accurate and up-to-date documentation of test systems.

Other lifetime costs.   Lifetime costs include all the running costs of the test system, such as the costs of regular calibration, spares, storage media, and any consumables that are required; for example, printer paper, ink cartridges, cables, cleaning kits, disks, and so on. Your organization may also factor in floor space costs for a portion of the lighting, security, and so on. You may also need to allow for the storage of spares and backup equipment. Up- and downtime management includes the costs of calibration and maintenance contracts, as well as the costs of having a production line or other system not running while the test system is being calibrated or repaired. Code testing for any software changes can also be an unexpected overhead. Net present value (NPV) calculations can help you establish a break-even point for your system when all lifetime costs are taken into account.

1.1.3 Results

Appropriate selection and application of test results are core to the effective use of your test system. Far too often, tests are completed and then the results have to be discarded. This can be due to inappropriate selection of what data to store, incorrect test setup, omission of a key piece of data from the test results, or other factors.

The end purpose of any tests you carry out will shape how you select results data. Test data may be used to analyze for improvement using ongoing process statistics, to confirm that equipment was performing correctly, or be straightforward go/no-go tests. Chapter 3 includes a further discussion on using results.

The format in which you store results could impact your test procedures and costs. Stacks of hand-generated results are generally useless unless they are diligently and consistently filed and sorted; the data is costly to access and analyze due to the high personnel costs of having people go through paper files. Computer storage is preferable for all but the smallest manual systems, and even then, the rapidly falling cost of computer equipment can make the advantages worthwhile. Even with computer storage of results, you will need to carefully decide on the format and value of the data you plan to keep. COTS and open standards issues (discussed more fully in Chapter 2) apply to software as much as to hardware. Designing your own database may be a satisfying exercise, but issues such as ongoing support, upgrades, and compatibility with other programs (even the word processor you use to write your reports) will usually mean that it makes more sense to purchase a commercially available database.

You will also need to consider what backup or long-term data storage facilities are required, depending on how long you want to store the data and how problematic a loss of stored data would be. The results of the test may be classified; for example, work carried out under "Commercial In Confidence" contract conditions, or work classified "Secret" under government rules. If any of these are true, then special storage facilities may be required.

You may have to plan for data migration periodically as older storage systems become obsolete and unsupportable; for example, data kept over an airplane's lifetime.

1.2 Make vs. Buy Decisions

The "make vs. buy" decision – whether to purchase equipment or test systems or develop them in-house – is an important one in any system design, and can arise for a number of reasons. You may have a specific application where there is no existing solution (whether you are considering a specific piece of test equipment or a whole solution/system), or you may be testing to a less common technical standard where commercial equipment is not readily available. It may also be a matter of deciding whether a specific task such as system integration or documentation could be carried out at a lower cost or more effectively in-house or by using a contractor. This decision can apply to:

- Test equipment.
- The whole test system.
- System assembly/integration.
- Software.
- Test fixtures.
- Contracting out the whole test process (due to other trade-offs, TAT [turn-around time], access, etc.).

For system components, the options are to purchase, re-use, or make the components you need. For issues relating to the re-use of system components, see Part 4 of this book, "Upgrading a Test System."

The "buy/integrate" decision may be a real paradigm shift for an organization used to building test systems from scratch. When working out costs, you have to consider not only the cost of buying or building the system or system components, but also the cost of the alternatives; for example, the overall costs of doing the test a different way. Even for an expensive supplier-built test system, you may see overall savings over the lifetime of the system by making a larger investment up-front.

Today, test equipment comes in all shapes and sizes. It may be a single box or a rack of equipment. For example, a one-box piece of test equipment can comprise a spectrum analyzer, oscilloscope, and even a power supply. A test system could be a vector network analyzer (VNA), which is still purchased as a single instrument, but arrives in a rack. It is possible to build a VNA out of the individual components, but at a severe disadvantage to the organization in terms of time and performance.

Note that it is not usually possible to buy a standard test instrument or test system for a widget if your widget is unique to your company, is highly complex, or you need to measure a number of quantities. However, you should break down your test requirements into test "instruments" that are available from manufactures. The "instrument" could actually be a series of test boxes integrated into a system by a manufacturer, and this will almost always be a more cost-effective solution than in-house design of test equipment. Re-inventing the wheel is not nearly as exciting the second time around!

1.2.1   Factors Affecting Make vs. Buy Decisions

The key issue with the "make vs. buy" decision for test equipment and test systems is the allocation and management of risk. In working with a third party, either a test equipment supplier or a system integrator, you can structure working arrangements to transfer the risk to the third party (bearing in mind that this can affect the cost of the contract, depending on the scope of the risk involved) or manage it in some other way. Even when risk is transferred by your contract with the supplier, it is still good practice to monitor any risks that have a large impact on your organization; for example, lead time for a mission-critical system. Payment of penalties still will not recover the time lost through a late delivery. Some of the issues that will need to be considered are:

Cost

If you purchase from a manufacturer, you will normally get a fixed-priced contract. However, if you design and integrate a system in-house, you bear the risk of cost blowout. Careful evaluation of any contractor, including their long-term business success and stability, is important whenever you contract out work. If your contractor goes out of business due to inexperience or through bidding lower than it costs them to do the work, then everyone loses.

Performance

If you design an in-house system, then you will also be required to prove the system's performance. If you purchase from a company, then that company is responsible for proving the system's performance.

Time

A manufacturer normally guarantees delivery time, and in cases where there are critical timelines, penalty clauses can provide additional surety for the purchaser. If you design your own system, then time blowout could occur. Additionally, staff who are working on this project cannot work on other projects, representing a possible opportunity cost to your organization.

Experience

Expertise in operating test equipment does not always translate into expertise in designing and implementing test systems, just as an experienced system designer may not be an equipment "super-user." The authors have never seen a block diagram of a test system that would not have worked; however, they have seen a number of systems that never achieved their design goals.

Support

If you design your own systems, you will need to support them as a unit; this is distinct from individual pieces of equipment, which can be returned to the manufacturer for calibration or repair. This may impact your company if key personnel leave.

Training/Documentation

This responsibility will rest with your organization for any in-house-designed equipment. Documentation must be done well enough that any competent engineer can understand and repeat the design to build an identical test system if the original designers have moved on or are not available.

Life of system

If the system is only going to be needed for a short time (relative to your company product), it may be simpler to lease equipment. However, if the system is to be used for longer time

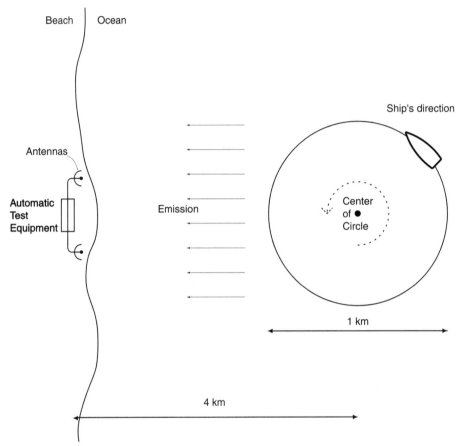

Figure 1.4   The test environment.

frames, then purchase may be the most suitable option. Usually, simple NPV (net present value) calculations will show when the system will pay for itself.

1.2.2   An Example

This is an example of how an expensive system still provided overall cost savings to the end-user. The key points of interest are the process that the engineer followed and the factors included in the calculations.

The test system being considered was for the measurement of electromagnetic emissions at selected frequencies from a Navy ship sailing in circles 2 km from the shore (see Figure 1.4). The original method was to take measurements manually and transfer the data obtained for sep-arate analysis. Using this method, it took up to three months to receive analyzed data back which could be acted on, partly because the data needed to be adjusted so that the ship appeared to be rotating on its axis so that a plot of emissions about the ship was produced. The engineer's options were:

1. To continue using the existing (original) manual test method.

2. To design an automated test system in-house.

3. To purchase a supplier-developed automated test system.

At first glance, the purchase of the supplier-developed test system appears to be the most expensive option. However, the project manager went through a costing exercise to examine the real cost to the organization of these three options.

Table 1.1 shows the factors that were taken into account.

Table 1.1   Factors Relating to Choice of Test Options

Original Measurement Method	In-house Design & Build	Supply of Full Test System
Time to do test	Time to develop system (data obtained by trying out some small design exercises in-house, i.e., with existing staff knowledge)	Cost of test system
Cost of manpower		Time saved over manual test (staff and equipment/ship costs)
Ship running costs		
Time to receive analyzed results (currently three months, partly due to the complexity of the analysis process and lack of automation)	Time to develop software	Time to receive analyzed results (can be faxed to ship at the end of each circle)
	Time to develop and prove algorithm for data reduction	Full warranty and local customer support provided
Delay between carrying out tests and being able to act on the results	Development of data gathering algorithm, including reduction of electrical errors due to multi-path effects and different wavelengths	
	Development of preliminary testing to reduce interference from other sources	
	Time saved over manual test (staff and equipment/ship costs)	

By comparing the total costs of the various test methods (Figure 1.5), the project manager found that the break-even point for buying a full system from a test equipment supplier was about sixty hours of test. Since the tests would take about eighty hours in total, the organization would save money by purchasing an expensive but overall more efficient system up-front. As the break-even point was reached during a single run of tests, each additional test run provided further savings.

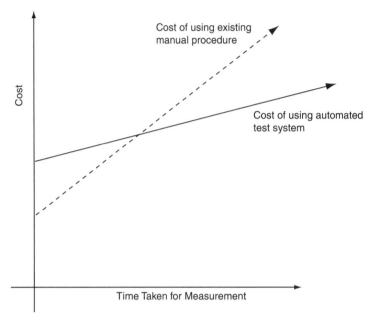

Figure 1.5   Cost of manual vs. system test methods.

The customer engineer and test system vendor were able to put together a good engineering solution by matching up operational needs with the vendor's expertise in through-the-air measurements and system automation.

TIP:

Remember that you are looking for a solution – not problems! If you buy a car, you don't gather quotes on engines, wheels, bodies, and so on and then try to put them together to make a "car." Consider the same approach for test equipment. Minimize your risk by thinking "system."

1.3 Architecture, Obsolescence Protection, and Upgradability

No engineering application remains static. Even very stable test environments will benefit from change as test technology improves – if for no other reason. One of the key factors in maximizing long-term flexibility is to use open standards wherever possible, and to apply a modular design philosophy to both hardware and software development.

Maximizing the flexibility of your test system will allow you to smoothly include new product tests in the system's specifications, incorporate your system into existing production lines or test systems, and interact well with other systems and processes currently in use in your application environment.

1.3.1   Planning for Future Upgrades

Your investment deals not only with the current need of your organization for a test system, but the future use to which the components of the system will be put will also influence aspects of the system design. It is important to keep the future needs of your organization in mind when you approach either software or hardware design.

If you plan to re-use components such as test equipment in other systems or other applications, using popular communication interfaces such as IEEE 488 will make it easier to use it with other equipment. Not only are open standards proven and reliable, but also more engineers will be familiar with these standards and able to make use of them in a relatively short time. Systems with a longer planned lifetime which are designed to be upgraded in the future should include features in the design which make future upgrades easier. Systems that will be upgraded for increased speed should be integrated with flexible communication buses, preferably with direct bus-to-backplane access if possible. Systems which will be upgraded to include additional tests or better test technology as it becomes available should be designed using a flexible architecture.

1.3.2   Design Philosophies: Hardware First or Software First?

In the past, many test systems were developed based on hardware specifications first with software designed around the selected hardware and test equipment. The increasing complexity of test equipment, control software, and the growing need for interchangeability and interoperability in test systems means that a parallel approach to hardware and software design delivers increased benefits to the designer.

Some hardware decisions, such as the choice of ASCII or driver-controlled test equipment, need to be made at the very start of the design project – especially with the increased availability of features such as IVI (interchangeable virtual instrument) drivers. The challenge in writing a TPS (test program set) is not to be tied down to a particular set of instruments or test assets, particularly if your application is in an area of rapid technological change.

Your choice of architecture will be affected by factors such as the level of test (component/module), budget, future plans for the test system, space available (e.g., airplane vs. lab), and so on. Component- vs. modular-level (functional) test requirements will also affect both hardware and software decisions.

Component-level tests, for example, require access to all nodes of a component. In-circuit testing does not require the board to be powered for many tests. For a passive component, a potential is applied to each node of the device. This removes the loading effect of any components connected to the same node, and is measured using traditional methods. Whether you use x-ray test, capacitive test, jet-test technology, or other in-circuit test methods will also affect your system design decisions.

A "rack and stack" test system works through edge connect or connectors or ports on the DUT. The DUT is stimulated to its working condition and then exercised through a series of tests to determine if it is working correctly. These tests are called test programs, and a collection of them for a DUT is called a test program set (TPS).

The design process is cyclic in many respects, that is, it will involve going through some iterations and once built, the system will continue to evolve. The most flexible approach is to plan for that evolution. Make planning for long-term system evolution part of your project strategy.

1.3.3   Choosing a Control Method

Your choice of control method (manual, semi-automated, or fully-automated) will depend on factors such as the speed required, the complexity of your application, the degree of expertise required or available in your operators, and so on. Chapter 3, "How Control Decisions Affect Hardware Architecture," deals with this topic in more detail.

Some decision-making tools will become available in the implementation of a fully-automated system, especially in large-throughput environments. Some AI (artificial intelligence) databases, for example, can learn the likelihood of faults on a particular board or product based on past fault statistics to decrease location time, therefore raising throughput.

If you choose a manual or semi-automated system, consider selecting equipment with full automation of the system in mind. This can lower your upgrade costs and increase your future flexibility, often at little incremental cost up-front.

1.3.4   Choosing a Computer Operating System
and Programming Language

The choice of an operating system or programming language is very important to supporting your system, upgrading future test equipment, and adding more DUTs. Systems such as UNIX® and Windows® are updated frequently, as are the capabilities of instrument drivers as standardization continues. You will need to look carefully at available drivers as well as programming code support from manufacturers to guide you to the most appropriate combination of operating system and programming language.

Open software systems, and commercial software systems in general, will be supported and have future upgrades available. Section 2.1.2 discusses open standards in software, but in general, the features that should be considered in any evaluation include stability, power, robustness, flexibility, connectivity, backward-compatibility (where appropriate), scalability, lifetime support costs, and system integrity.

Different packages will provide features valuable in different applications. Graphical or iconic programming packages are excellent for proving a concept, but they also need to be evaluated for speed of performance if you need optimization of throughput. To gain the best performance for a leading-edge application, you may need to have access to all the manufacturer's bus commands. If your system will require multiple (human) language support, you may prefer a commercial package with multi-language help functions, instructions, and warnings.

Chapter 3, "How Control Decisions Affect Hardware Architecture," deals with program structures and operating systems in more depth. However, the subject of software is large enough to warrant several books of its own, and the authors recommend using additional resources to gain detailed information.

1.3.5   Writing Test Specifications and Documentation

The ability to upgrade or modify an existing test system will almost always depend on the documentation provided with that system. If a test system, its test specifications, its software structure, and its hardware setup are thoroughly documented, it will greatly simplify the task of the engineer charged with making any changes.

The same applies to building a copy of an existing test system. Multiple test systems add benefit to an organization and are easy to maintain if they are built and managed to the same configuration. The quality of your original documentation, and the thoroughness with which any upgrades and other changes are included in that documentation, will affect not only the cost of building a duplicate system, but also the cost to maintain multiple systems.

Investing time and care early in the test system project to developing good documentation will pay dividends throughout the lifetime of the system. Chapter 14, "Documentation," deals with this topic in more detail.

1.4   In-house Resources and Competencies Relevant to Test System Design, Test Suite Programming, and System Build

Technical expertise is not the only resource relevant to test system design. Sources of information and being able to make use of them will be invaluable. A team of people in your organization will also be part of the project as it progresses.

1.4.1   Access to Organizations and Information

When designing test systems, a number of organizations can provide very good technical documentation to assist you with measurement needs. These organizations include ANSI (American National Standards Institute), IEEE (Institute of Electrical and Electronic Engineers), and ISO (International Standards Organization).

The IEEE has very detailed information and a number of proceedings, which are worth the small cost usually asked for. IESS (INTELSAT's Earth Station Specifications) provides information on satellite earth stations, ITU (International Telecommunication Union) provides detailed information on telecommunication systems. Most countries have standards organizations for areas such as safety and metrology. Many of these ultimately reference organizations such as NIST (National Institute of Standards and Technology) in the United States, or British or French organizations. ISO standards documents are also excellent references.

1.4.2   Team

Integrating a test solution will normally require the formation of a team. The size of the team will of course depend on the complexity of the tests to be implemented. However, a range of skills will normally be required. Engineering skills will be required to determine the quantities that need to be measured and to what accuracy. The engineering team will require experience in a relevant measurement discipline; for example, RF, microwave, or digital test. It is no use assigning a digital engineer to design a test solution for a satellite low-noise amplifier. Equally, RF engineers may not have the best programming skills for your application, and software engineers may not understand why an engineer wants to set an instrument up with a particular test configuration.

Technical officers or skilled technicians will be required to build the system. They bring with them better soldering skills, cable-making skills, and practical experience in getting paper designs to work in the real world.

A test system manager who can coordinate all personnel involved both during and after system integration, and who is responsible for the well-being of the system during its lifetime, will make the test system project run more smoothly and will maintain the integrity of the system during its lifetime. Stories such as an $80,000 spectrum analyzer being used as the world's most expensive radio, or a $700 torque wrench ending up in the toolkit for a $200 push bike, are part of the "urban myths" of any engineering organization.

Someone capable of writing technical documentation is also required. Engineers generally assume the person they are writing the manual for is at least as qualified as they are. Since the documentation is such an important part of the system, it should be done by a qualified technical writer, especially if the system is large or if multiple systems will be built. This allows people never involved in the test system to be able to understand it well enough to implement design changes after the original designers have moved to other roles.

Staff will include technicians, administrative staff, engineers, electricians, fitter and turner staff, as well as other project staff.

As with any team project, communication skills, appropriate levels of responsibility and authority, and a clearly understood goal will help make your team successful. Recognition is a key part of reinforcing excellent work. Enjoy the opportunity to celebrate your team's successes and achievements.

Using COTS and Open Standards to Maximize Flexibility and Control Costs

T his chapter explains the importance of COTS (commercial, off-the-shelf) equipment and open standards, and how they can make your system design easier. More importantly, they can make ongoing support easier, lower your lifetime system costs, and protect your initial investment by making system upgrades easier.

KEY POINTS:

- Both COTS and open standards can enhance your system design.
- COTS offers features such as better availability, support, documentation, and product upgrades. Open standards offer superior obsolescence protection through more flexible upgrade paths and easier interoperability.

2.1 Understanding COTS and Open Standards

Commercial, off-the-shelf (COTS) products are products available in commercial quantities from a manufacturer. They typically come with warranty, documentation, access to repairs, spare parts, training, and support. COTS products are also more likely to have upgrades available in the future such as revisions to take into account the latest operating systems, test languages, or improved models with better technical performance or increased feature sets. Both markets and technology change over time, so flexibility is an important point to consider in planning for the long-term usability of your system.

There is increasing pressure in industry and in organizations to cut the development and running costs of test systems. For a system which is intended to have a long working lifetime, operation and maintenance costs will have a large effect on overall cost of ownership (or system lifecycle costs). COTS products, components, and software can help companies and organizations achieve this.

2.1.1   Hardware

COTS equipment will come in common form factors such as "rack and stack" (test equipment and system components such as switches which have a width of 19 inches – the width of a standard rack – and where the height of the equipment is measured in EIAs, or Electronics Industries Association units) or VXI (an open standard based on a mainframe and "test equipment on a card"). It may have a built-in command language, be ready to program, and will allow the user to add and remove options to meet their requirements. An important point is that the manufacturer of the equipment will be responsible for guaranteeing that it meets its performance specifications, whereas equipment designed in-house requires you to verify that it is performing correctly. Most test system users will accept that a spectrum analyzer from a reputable company will meet its performance specifications, but may argue the point when in-house equipment is used, especially if contracts or penalty fees are involved. COTS equipment can provide peace of mind.

The most compelling reason to remain with COTS equipment is that each individual piece of equipment is guaranteed to have a certain level of performance. This description of performance is the technical specification of the instrument. A range of information will be described in this document, from input levels, accuracy, and power requirements to equipment weight and dimensions. Equipment purchase will then involve choosing the instrument that can meet the performance and features you require. In-house-designed equipment will always have uncertainties about performance until it is fully tested, a process which itself requires test equipment. Section 1.2 of Chapter 1 discusses the "make vs. buy" decision in more detail.

An open standard is a standard that has been developed with the involvement of major companies and users in an industry, rather than just a single manufacturer. Open standards can start life as a company's internal standard (for example, both MMS – now managed by an industry consortium – and the IEEE 488 interface bus originated from Hewlett Packard's Test and Measurement Organization), but they become much more valuable to users once they are given to and adopted by industry as open standards and are used by a number of companies. Open standards help a test system developer in a number of ways.

Open standards are currently in place to describe both hardware and software. "Rack and stack" can be viewed as a standard, even if only in general terms, since equipment is designed to fit into 19-inch racks and be a certain number of EIAs high. The VXI standard goes further in describing communication interfaces, heat, power, and EMC specifications. Although different hardware platforms can generally be used together, a user must make a fundamental choice of a hardware platform to fully take advantage of hardware standards. A test system designer may choose to use a mixture of different hardware platforms to take advantage of particular functionality offered by each platform. The goal of the system designer is to make informed decisions that simplify rather than complicate the test system and measurement task.

If for some reason it does become necessary for you or your organization to build a piece of test equipment in-house, then try to ensure that it is designed using the hardware platform standard that best suits it. VXI kits with design guides, for example, are available to make this task easier.

2.1.2 Software

The design task becomes more complicated in the area of software development. Typically, software development can account for over 50-80% of a test system's development. Software needs to be maintained and upgraded just as hardware does, and open standards in software can make this task easier. Open standards in software, as with hardware, are the backbone of mainstream test system applications. Chapter 17, "Using Standard Software and Open Standards for Obsolescence Protection," deals with the system lifetime aspects of this topic in more detail. Software design is itself a major field and information in this text (which focuses on system hardware) should be augmented with reference to texts focused on software.

Commercial, open software products can lower individual system costs, and can simplify lifetime support, system integration, and connectivity. They make systems more easily scalable and backward-compatible. In an environment of increasing inter-system communication, software interoperability is a key tool in enabling new capabilities and links to other systems.

DUTs with a long operating life and their associated test software can outlive test systems in many applications; for example, support systems for aircraft or radar systems. Commercial test instrumentation and software applications used in the support test system can change more quickly than the technology or design of the DUT itself. There have generally been two solutions to the problem of changing test system equipment and its impact on test system software:

1. To modify the test software TPS (test program set).
2. To make sure that you have a continued supply of the particular test equipment you need over the life of the system.

Ensuring availability of test equipment means either purchasing a number of spares or negotiating a production or long-term support contract with a manufacturer (if you will be purchasing a significant volume of equipment over time). Test equipment can be obsoleted by a manufacturer for a number of reasons, typically either as a business decision based on sales volumes, or at times because of a supply problem with a component which cannot be solved (for example, if the component manufacturer no longer produces a particular component and no replacement is available). Even if you were able to overcome this supply problem, for example by purchasing spare units, you would be tying your system down to one set of test equipment assets which would become dated over time, and which would prevent you from taking advantage of new features such as increased measurement speed or more accurate measurement technology as it becomes available. The ideal situation is to aim for functionality dependence and equipment independence.

Changing TPS software to support new and different test equipment in your system is an expensive and logistically difficult process. It also involves the burden of tracking software and documentation versions, especially if you have multiple systems at different locations. Making software and systems decisions at the start of your project to minimize these issues during the lifetime of your system will save you significant amounts of time and money down the track, and is a worthwhile part of your initial investment in a system. Chapter 17 deals with this topic in more detail.

In the search for inter-operability, open standards equipment and software provide the best hope of connecting "boxes" together, even when different manufacturers' equipment is used. Always try to reduce your test system to the integration of boxes, not the design of boxes. The user may wish to design a specialized piece of equipment to replace a COTS piece, but if your test system is dependent on the timely building of this equipment, you may find your whole project delayed. Table 2.1 lists some issues addressed by COTS and open standards.

Table 2.1   Issues Addressed by COTS and Open Standards

COTS-Related Benefits	Open Standards-Related Benefits
Warranty	Superior obsolescence protection
Documentation	System development costs
Future upgrades	System repair and maintenance costs
Lead time/delivery time	Lifetime ownership costs
System development costs	
System repair and maintenance costs	
Lifetime ownership costs	

2.2 How COTS and Open Standards Maximize Flexibility and Control Costs

2.2.1 The Benefits of Multiple Suppliers

By allowing equipment from different manufacturers to work together, open standards help build ongoing competition into the marketplace, which provides a number of benefits to test equipment buyers. It also benefits test equipment manufacturers, as they can sell to more customers using open standards products than proprietary equipment. Competition means that cost savings achieved by the manufacturers, either through improvements in their manufacturing processes or advancements in test technology, are generally passed on to the user. The need to keep pace with improving test technology means that suppliers will obsolete their own products with better versions almost as quickly as they can be developed. Time to market is a strong driver in the test equipment market, just as in many other industries. Competitive pressures also make quality and customer satisfaction increasingly important business drivers for suppliers – all to the benefit of buyers.

2.2.2   The Benefits of COTS Production Volumes

The benefits of COTS are linked to the business potential of having a large number of customers for a product. In addition to the benefits of availability, warranty, documentation, technical support, and likelihood of future upgrades, commercially available products have a number of other benefits that can influence the overall cost of ownership, as well as the development cost of your system. Non-recurring engineering costs (NRE – discussed in more detail in Section 2.2.3) for COTS products are spread over many units and the unit price is commercially driven.

Leading-edge equipment will always cost more, since the last 10% in performance can be as expensive as the first 90%. Competitive environments and continual product improvements as technology improves will mean that COTS equipment on the whole will provide value for money.

Availability

COTS production runs mean that you will have relatively quick access to a product. The manufacturer will either have stock available, or (if they build to order) will have regular production runs and will be able to quote a definite lead time to you.

It is still important to remember that quoted lead times can at times be affected by external factors such as problems with supply of key components to the test equipment manufacturer or an unanticipated influx of orders such as possible military purchases at a time of regional unrest. Manufacturers will have production planners on staff to plan for or deal with these events, so they should be rare; however, they will not always be able to overcome all difficulties.

Warranty and Support

The production volumes of COTS equipment mean that it becomes more efficient for the manufacturer to provide additional warranty for their equipment, thus lowering the per unit warranty costs and providing the buyer with a more easily administered warranty program. The larger installed base typically achieved with COTS (rather than custom equipment) also increases the obligation of the manufacturer to provide effective and efficient post-sales support.

You should have access to ongoing worldwide support for the product you have purchased. For a custom-designed product, the designers might be busy working on their next project, or they may have left the company. If they have not provided excellent documentation, you may end up in a situation where no one knows enough about the product to be able to support it properly. Proper documentation is time-consuming and therefore expensive, and you have a better chance of getting it with a COTS product.

COTS equipment will normally always have MTBF (mean time between failures) data available, support packages, and other detailed information to minimize risk or uncertainties. Product maintenance, repairs, and support should be cheaper for COTS equipment than for custom equipment, again due to the volume of sales and shared costs. Spare parts and repair manuals should be more readily available for COTS equipment.

The idea of efficiencies of scale, however, also applies to the test equipment purchaser and may affect your lifetime support costs for test equipment and test systems. Depending on the type of support structure you decide to use, your costs could increase if you have bought from a number of different vendors. For example, if you have negotiated an on-site calibration contract to minimize turn-around times (TATs) and disruption to your work environment, the costs to have a number of different companies come on-site to calibrate a smaller amount of test equipment each will be higher than contracting with one or two companies. Each company will have a fixed overhead cost to set up at your site as well as the variable cost per piece of equipment calibrated. A large number of suppliers means that you will pay the overhead or setup cost a number of times.

An understanding of and allowances for likely system downtime should also be part of your support plan, especially in a high-volume or time-critical application. Many new test system designers neglect this aspect of test system ownership. Even if the system does not need repair, routine maintenance and calibration will be required. In-house-designed equipment requires in-house experts to repair, re-align, recalibrate, and generally maintain the equipment. If this is not part of your company's core business, then this scenario will cost you time and money that may not be budgeted for. COTS equipment, on the other hand, can have a detailed life support plan designed for it, and you can put a support contract in place to guarantee repair TAT or a minimum downtime if you need to meet critical requirements. A guaranteed TAT would usually be in addition to the terms of your normal equipment warranty (and thus an additional cost) or part of your calibration contract, and once the warranty period was over, you would put a maintenance and calibration contract in place with any specific performance guarantees that you have negotiated. As these are contract arrangements, the system's yearly support costs would be known to your company, as would be planned downtimes for calibration.

Many pieces of test equipment now have built-in test routines that can help when confidence testing of the system or even fault-finding is required. This will lessen the need for routine maintenance simply for system assurance, but a maintenance contract to cover repair costs is still a good investment as it makes your annual support costs known and avoids cost blowouts which could occur if more than one piece of test equipment requires repair in a short time.

Documentation

Documentation is a key factor in the usability and maintainability of test equipment or a test system, and the costs of providing good documentation are high. Tools such as user manuals, service manuals, and application manuals can make a huge difference to how much a piece of equipment is used, how well it is used, and the benefit it brings to an organization. Many companies have seen expensive equipment under-utilized because a poor documentation set or user interface made it too much of a problem to use.

As with other NRE costs, the cost of developing COTS product documentation are spread over the whole production run for that product, and the cost per unit is lowered.

Potential Upgrade Paths

There is an advantage to being able to arrange incremental upgrades (evolution) rather than having to go through a complete system rebuild if you need to upgrade capabilities or want to take advantage of new features as they become available (evolution). If you are in a rapidly evolving area, you will want to be able to include new features and capabilities as easily as possible without a large investment in updating your whole test system. Using COTS equipment, especially when combined with open standards, lets you plan for system evolution.

With standardized product families and interfaces, and the availability of thorough documentation, COTS solutions can be rapidly scaled to meet varying demands, and even reconfigured quickly to accommodate changes in test routines or fixtures. New technology can be quickly incorporated into the ATE (automatic test equipment).

Product upgrades are more likely with a COTS product than a custom product. The manufacturer's investment in a COTS product is large, and they are likely to have a large installed base for their product (a large number of users). The manufacturers have a much better chance of a good ROI for a product upgrade with a large number of existing users, and so they are more prepared to make the investment in new R&D.

A useful point to remember is that COTS test equipment can more easily be used in other applications or even sold to other companies or organizations once it is no longer required for its current application, and it will still have some worth. In-house or proprietary equipment may not, and if it does, the potential market will not be as large as with COTS equipment.

2.3 COTS and NRE Costs

NRE costs are the development costs incurred by a company to bring a particular product to production. These costs are usually spread out over a whole production run, or over the anticipated lifetime of the product for a commercial product. However, for a custom-designed and manufactured product or for a product with a very limited production run, the design costs must be paid as part of the price of a single custom product, or they will contribute a large amount to each product from a small production run.

Buying COTS products means that the NRE costs will have been spread over a large production run by the manufacturer, and you will not end up paying an unreasonable premium for one-off products.

WHAT ABOUT THE NRE OF THE TEST SYSTEM YOU DESIGNED?

A related NRE issue is the NRE of designing a custom test system. The intellectual property (IP) of your system relates to the design of the system itself. Retaining the IP for your system means that you would be able to resell your system design if you can find other customers interested in buying. Thus, you (or your company) can recoup some of your own NRE costs in the same way that a manufacturer recoups the NRE costs of the components it sells.

2.4 COTS and Open Standards

COTS does not necessarily mean that you are getting a product based on open standards, as a COTS product may still have some proprietary aspects; for example, its communications interfaces. Open standards add another dimension of flexibility and investment protection to your system design.

Open standards are common standards among a number of manufacturers. The IEEE 488 interface is a classic example. The key benefit is that products from a number of manufacturers will work together easily. Being assured of the behavior and capabilities of an open standards-based product or interface means that a developer can focus on systems development and implementation rather than troubleshooting an interface or a proprietary communications protocol. More and more test equipment manufacturers are using open standards for both hardware and software, increasing the choice available to buyers. Open standards mean that you are not tied down to a single supplier, either for the initial design and build or for later upgrades and system revisions. The number of companies that manufacture switching solutions using the VXI standard, to take one small example, means that a myriad of switching products are available in all common topologies with scanning, full-access, blocking, multiplexers, and high-current and high-frequency variants. Having access to a range of possible suppliers also makes open standards a safer option for buyers, as the breadth of choice increases.

Proprietary interfaces, communication systems, and other product specifications limit your ability to upgrade, re-use, or migrate to new test applications as they become available. Open standards give obsolescence protection by allowing easier upgrades and by giving you more than one possible supplier. In fact, it opens up your list of suppliers. You have the ability to substitute one manufacturer's product with one from another manufacturer. If one product is no longer in production, you can choose another with the same capability (either the same set or a superset of the features you need). You can even use a different instrument, as long as it can measure the quantity you need to the same specifications. For example, a digital multimeter with frequency measurement capability can be substituted for a counter, as long as the digital multimeter's specifications are adequate and the two instruments use a common command language.

Open standards are established and maintained by international standards bodies such as the IEEE or the ATM Forum, and involve manufacturers, users, and other interested parties. There are also other types of standards; for example, an industry standard such as Windows®, which is used by a number of applications but is defined by a single company. De-facto standards describe standards that may be emerging and slightly different versions are in use. Market development will gradually establish which version will become more widely used, and in some cases, marketing and market share will have a greater impact than technology. The emergence of VHS™ as the industry standard for video players over the technically superior Beta™ system shows the importance of appropriate promotion and accessibility of a standard.

Open standards are the best standards to work with if they are available. They provide the best protection for your test system and are normally the easiest to work with as they are proven and widely established. They also tend to be the most cost-effective since a number of companies manufacture them rather than just one company manufacturing a proprietary standard.

Industry standards are useful as well because they are accepted protocols/hardware in your industry. However, since they are generally controlled by a single company rather than a community of manufacturers and users, industry standards can change, so they are not as future-proof as open standards. Additionally, if you wish to alternate or maximize your test system by covering multiple tasks, one industry standard may not be the industry standard for another application.

SOME NOTES ON DE-FACTO STANDARDS, STANDARDS BODIES, AND INDUSTRY CONSORTIA

Standards need to be fully defined to be at their most useful, and may be managed by a number of companies and key users who are involved in the technology area. Sometimes, getting consensus (especially in an area such as a complex communications standard) can take a number of years. What approach should you take if you need to go ahead with a product implementation? Some companies try to establish a "de-facto standard" by trying to gain significant market share. They may be driven by a need to get a product shipping, or by their own customers who want to get their products out into the market (for example, switch manufacturers will push test equipment suppliers to release their leading-edge communications test products so that the switch manufacturers can test and release their own products). This is a case where company factors such as market share can be important in your considerations. The supplier with the largest market share may well have the strongest voice in defining an emerging standard. If you decide to use an emerging technology, where standards are still developing, you may just have to bite the bullet and choose.

Consider:

1. How fully defined is the de-facto or draft standard you are considering? The more defined the standard, the less risk there is in implementing it.

2. Is information on the draft or de-facto standard freely available? This will influence whether other companies take it up, strengthening its position as a standard if it has a larger user base.

3. Is this standard developed or influenced by consensus? A "standard" that is imposed by market volume pressures is in some respects still a proprietary standard that may become a de-facto standard if the company's market share is overwhelming. A standard developed by informed consensus has a better chance of being effective and robust, due to discussion by a range of experts and developers, and has a greater chance of being broadly accepted.

Example of the ATM Forum

The ATM Forum (www.atmforum.com) is an international non-profit organization. It exists to promote the use of the ATM (Asynchronous Transfer Mode) communications standard, to maintain a set of common technical specifications to ensure interoperability between all ATM products and services, and to provide marketing and education which will increase the understanding and acceptance of ATM technology. Any organization interested in the support and promotion of the ATM

Example of the ATM Forum (continued)

standard may join, and the membership list includes manufacturers, developers, customers, integrators, and other organizations from a range of industries.

Principle members may influence specifications, submit contributions, and vote on contributions and specifications. Hence, manufacturers of ATM equipment find it valuable to have a voice in this forum. Over 600 companies have joined the ATM Forum.

2.5 Disadvantages of COTS and Open Standards

COTS and open standards are NOT guarantees of success. They make the job of designing and implementing your system easier, but you still have to work through all the issues. In some cases, COTS without open standards – or even open standards equipment – may be a disadvantage to your system design.

There will be times when you are unable to source open standards equipment with all the features you require, even though COTS equipment (which may not be fully built using open standards) is available. COTS equipment with proprietary features can tie you to a single vendor. Having a choice of supplier gives you more negotiating power, a wider choice of products, and more flexibility of design. You will most likely only work with a small group of suppliers that have been evaluated as reliable, but if the need arises, having a choice of suppliers is advantageous. If particular features of the equipment you purchase limit you, you limit your future as well as present options.

Conversely, you may find that you only need one or two features on an item of test equipment, and thus in the short term, you will not be using all of the features that you have paid for.

Maintenance and support has value, and will cost money whether you do it with in-house resources or ask a manufacturer to provide it. A number of different vendors may mean that support is more expensive than if you use a smaller number of selected vendors. The smaller volumes of work involved will result in an increased reporting and management workload, as you will need to communicate with a larger number of different contacts. Placing a larger support contract will also gain you a larger portion of that manufacturer's attention, as you will be a proportionally larger customer for them. If your application has a long anticipated lifetime, you may also find that a manufacturer will not stock spares and provide support for as long as you require. In this case, you will need to upgrade your system to newer equipment or make your own arrangements for equipment support (for example, by purchasing spares of any equipment which is obsoleted).

If you have a highly specialized application, you may not be able to purchase a COTS or open standard solution, perhaps because the market is not large enough for a full commercial product run, or because specific technical requirements mean that current open standards are not the best solution.

ON RE-INVENTING THE WHEEL....

The authors remember a scientist who believed that he had saved money by designing and building his own phase noise test system rather than buying a commercially available one. He had purchased some second-hand equipment and designed and built other pieces to produce a custom system. On examination, the system took up nearly a six-foot rack, had cabling all over the place, required constant tweaking, and was not portable. The "designer" was the only one who could use it, repair it, and explain how it worked. The currently available COTS system could be carried by one person, had a three-year warranty, came with a support plan, and could be driven by most technical people.

The scientist had spent considerable time on this project, and had produced something which was not easily supported and which would become unusable as soon as the designer left the organization. By not considering the value of his own time and efforts, he had underestimated the cost of this project to the organization.

Beware the scientist who sees something produced by a company and then excitedly proclaims that it could easily be designed and built in-house! That person's expertise should be applied to developing something NEW, rather than repeating someone else's work.

How Control Decisions Affect Hardware Architecture

T his chapter examines system control decisions and how these affect the system hardware and the skill level required from your operators. If you intend to start with manual or semi-automated control and upgrade to fully-automated control at a later stage, you can plan for this during the original design to make the later upgrade cheaper and easier than it might be otherwise.

KEY POINTS:

- The population and complexity of your DUTs, and the level of test required, will affect the time to test and cost of test. Additional constraints to plan for are available time and available skill levels in your organization.
- Bear in mind that the Test Executive and test program sets will turn out to be your major cost drivers in test system automation.
- If your project calls for multiple systems, consider how they will be deployed. You may design different versions of the system for development, manufacturing, and repair center deployment.
- There are also factors in your initial design that can make future control upgrades easier.

3.1 Choosing How to Control Your System

There are essentially three classes of control for a test system:

1. Fully-manual control (Figure 3.1(a)).
2. Semi-automated control (Figure 3.1(b)).
3. Fully-automated control (Figure 3.1(c)).

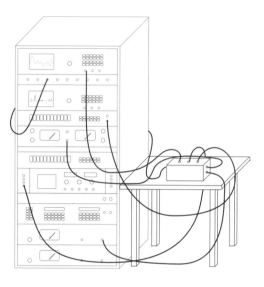

(a) Fully-manual

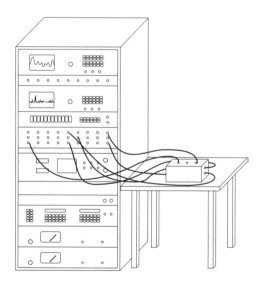

(b) Semi-automated

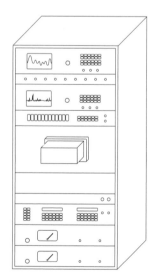

(c) Fully-automated

Figure 3.1   Three classes of test system control.

The factors affecting the decision of which method to choose will include cost, the volume of tests required, the speed of test required, and other factors. The type of control you choose for your system is a key decision, and needs to be made early in your project as it will influence the type of equipment you purchase, how you design any software you use, and how you design the test system itself.

Most people who are new to test systems will feel more comfortable with initially designing a manual test system. This allows them to focus on the technical requirements of the test equipment, test process, and analysis of results without the requirements of software design and implementation. After gaining some experience in this form of test system, it becomes a natural step to progress to semi-automated and finally automated systems. A manual system allows the engineer to develop and understand the measurements, test equipment, and any idiosyncrasies of the "system" before having to deal with coding issues such as interface, drivers, and bus problems, which are not really measurement issues. Once the complete measurement matrix has been debugged, the engineer can turn to improving throughput with automation.

The decision of whether to choose manual, semi-automated, or fully-automated control will depend on a number of factors, and often there will not be a clear-cut solution for a particular set of circumstances. Often a decision will depend on your plans over the next three to five years, as you may either plan to include more automation in the future or build the test system with greater automation now to take your future requirements into account.

It is possible to include a planned upgrade path in your design to move from manual to automated control in the future. For example, the future upgrade process for a manual test system that will be upgraded to either full or partial automation within the next two to three years can be simplified at the design stage. All the test equipment for such a system should be purchased with bus capability installed. This capability will not be used for the fully-manual test system, but will make the upgrade process to a degree of automation much easier and at a lower cost – the equipment would otherwise have to have bus capability retrofitted or be replaced if this were not possible.

The system designer should balance currently known and possible future technology enhancements when planning for future upgrades. A focus on a well-structured approach to hardware and software will offer the most flexibility for future system upgrades. For example, designing software so that it is independent of particular hardware will allow it to more easily carry across platforms with minimal rework as technology changes.

The overall decision is based on whether the cost of automation (including software development time and fixtures) is outweighed by the benefits obtained. The complexity and population of DUTs will be one of the more important factors, as will the throughput volume of your test environment. Complex DUTs with longer testing times or high-volume environments suggest that full automation is warranted. A rapidly changing test environment such as a development lab may prefer a fully-manual test environment, as the cost of developing or updating test automation software is not worthwhile if it has to be done often.

Table 3.1 shows some of the factors that a test system designer may take into account.

Table 3.1   Factors that Influence Decisions toward Various Control Methods

Manual	Semi-Automated	Fully Automated
Cost of automation outweighs benefits	Balance of cost to automate and time to test	High-volume environments mean that repetitive tests warrant automation
Speed of test is not critical – long test times are acceptable. Budget restrictions and usage patterns mean that cost of automation outweighs the longer time to test using a manual system	Volume of environment means that a trade-off between time to test and cost of automation is the best solution	Lowering time to test is a critical cost benefit
Test requirements may change regularly, meaning that test automation is not worthwhile	Some flexibility in test procedures required	Test requirements are known and likely to remain stable; modular test software design used to allow ease of test update
Need to get system up and running quickly	Benefits of some automation will outweigh the additional system development time; partially automated test system is a short-term trade-off to allow system implementation while the software for a fully-automated system is developed	Savings from faster, more reliable test far outweigh test system development time; project manager has enough time to fully automate the test system
Some "informality" in results is acceptable; setup, calibration, and self-test procedures are not overly time-consuming; highly trained staff are accessible if required for troubleshooting	Knowledgeable staff are available to manage the test system; balance of system interaction and user boredom	Low access to highly trained staff means that automation gives more repeatable results; all setup procedures, calibration, and self-test results as well as the test results themselves must be fully documented and accessible
Good for development labs that have specialized requirements or systems that are time-shared, or may be pulled apart to use test system components in other configurations	Good first step in producing fully-automated test system	Very high-precision requirements in test equipment or test parameters mean that the test system must be fully automated to avoid errors that can creep in even through small variations in human operator actions
		Most effective solution if large number of components or configurations need to be tested

3.1.1 Manual Control

Fully-manual systems depend totally on the actions of the system operator. This can provide additional flexibility for changing test environments, but also limits the speed and repeatability of the system's test results (see Figure 3.2).

Equipment is generally installed in a rack (although "benchtop" systems where the equipment is laid out and connected on a bench are also possible; see Figure 3.3) and all outputs and inputs are available to the operator. The operator connects manually to each item as he or she needs to using cables, sets the equipment as per a documented procedure, and records the results.

One of the advantages of manual systems is that they are easier to get up and running than those that require some degree of automation. Software development times for a semi-automated or fully-automated test system can account for the larger proportion of system development

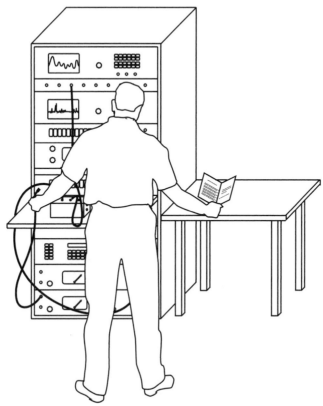

Figure 3.2 A system operator following written operating procedures for a manual test system.

time, particularly if the test system is complex. Manually-controlled systems generally require the use of less expensive test equipment which does not need to have the ability to be programmed. The equipment does, however, need to have full front panel access (all functions accessible through buttons or dials on the front panel), which can limit the choice of equipment available. Shortened development times for a manual system also mean that development costs are lower, and they are comparatively fast to get up and running. In terms of the test system's lifetime, it will also be easier to upgrade a manual system and add tests as system test needs change.

Manual systems rely heavily on test procedure documentation, or standard operating procedures (SOPs, discussed in Section 3.2), and require more skilled operators than a semi- or fully-automated test system, as the test system operator controls all steps of the test process without the assistance of any automation. The results of many tests may require interpretation, and a skilled technician knows which is the next best test to run to isolate a fault or prove a function. Generally, greater degrees of automation require less skill on the part of the operator (see

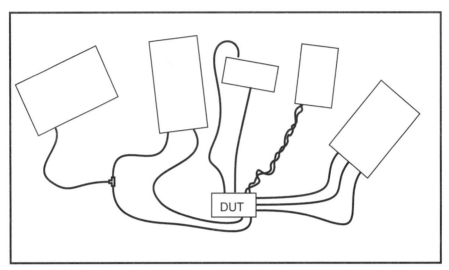

Figure 3.3   View from above of a benchtop test layout.

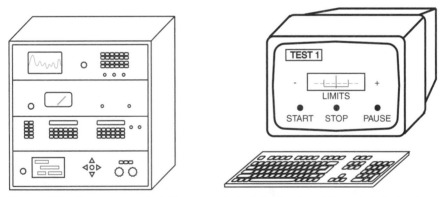

Figure 3.4   Computer control allows you to just display the data and control options required by the operator, rather than the complicated test interface of some complex test equipment.

Figure 3.4). Conversely, a fully-manual test system requires a greater skill level to gain meaningful results.

Since fully-manual test systems are both labor-intensive and procedure-intensive, they have higher operating costs and will have longer test times than a semi- or fully-automated system.

Manual systems are very slow, even when skilled operators are available. So much time is spent on setup, on transcribing results, and on assigning pass and fail units based on actual parametric data required to validate the DUT. The setup time for each test needs to be considered, as well as the number of tests to be run based on the complexity of the DUT. Long testing times can become a disadvantage as the task becomes repetitive and boring, and skilled operators can be better applied to other more complex tasks. Inexperienced operators start by following test procedures blindly and may have trouble establishing factors such as where errors are generated across cables, when a cable has been degraded, or when and when it would not be acceptable to make use of adaptors.

Errors are also more of a concern with manual systems than with semi-automated or fully-automated test systems, although the effects that these errors have on the validity of the results will depend on the sensitivity of your test application. Systematic errors can occur through setup errors or deterioration of equipment such as connectors. Switch interfaces and patch panels are not required for a manual test system; however, the number of connections and reconnections necessary in a manual system mean that there will be more wear and tear (and thus eventually greater losses) on cables and connectors. Reliability should be one of the main goals behind a regular maintenance program for connectors that interface the instruments to the system, along with the cables and adapters. Once a cable is used in a particular section, that cable should always be used in that section until it needs replacing. This avoids the need to recalibrate the test system to the measurement plane every time you move a cable. The same applies for all test system components.

More detailed discussions of errors and uncertainty can be found in various metrology articles and papers. The errors mentioned in this book conform to the conventions generally listed.

Transcription errors and/or "fudged" tests can also degrade the repeatability of test results from a manual system. The opportunity for errors in data entry often occurs twice: once when the results are transcribed onto paper and then again if they are entered into a computer system; this increases the risk of transcription errors. The necessity to repeat tests if procedures have been incorrectly followed can also further slow down the throughput of the system.

Manual systems can encourage informal test procedures, such as the use of cardboard cutouts for limit tests (see Figure 3.5); however, this also means that higher operator skill levels are needed if test requirements change or to troubleshoot any difficulties.

The "cardboard cutout" method (which uses either a cardboard cutout or limit lines set electronically on the test equipment) is valid if all the other test parameters are followed. If the signal output on the screen falls within the cutout with the test equipment setup correctly, then the test is deemed to have been passed. The problem is the result can also be obtained with the test equipment set to the wrong parameters! If the limits are set very wide, then everything will pass through them. You need to monitor that the cutout method is being followed with the correct setups as well; SOPs will normally take care of this, but you always have to take the possibility of ignorance into account.

As the reporting of results is also a manual process, this adds both time and complexity to your test process. In addition to the results from all tested devices, the test system itself must have traceable, documented performance. The results of the system's start-up test procedure (to validate the system itself) must also be documented for each test run. A self-check on a manual

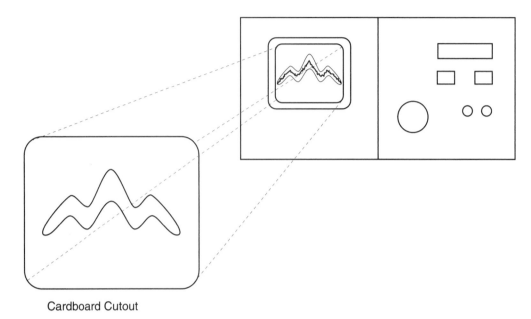

Cardboard Cutout

Figure 3.5   Using a cardboard cutout as a guide to pass/fail limits on a spectrum analyzer.

test system is almost impossible. More complex and more frequent calibration procedures will also be required.

During manual testing, the user must be aware that only the individual instruments are calibrated; however, the test system as a complete unit is not. Hence, the user must apply their own calibration methods or accept some error. To give an example of this, a signal source may be calibrated to within certain limits on its output. However, if a signal of this level is sent down a cable and through a switch, then through an adaptor and into a device, the signal level at the device can be significantly altered. The system as a whole is not calibrated, even though the signal generator is. The system operator would need to measure the signal level before it is injected into the device, after the signal has traversed the cable and the adapter, and alter the signal source level to compensate. This would have to be done every time a cable is attached – it is introducing an error that can be quite large and at best is unreliable.

The three major areas where test strategies are most commonly put into place are production, service and repair, and product development. Of these, manual systems lend themselves best to development and some service areas where skilled operator expertise is more likely to be available and where longer test times are balanced out by the advantages of greater flexibility in test setups. Once full-scale production begins, manual procedures can be a problem, as they are simply too slow to be effective. The cost of production could make product production unviable if test procedures take up too much time. The high throughput levels alone in a full production environment require automated test systems, and the increased accuracy gained by greater control over the test process is also an advantage in marketing the end products.

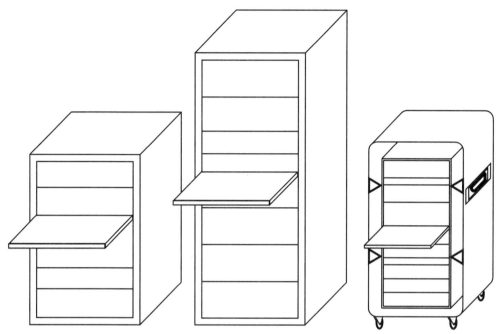

Figure 3.6   Racks in different form factors.

Manual systems normally do not take advantage of the different form factors available in instruments today, because of the need to be able to push buttons and read screens. Hence, size, portability, floor space, and access to systems can sometimes be problematic. The advantages of open architectures such as VXI and PCI are lost if you decide to buy less expensive equipment that is not open to automation – eventually you have to upgrade and buy into the standards anyway to reduce overhead in software design, build, and eventually, support.

Manual systems can be broken down into their individual instruments and re-deployed more quickly than instruments that need programming or computers to operate, since they normally have buttons, displays, and screens. This needs to be weighed carefully against the cost savings of using open standards. How often will you have to move – really?

Vertical form factor is most common (see Figure 3.6); it saves on floor space, and it is almost always possible to get at least two to three meters of height (6 to 10 feet) to position a test system where you cannot get the depth or width. A vertical form factor also has many advantages for cooling and cable distribution as well. Bench space is generally horizontal, which is a poor use of space. Do not be tempted to stack test equipment up on the bench; the likelihood of accidents is too great, and you may damage equipment as well as people.

Concurrent engineering principles are well-suited to a manual test system development environment. The tests used in the design and prototype stages are normally manual. Scientists develop enough tests to prove fundamental concepts – final prototyping and first article testing are most often left to engineers and technicians most skilled in the setting to work of a test system.

A manual system is appropriate for environments where test requirements change frequently or where the DUT complexity of component population is low, making the cost of automation an unnecessary expense. Manual systems generally offer go/no-go testing rather than qualitative test results, as these take much longer on a manual system.

3.1.2   Semi-Automated Control

Semi-automated test systems are the most common type designed and implemented, as they balance the advantages of both manual and fully-automated systems. The form of control here clearly determines the level of automation. The more test equipment under the central computer's control, the greater the likelihood of results being recorded correctly – the repeatability of tests carried out under computer control increases the reliability of the results. The operator's role is to place the DUT into the best position for the computer to have control of the measurement devices. The operator can then focus on the interfaces and getting the cabling correct (see Figure 3.7).

Semi-automated test systems have a moderate cost. Designers have more flexibility in the choice of equipment, as front-panel access is no longer a requirement as it is with a fully-manual system. The test equipment may be a mix of architectures such as "rack and stack," VME, VXI, and so on, depending on your application. The mix can also be of test equipment with individual displays as well as test equipment that can only be interfaced through a computer to get central display capability. All test equipment, however, must be bus-controllable if you want to have computer control over actions or results. A mix of equipment is made easier in a semi-automated system, which also means that it is a little easier to upgrade individual components than it may be in a fully-automated system that may have some architectural restrictions.

Semi-automated test systems generally provide a set of procedures electronically for an operator to follow and automatically transfer results into the computer. The connection to the DUT may be manual, needing to be set up during testing to suit different purposes. Semi-automated systems involve software control of equipment as well as operator SOPs or guided operator control, and the operator does not need to be highly skilled as decision-making is transferred to the computer program, also called the Test Executive (see Figure 3.8). Semi-automated systems are fast compared with manual systems, but cannot match the speed or throughput of fully-automated test systems.

A patch panel can be employed to bring all the measurements and connection points up to the operator – in addition to making all the connections convenient, it saves time finding the correct connector (see Figure 3.9). All the signals that are needed to test a device can be delivered to the patch panel then routed to the DUT directly or through a supporting jig of some type. Often if the DUT is a circuit board, then it will go on a fixture and be hooked by the software to the patch panel and switch the correct paths to the patch panel via the switch matrix. The signals can be measured at the panel to assume correct levels and frequencies and thus calibrate to the mea-

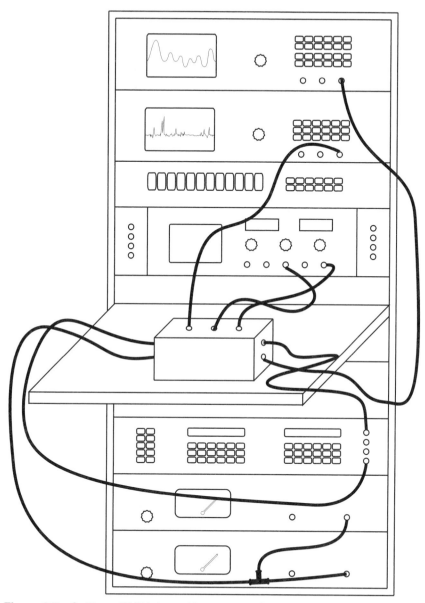

Figure 3.7 Getting a DUT into position on a semi-automated test system.

suring plane of the panel. Some signals may need further conditioning, such as some form of modulation, maybe a PIN switch to produce pulses, or splitting of the signal so that the condition can be monitored for such purposes as amplitude leveling. Adding a patch panel to the interconnect immediately gives you control over cable losses and errors, impedance matching, and adaptors by giving you the ability to calibrate to the point you need. This does not mean that the

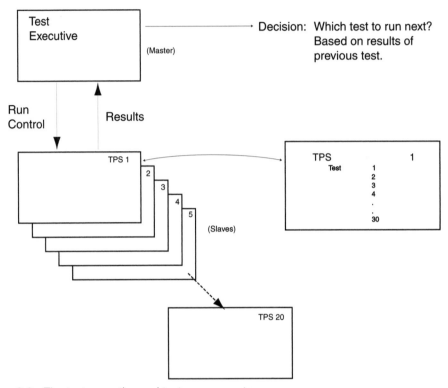

Figure 3.8   The test executive and test program sets.

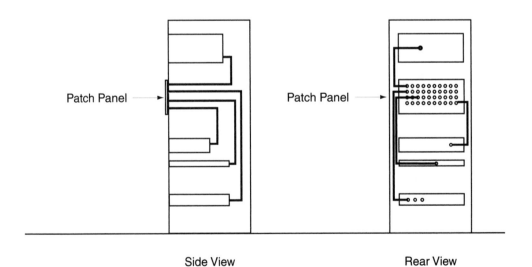

Side View   Rear View

Figure 3.9   Cabling in racks.

losses and mismatches are not there anymore, just that presenting a consistent and reliable measurement plane eliminates having to calibrate and calculate losses and the power or voltage to
overcome them at the end of the cable where you require the correct signal level.

Losses through cables must always be considered, as with any system setup. Once you
have run all the cabling to the panel, behind the covers of the racks, then they are left in place
and your DUT attaches where they terminate – at the patch panel.

Software needs to be structured, for example using a Test Executive, which is a software
manager of modular programs for specific tasks called test program sets (TPS). The costs of
software development and implementation add to the cost of these systems. Software control for
the switch has to be capable of being expanded over time – actually, over and over. Many systems are expected to support parent systems for more than 20 years, which is certainly a challenge in today's rapidly changing technical environment. If a driver is written for the switch
matrix, under the Test Executive or as a TPS, then you have to be able to add new path possibilities as more matrix capability is added. If you decide to write a specific driver, then be prepared
to write and document exactly how you do it, for the benefit of future operators and designers.

Semi-automated systems also lend themselves to less complicated software development
cycles. A developer can use programming environments such as HP VEE™ or National Instruments' LabView™ to quickly develop functioning code. The developer can also make use of
plug-and-play drivers and libraries. Hence, a fully functioning test system can be developed
without "true code cutting." Of course, true code such as C can then be developed to speed
things up after the proof of system is successful. Result storage and data manipulation also
become available with semi-automated systems. These systems also allow the same suite of
equipment to be used by different applications when different software is loaded. However,
beware of the universal tester concept; always have a requirement that can be qualified and
quantified before launching into code.

If a semi-automated test system is being considered, take advantage of the VXI and instruments on a disk form factor, since these are a great method of reducing space, cost, and generally
shrinking the whole system.

Calibration can also start to be planned and introduced from a system perspective. Users
can also halt the process and return to a manual setup if they wish to experiment or do tasks out
of the ordinary, providing they can get access to the control of the instruments (through the front
panel or drivers).

Semi-automated test systems (see Figure 3.10) are sometimes the best way to develop a
fully-automated system. By setting up a semi-automated test system as an intermediate stage to
developing the fully-automated version, test engineers and software programmers can view the
instruments in action and discuss and interpret the test requirements together before attempting
to fully automate the system. Many system houses will develop test systems using a semi-automated, intermediate stage and then move to fully-automated test systems once full production
begins.

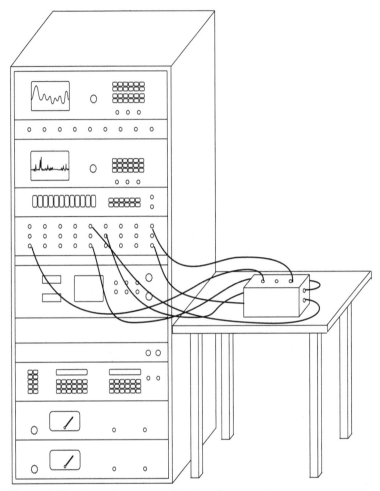

Figure 3.10   A semi-automated test system.

Semi-automated control particularly suits DUTs that are attached to jigs and fixtures since many of these then hold integrated circuit cards, sometimes by edge connection or a variety of connectors on different parts of the module.

If your DUT is extremely complex and there is little difference in the overhead of designing and carrying out manual tests compared with fixture development for automated testing, then you may want to consider not testing the DUT in that way. It may be better and more cost-effective not to automate some of the tests. Section 4.6, "Evaluating the Cost-Effectiveness of Tests," introduces some methods of evaluating whether a particular test method is worthwhile.

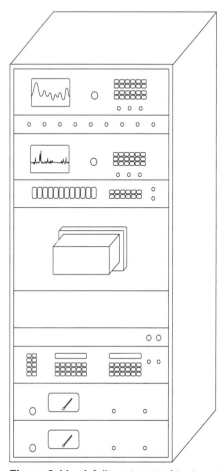

Figure 3.11   A fully-automated test system.

3.1.3   Fully-Automated Control

Fully-automated test systems (or automatic test equipment, ATE; see Figure 3.11), are completely controlled by software. The test equipment settings and signal application to the DUT are controlled through the switch matrix and interface panel. This is the most expensive implementation method, and also the fastest. Extensive use of fixturing gives the operator a single-action connection to the DUT. The operator attaches the DUT to the interface, starts the test procedure, and removes the DUT once tests are completed. There may even be an automatic handler implemented in this type of test environment to further speed the test process and avoid repetitive operator tasks. Fully automating a test system means that skilled staff are freed up to carry out more valuable work. Full automation also means that all the test equipment is going to be bus-controlled, and thus can be more expensive. At the high end of the test equipment market, access to greater functionality can also come with a range of features that increases the price of the test equipment further; the test system designer will need to make trade-offs between cost and features at times. Chapter 4, "Choosing Test Equipment," and Chapter 5, "Sourcing Test Equipment," deal with getting the best results from equipment selection and business relationships with suppliers.

Automated control means that all the settings of the test equipment are known through the computer control software. Whether the operator or computer records the test results is up to the system designer, although much of the speed benefit of a fully-automated system is lost if manual recording is used. Recording all results automatically to disk also allows trend analysis over a series of test results.

A fully-automated test system allows the system designer to create a test setup that will remain unchanged. Such a test system can be made highly accurate by full calibration to the test equipment measuring plane or generation point. All cable lengths should be calibrated. Cable and connector losses need to be considered for better accuracy and quicker measurements.

Increased development costs mean that the cost per test for a fully-automated system is higher, but this is offset by greatly decreased test times and over large volumes, the test cost per unit will drop. In a large-scale manufacturing environment, for example, such as the manufacture of electronic components where millions of products must be tested each year or extremely accurate results are required, fully-automated testing is essential.

Important considerations for a fully-automated test system include:

Go/No-go testing

This can be viewed as simply testing whether the DUT will perform within some limit or be outside the limit. If the DUT is outside the limit, then the test result is considered a no-go result and the device fails. Alternatively, if the device is within the limits, then the test is considered a go result. If the test is a no-go, the system may try to isolate the fault or it may reject the device and start testing the next device. Failed DUTs may be sent to other testing areas to fault find or simply be thrown away – this depends on DUT price, cost to repair, etc.

Parametric recording

This is the recording of all test results as well as the condition and the serial and model numbers of all the equipment used in testing or measurement – this ensures a traceable path from the DUT all the way back to national standards. These results should be kept for as many years as the relevant laws require; most countries require five years.

Increased complexity of the upgrade process

Upgrades of a fully-automated test system can be made more complex as software must be rewritten. To upgrade the test system will require a modification to the software, unless it is simply placing a more highly specified but otherwise identical instrument into the system, such as some new models. However, keep in mind that old software and new test equipment models do not always work well together. Generally it is safe to assume that modifications will need to be made to the software. Hence, it is very important that software is developed and maintained in an orderly fashion. The more robust the development design requirements, the easier the software is to modify.

Test equipment spares

The high throughputs of most fully-automated test systems mean that system downtime has a significant effect on an organization. For critical or high-volume applications, high sparing of test equipment is necessary to avoid system downtime. Test equipment vendors can help you establish an appropriate level of spares. Many vendors work on a common rule of thumb of ten percent sparing of components.

The ability to reconfigure by software

A fully-automated test system can be reconfigured under some circumstances simply by loading a different program. This arrangement should be considered if different production runs for different equipment are being undertaken. For example, during day shift, the system can test production of model A, and during night shift, test repairs to model B. This reconfiguration by software can be extremely useful if your workload in individual systems is random or out of your direct control. All the test functions called by each version of the software must be present in the test system, however, or the program will not operate.

Software development as one of the major cost drivers

Writing software has numerous time overhead costs. Some sources suggest that ten lines of software per day is the most that can conceivably be written by a programmer once the code is fully documented and debugged. Remember that software designers generally do not have test and measurement engineering experience, and that the finer points of instrument control for setup during a measurement may need to be clearly specified to the programmers, as will measurement theory and how to reduce errors. For example, a noise measurement in a spectrum analyzer uses a different detector than a normal trace display. The analyzer will measure the noise with either detector; however, only one will return a correct result.

3.2 Standard Operating Procedures (SOPs)

Standard operating procedures are the written step-by-step instructions for an operator to follow to set up and complete a test. They cover all cables, adapters, correct switch settings, the test itself, which results to transcribe and how to transcribe them, and setup for the next test or shut-down for the test system. Action for failure of a test must be included in the SOP together with corrective processes. SOPs should include features such as an everyday system health check (or cycle of use) and calibration plan so that the system's parametric state is known. If test equipment requires special intervention, for example reprogramming a vector network analyzer when the command set, control language, or software changes, then those details should also be included. Good SOPs are the essence of what standards such as ISO 9000 are trying to achieve – a general three-ring binder of how to do everything that even someone without relevant experience could follow and work out what was going on.

Well-designed SOPs give the organization easy-to-use equipment, repeatability of processes, and standardization of results. They also aid in training new operators as they clearly describe all relevant procedures. As with all aspects of test system design and operation, your SOPs should make your processes repeatable and controllable – you certainly do not want to be in a situation where different operators get different results from your system! In doing so, they also lessen the risk of damaging equipment through incorrect use.

SOPs are a key client communication tool for your organization. You can negotiate for your client to agree to their contents as part of a pre-acceptance testing process. They can be used to trace the accuracy of your system. For this reason, they should be well-thought-out and clearly written documents. They should also be written in such a manner that the least experienced operator could interpret them and work accurately from them. They should not be too verbose, yet they should discuss all relevant information – never assume that something is obvious.

Suitable SOPs are often necessary to fulfill particular audit requirements as well. If your organization is delivering government work, then there is an expectation of a minimum standard of workmanship to specific guidelines. The SOPs can become part of your bid documents in a competitive tender for government work. Keeping good records in a manner that anyone can use and understand has many additional benefits for training as well as general workshop behavior.

SOPs will also need to be maintained so that multiple copies or erroneous versions are not left lying around the equipment or in a location where an old version could accidentally be issued to and used by an operator. They should be endorsed or approved by the chief engineer of the relevant section.

3.3 The Test Executive and Test Program Sets

The Test Executive is the program that the operator will interact with during the running of the test system. It is the overall manager of all the TPSs that are in the system. The Test Executive allows the user to select a TPS from those available and execute that TPS. A large system will contain many TPSs for each assembly or module that is going to be tested. The executive also maintains the housework-type functions of a test system, such as logging in and security functions, storage and retrieval of results, and generation of reports.

TPSs are developed to control a single test or group of functions to be tested on a DUT. The program will control all switches, sources, and instruments during the test. For software control of the system, generally there is a Test Executive that manages all the individual TPSs. Each TPS has all the tests for one DUT type. These are written specifically around the equipment selected for the rack. In most cases a TPS will be written for specific test equipment; this is because a lot of functions will be unique.

Chapter 17, "Using Standard Software and Open Standards for Obsolescence Protection," also discusses aspects of TPSs and their development. Also consider other reference material, as software design is a significant topic in itself.

3.4 Using Results

Careful selection and storage of results allow more than just identifying failed units. Section 1.1.3, "Results," discusses some aspects of selection and storage of data.

When test systems have been operating for a while and a large number of the available population have been tested by the system, then it may be possible to extract data from the results of the test system over time to correlate good or poor units in circulation. For example, if the same unit always has to be adjusted and another never needs adjustment, then the better unit is the one that never needs adjusting. Systems can be designed to bring poor units that may still just pass the test process to the notice of the manager of the system in a higher level report than is seen by the day-to-day operator.

During production line testing, the results of tests that pass all the time may lead you to remove those tests and focus on tests upstream that give you the confidence that those tests will pass all the time if the upstream ones pass all the time.

Care must be taken when driving test conditions that you do not miss something that will have an adverse effect on your DUT; for example, that it does not fail under certain conditions that are commonly experienced outside the test environment. Certain model cars, for example, were known to fail electronically when near particular television towers. No one at the car manufacturer had considered a signal stronger than those at their development site. The television signal swamped the open door signal, and the doors simply would not open for the key-unlock device.

Results that are obtained by using superior test equipment can be used to further give a competitive edge to your product in the marketplace (see Figure 3.12). If you can show by using better test equipment that your noise figure (in the case of a receiver) is better than that of your competitor, and this information is of advantage to you, then it would be careless not to use it.

Getting these results consistently means designing them into your test procedures in the first place; hence, you need good test equipment to start with. Once you have good test equipment, then you can clearly see the real limitations of your setup, your product, or the test equipment. If the test equipment shows your product or DUT in a positive light, then take the opportunity to make this advantage known to get the best promotional results from your product.

3.5 Making Future Control Upgrades Easier

Plan for your upgrades. To help future-proof your system, always design your system with upgrades in mind. Try to determine what your future needs will be compared to your current needs. This means that open standards are used wherever possible and that proper software design techniques are used. Documentation is critical; it must be relevant and complete and to the required standards for the task. Many houses will have their own standards; whatever they are, they guarantee for that organization that they will be able to reliably reproduce their processes. These may be ISO 9000 documents proving conformance to a specified methodology.

Upgrading to new models of existing equipment in the system is perhaps the simplest way to upgrade; however, as mentioned before, some new models may not be completely compatible

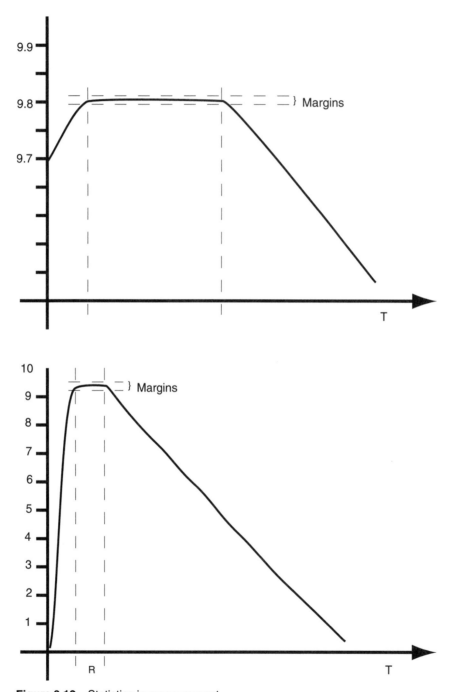

Figure 3.12   Statistics in measurement.

with the existing software. Computers are always a problem with automated and semi-automated test systems, and it tends to be a company and user decision whether to use PC, UNIX, or other operating systems. Everyone has their preferred system, and the choice of operating system will often be influenced by the requirements of the test application itself.

Also plan whether you are going to upgrade the level of automation of your system and plan the initial design to make this change easier later on; for example, deliberately include blank facia panels and use larger racks than initially required.

3.5.1 Reasons for Upgrading a Test System

Upgrading a test system can be an expensive and time-consuming effort. Reasons for upgrading a test system would need to justify the expense and effort involved. They can include:

- Better test coverage. More tests, more accurate tests, or faster tests all reduce costs and time taken overall. Eliminating redundant tests through improved analysis or results also decreases the overall test cost.
- Redeploying skilled staff to more valuable and complex applications by using automation leads to the overall reduction of costs for your organization as capacity is increased. Their processes and skill can be built into the test system to give consistently reliable test results without having to tie up expensive test technicians and test engineers on repetitive tasks. In a restricted employment market or where an organization is training a number of less experienced people, test system automation increases the flexibility of your organization and access to senior engineers.
- Gaining greater production figures. As new equipment comes on the market or your design becomes so advanced that you can reduce your test requirements, you can take advantage of the latest in test technology to improve your throughput and make more devices, faster at lower cost per item. You can even claim better specifications in your marketing material by using more advanced equipment that is not in itself limited, and thus improve your competitive position in the market.
- A reduction in support costs. If test equipment in your system becomes obsolete, or if your in-house-built equipment fails and the original designer is not available, then you may have to upgrade your equipment to keep on working and giving the same support or better than when you started.

If you do decide to support your test equipment beyond the manufacturer's provided support life, here are some practices that will be helpful:

- Make a lifetime spares purchase from the manufacturer if you are notified of the end-of-support-life date in sufficient time.
- Search second-hand equipment suppliers and Web sites.
- Watch for government disposal auctions.

- Use your professional network to keep an eye out for unusual sources of the equipment you require.

Supporting equipment past the manufacturer's support life complicates your organization's whole support and logistics processes. Unless there is a compelling reason to remain with a particular piece of equipment, then when a manufacturer decides to drop support, so should you. The benefits and cost of doing it yourself are low and high, respectively.

Upgrading from a manual to semi-automated or a semi- to fully-automated test system is a reasonable reason for analyzing what needs to be done to get the best life out of a test system. This involves serious software changes and should not be taken on lightly, but it remains an appropriate reason to consider upgrading.

If you intend to upgrade your software capability, and not to upgrade your hardware capability or upgrade it minimally at best, then you need to understand the trade-offs concerned. To upgrade the routines to give better throughput or results would in most cases be as big an effort as rewriting the software based on the same principles and objectives as before, from scratch. You need to decide whether you will update both hardware and software with relatively little incremental effort, or just try to upgrade your existing software. Test equipment manufacturers will be driven by market forces to continue to improve their equipment, so you will find that even though your objectives do not change, the way to accomplish them will change over time.

At final analysis, it will be a mix of events and conditions that leads you to upgrade a test system or to consider an upgrade and to carry out the analysis. You will have to do the figures at some stage to determine whether you are still getting the best value out of your system, and establish whether an upgrade would be a profitable exercise for your organization.

PART 2

Test System Design – Building a Completely New System

Designing a new test system (as opposed to upgrading an existing test system) involves translating an operational or technical need into a set of test specifications and a working system solution. Eliminating redundancy and choosing the minimum set of test equipment that meets your requirements helps you manage costs and test cycle times. Managing relationships with partners such as test equipment vendors can also provide you with additional sources of information on possible solutions such as special options or custom work.

Making sure that good documentation is provided with the test system is a significant investment in ensuring that overall system lifetime costs (which include operation, maintenance, repair, and upgrade) are kept as low as possible.

CHAPTER 4

Choosing Test Equipment

T his chapter explains how to determine what test equipment you need to obtain the most effective test solution using a method such as the test parameters matrix described in this chapter. It also examines how to get the most from your test equipment by eliminating redundant tests or pieces of equipment and considering some of the investment decisions involved in the purchase of test equipment. Some of the trade-offs test designers have to consider are also discussed; for example, between the costs and benefits of some tests, or test coverage vs. test development time.

KEY POINTS:

- An effective test system solution is based on technical specifications, budget, and project timeframe.
- Good planning improves your system lifetime ROI.
- Use the test parameters matrix to fully specify your test alternatives and avoid reworking your design.
- Know when to contract your work packages, and which ones.
- Eliminate redundant tests and evaluate the cost-effectiveness of tests before choosing your test equipment.
- Plan now for future upgrades to save money and later rework, and to help with obsolescence protection.

4.1   Designing an Effective and Efficient Test Solution

In designing a test system, you will be influenced not only by engineering specifications, but also by budget and time constraints. The key issue for any engineer is how to design an effective system in the least possible time and with the lowest possible cost. A good design will address all three issues, and this chapter outlines some tools that can help you go through the process quickly.

It is tempting to build a test system simply by starting to connect pieces of test equipment together. However, starting without a plan will almost always lead to redundancy or rework. Your test system should perform your required tests in an efficient manner and with the minimum amount of test equipment and fixturing required for an effective solution. Unnecessary redundancy – i.e., redundancy which you have not deliberately included in your system – wastes time and money, either through rework as you improve the system or by requiring a higher upfront cost for equipment, cables, fixtures, and so on. Either case will lower your ROI for the system. Starting with a cost-effective design involves more time spent planning at the start of your system design project, but it is a good investment which will pay off in an easier system implementation. By planning for future upgrades in your system design, you can also ensure that your long-term cost of ownership is minimized; this will give you a higher long-term ROI.

The test parameters matrix described in this chapter will help you evaluate the minimum number of pieces of test equipment that will solve your test requirements. Guidelines on common design trade-offs will help you through the process of eliminating redundant tests and evaluating the cost-effectiveness of tests. Most engineers will build their own guidelines or rules of thumb over time. This chapter covers rules of thumb relating to "coverage vs. development time" and "costs vs. benefit of test" which are easy to apply to most situations.

4.2   Drawing up the Test Parameters Matrix

While it may be easy to work out what test equipment you need for a small test system, complex systems with a large number of signals can be difficult to specify, or at the least are difficult to specify without redundancy. The test parameters matrix works by building a matrix of the signals you need to apply to your DUT to verify all inputs and outputs of the DUT. You can then use the matrix to eliminate any redundant tests, and draw up a list of the minimum amount of test equipment required.

You may decide to break out this part of your system project as a separate work package and assign it to a third-party company or consultant. The benefits of doing this include access to test equipment expertise and freeing your time (or your engineers' time) for other work. If there are projects or work packages that are more urgent or offer greater benefits for your investment of time, then contracting out this task is a more effective use of your resources. Even if you contract out the selection of test equipment, though, it will still help to evaluate your contractor's work if you understand the selection process itself.

TIP:

WHEN TO ASSIGN THE "SELECTION OF TEST EQUIPMENT" TO A THIRD PARTY OR CONSULTANT

- A specialist will be able to provide a solution more quickly, in circumstances where your project is under time constraints.
- Your engineers (or you) have a more valuable or more urgent use for their time.
- Due to internal costs and the time involved, a contractor will be able to provide this service at a lower cost than performing this task in-house.

To draw up the test parameters matrix, start with a block diagram of the DUT. If you are designing tests for a complex system or circuit board, first consider your DUT in terms of functional areas, as even a simple device can give you a large test parameters matrix. To build up the matrix, begin by listing the number and types of inputs and outputs for each device and the parameter you need to measure. You will end up with a matrix of signals (voltage/frequencies, etc.) which need to be applied or measured. To populate your matrix with possible test equipment, you will need to consider measurement techniques, the accuracy of measurement required, and the control method you have decided to use for your test system (see Chapter 3).

Whether you decide to use this or another method of building a test equipment list that suits your work style better, the method you use should be:

- Thorough.
- Able to identify redundancy.
- Flexible enough to allow easy updating with any system revisions or upgrades.

Figure 4.1 and Table 4.1 show how to develop a test parameters matrix for an amplifier that is a sub-component on a circuit board, or a higher power standalone device.

Table 4.1 shows the matrix of possible test equipment for this amplifier for each of the three control methods discussed in Chapter 3 (manual, semi-automated, and fully-automated). We will examine the differences these control decisions make to the equipment for your test system, and also how an upgrade path from a manual to an automated system would work if this were planned in stages over time. The matrix in Table 4.1 also contains some of the information you will need later in the racking process, such as connectors and cabling options.

The major benefit of using the test parameters matrix is that you fully specify your test requirements. By using this or a similar process at the start of your test system project, you will avoid missing any of your required tests or missing opportunities to make multiple uses of a piece of test equipment. Neophyte engineers also often miss test throughput time, particularly

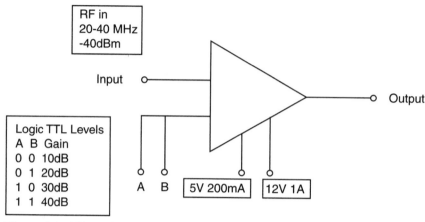

Figure 4.1   HF amplifier.

Test Requirements for HF Amplifier

Frequency Hz

Gain dB

Level – Frequency Response

---

that the measurement time for the programmer or designer includes the setup time as well. Although it sounds straightforward, these are the most common errors made by test engineers on their first test system project. Having to rework a design to include missed technical specifications will cost time and cause frustration, particularly if the engineer has reached the build stage of the project before realizing that changes need to be made.

The matrix will have more than one piece of test equipment listed for most tests. Once you have eliminated any redundant tests (see below), you will use rules of thumb, experience, and your knowledge of measuring techniques to decide on your final list.

4.3 Eliminating Redundant Tests

You may receive a set of test requirements that your test system must meet, or you may be drawing up the test requirements yourself as described in Section 4.2. A well-specified set of test requirements should not normally include any redundant tests. However, it is still worth checking for redundancy; for example, where the results of one test may be covered either explicitly or implicitly in another test, to avoid overspecifying your test equipment or test automation software. For example, the test parameters matrix in Table 4.1 includes a specification in the middle of the pass band for level, which is redundant because we are also testing frequency response.

Another factor that can increase the speed or efficiency of your test system is to eliminate range changes where possible. If you need to change from the 1-volt range to the 10-volt range,

Table 4.1 Test Parameters Matrix for HF Amplifier

	Required Parameter	Manual System	Semi-Automated System-Bus Control	Automated System-Bus Control
DC Supply	5V 200mA 12V 1A	DC supply x2, or dual DC supply	DC supply x2, or dual DC supply	DC supply x2, or dual DC supply
RF In	20 – 30 MHz -40 dBm	RF signal generator Scalar network analyzer	RF signal generator Scalar network analyzer Vector network analyzer	RF signal generator Scalar network analyzer Vector network analyzer
RF Out	Frequency response, flatness At 25MHz – 0dBM with 40dB gain stage active	Spectrum analyzer, scalar network analyzer, power meter	Spectrum analyzer, scalar network analyzer, vector network analyzer	Spectrum analyzer, scalar network analyzer, vector network analyzer, vector signal analyzer
	Gain	Spectrum analyzer, power meter, scalar network analyzer, oscilloscope	Spectrum analyzer, power meter, scalar network analyzer, vector network analyzer	Spectrum analyzer, power meter, scalar network analyzer, vector network analyzer, vector signal analyzer
Frequency	Stability, accuracy	Oscilloscope, frequency counter	Frequency counter	Frequency counter
Max Output Level	1dB compression point	Spectrum analyzer, scalar network analyzer, power meter	Spectrum analyzer, scalar network analyzer, vector network analyzer	Spectrum analyzer, scalar network analyzer, vector network analyzer, vector signal analyzer
Digital Control	2 inputs, 2 states 0V, 5V	DC power supplies	Power supply, digital IO cards in controller	Digital IO cards
Interface		Manual connect to individual instruments by cables (see Figure 4.2)	All inputs and outputs connected to a patch panel, all instruments in test system connected to back of patch panel (see Figure 4.3)	Connection to fixtures by edge connection or to connectors; fixture attaches in one movement to test system/all fixture connectors parallel for best electrical connection (see Figure 4.4)
Connectors		BNC, APC-7	BNC, APC-7	Fixture – high-grade quick connect - BNC, APC-7
Cables		High-grade	High-grade	High-grade; custom-made for correct sex and type, e.g., type N (f)
Switches		None	Switch all inputs and outputs to a patch panel with connectors on it	Switch all inputs and outputs to the back of the fixture connection panel
Recording of Data		Manual entry to log book or computer	Some entries manual, some automated	All entries automated to computer

PM – power meter

DIO – digital IO

NOTE: SNA and VNA have inputs and outputs; the output is sampled continuously, which corrects the input.

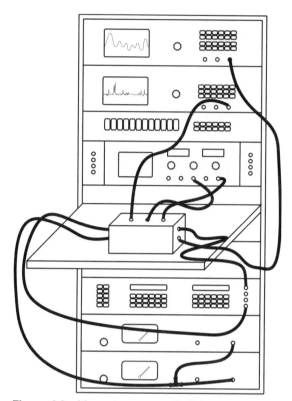

Figure 4.2 Manual connect to individual instruments.

then back to the 3-volt range, it would take more time than going through 1-, 3-, and then 10-volt range changes. These types of range changes eat up microprocessor cycles and reduce the test system's throughput time. For fastest operation, group all your measurements where possible so that you only use each item of test equipment once in your test cycle.

It is also important to note the effects on the accuracy of your measurement if you work at the extreme ends of a measuring range for a piece of equipment. Accuracy often includes a "% of range" factor, so working at the low end of the range gives a proportionally larger error band than working at the high end of the same range. Checking your error bands may give you opportunities to make multiple uses of a piece of test equipment. Most oscilloscopes can now make counter measurements, for example, so if the accuracy is acceptable, then using the oscilloscope eliminates equipment (the counter), cables, and switches, and can avoid equipment range changes as well.

When you design a test system, take care to analyze all tests and test objectives carefully. The tests themselves must give meaningful information about the health of the DUT, with this information being gained with the minimum possible time and resource overhead. The tests must make use of the test equipment in such a way that tests do not need to be repeated. It is

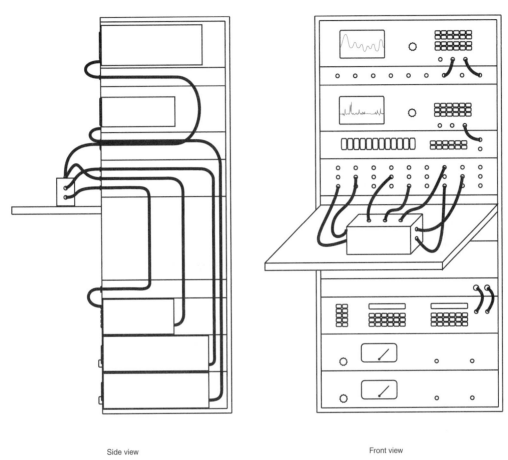

Side view   Front view

Figure 4.3 Instruments connected to the back of a patch panel (side and front views shown).

advantageous to create a state where measurements can be made with a fixed set of conditions and other tests can be done under the same test conditions.

It is likely that the number of tests or the test methodology in the system will change over time. If the test system software (for semi-automated and fully-automated systems) has been designed with future flexibility in mind, then the older code can be re-used with new or modified tests added. This is only possible, however, if the existing system software is fully and clearly documented. Avoid adding to the TPS or making changes to a system before you have examined what is already present, as you may find that some current measurement software is made up of modules that can also be used for your revised test requirements. Good documentation will also help you avoid duplicating test software at any stage in the test system's lifetime. The system design objectives are where you will pick up the redundancies. Compare these when you plan to add new tests or when you want to replace test equipment.

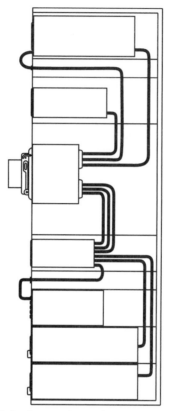

Figure 4.4   Connection to fixtures by edge connect.

4.4   Using the Test Parameters Matrix to Choose Test Equipment

The test parameters matrix will allow you to choose a list of the minimum test equipment that will meet your test requirements. Table 4.1 lists the possible test equipment selections for the HF amplifier in the example, with a list for a manual, semi-automated, and fully-automated system, including multiple units where they are required.

In most cases, you will end up with more than one reasonable solution for the test parameters matrix. The matrix developed in Table 4.1 has a number of possible test equipment configurations. The next stage in your design process is to start making decisions about the most effective solution, given any technical and budget constraints. The first step is to consider the equipment itself, including features and capability, and then to consider test development trade-offs, depending on factors such as development time and ROI constraints for your project.

Sections 4.5 and 4.6 discuss some of the issues involved in selecting specific tests and test equipment, while Section 4.7 lists one of the possible choices of test equipment for a manual, semi-automated, and fully-automated test system for the HF amplifier used in this chapter.

You may wish to show your test parameters matrix to selected test equipment vendors to give them a complete picture of your test objectives. Knowledgeable equipment vendors may have some lateral ideas you have not yet considered. They may even be prepared to release information about upcoming new product releases under a non-disclosure agreement if the new product is suitable. Being able to choose from the very latest test equipment will also help you extend the support life of your test system.

4.5 Getting the Most from Your Equipment

There are two main areas where you can influence the ROI of your system design: choosing specific pieces of test equipment and getting the most effective use of the equipment once you have chosen it.

Cost is normally one of the major concerns when choosing test equipment. Equipment should be functional enough to meet your current test requirements as well as any planned short-term additional capacity. It is normally not a good idea to purchase expensive equipment features based on long-term requirements. Most modern equipment can be upgraded at a later stage or sometimes traded in to the supplier with a later purchase. Time value of money calculations will usually show that if the cost of the feature is high and the time before it will be used (i.e., a return on the investment) is long, then the money can be better invested elsewhere in your project. Whatever equipment decisions you make, amortization of the test equipment should be included in your project costings.

TIP:

Whenever you buy test equipment, even if for the benchtop or a fully-manual test system, always invest in bus control if it is not standard. (This is usually a low- or zero-cost option if ordered at time of purchase.) This means that you will easily be able to use this piece of equipment in an automated test system at a later stage, or upgrade your manual system to partial or full automation.

The cost of test equipment compared with the production cost of your product or the importance of your test will also influence your buying decisions. Several types of instrument may be appropriate for a particular test; for example, a spectrum analyzer, scalar network analyzer, vector network analyzer, and power meter can all make RF level measurements. However, the accuracy of your results, for example, may vary. Some tests may be too expensive to be cost-effective, depending on the cost of the test equipment and the benefits you expect to gain from carrying out the test. Some pieces of test equipment can also be too expensive to use unless the throughput of your system is high enough to give you a good return on your investment. In Table 4.1, for example, the vector signal analyzer is only included in the possible equipment list for the fully-automated system, as the throughput in a manual or semi-automated system is unlikely to be high enough to warrant the cost of this piece of equipment. You may have an application where accuracy or a particular test capability is important enough to justify more expensive equipment. This is the point at which you will start to make trade-offs to choose the best of the available test solutions.

Table 4.2 lists three top factors that should be considered when you choose equipment for a test system.

Table 4.2 Some ROI Factors for a Test System

Some Factors that Influence Equipment Investment Choices for a Test System
Do the benefits of additional test capability outweigh the cost of that capability?
Will a smaller investment meet current and short-term upgrade needs?
Will faster test equipment give you a high enough test system throughput to make the more expensive equipment worthwhile?

4.6 Evaluating the Cost-Effectiveness of Tests

Engineers develop their own rules of thumb for test system design. The guidelines we have included here cover some of the main issues a test engineer will encounter.

1. Decisions on tests and test equipment. Here we consider:

    • Cost of test vs. benefits of test; for example, where a test ends up being more expensive than the DUT itself. This comes down to component populations on the DUTs vs. cost per item.

    • Coverage of tests vs. development time constraints.

2. Getting more effective use from the equipment you have chosen. Here we consider:

    • Using data buses vs. relay control lines.

    • Planning for multiple users.

    • Planning now for future system upgrades.

4.6.1   Cost of Test vs. Benefit of Test

Once you have a couple of options for test equipment which can carry out a particular measurement, the first decision is usually to consider what degree of accuracy you require and the cost of the equipment. A spectrum analyzer and frequency counter can both measure frequency; however—providing the requirements for dynamic range are met—the counter is typically the more accurate of the two. This trade-off process in specifications is where your business relationships with suppliers can be beneficial. An experienced supplier representative can give advice in particular circumstances by providing application notes or similar material on test techniques.

> **TIP:**
>
> Always budget for the best cables you can afford. The benefits in accuracy, reliability, and minimizing losses will pay back your investment; the reduction in maintenance and connector problems cannot be emphasized enough. Always have your cables terminated in the correct connector to avoid having to use adapters, as they increase errors and uncertainty as well as wear on the connectors themselves.

The costs of some tests may outweigh the benefits you receive from them, depending on the test equipment and fixturing required to do the test. For low production volumes, the cost of a fixture may outweigh the yield benefit of carrying out the test, and it may be a better investment to focus on improving the assurance of the manufacturing process itself. You will need to trade off failure rates against the incremental improvements in yield and decrease in product returns. In addition to a purely economic trade-off, the type of market you are in and the effects of customer satisfaction on your long term sales – i.e., not just the sales for this particular product – will play a part in this decision. Your profit margins will also be relevant. For high-profit-margin products, you can weight your decision more strongly toward the investment in test, particularly if the costs of rework or repair by replacement are high.

Your choices when you are making test trade-offs are basically:

- Can the test be omitted? (Are the results going to make a difference?)
- Can the test be done another way? Do you need to test 12 or 4000 points in a frequency response measurement – the answer to this question gives two different methods and costs of performing the tests.
- Can the test results be derived from other data? Statistical derivation, for example, can be used in many cases where complex microwave measurements are used.

Each of these options is discussed below.

Omitting the Test

This decision depends on a number of factors relating to your product, your application, your customers, and the marketplace or field of action for your product. The test engineer's judgment and your company's or organization's standard operating practices will play the major role in this decision. Table 4.3 lists some of the factors that will influence your thinking on this decision.

Omitting a test is a serious consideration, unless it is clearly redundant or obviously serves no purpose. The decision should take into consideration what you need to supply under contract to satisfy a test requirement or contractual obligation. The tests you are going to run and spend engineering time developing should already have been well-tested for suitability – even so, you should continue to evaluate your decisions.

Table 4.3   Factors Affecting Cost vs. Benefit Decisions

Factors Which Weight Investment Decisions Toward Testing	Factors Which Weight Investment Decisions Against Testing
High profit margins	Low profit margins (focus on improving manufacturing processes instead)
High cost of repair or replacement	Repair costs or module/product manufacturing costs (for repair by replacement strategy) are low
Customer satisfaction crucial to long-term company success	Good manufacturing processes give close to zero failure rates, or existing failure rates deemed to be acceptable
Revenue/profits from improved yield outweigh cost of fixture or test equipment	Cost of fixture or test equipment outweigh revenue/profits from incremental yield
The product is required for a mission-critical application	Consequences of product failure are judged to be acceptable

Doing the Test Another Way

The test parameters matrix in Table 4.1 shows a number of equipment alternative; for example, for tests such as frequency response or flatness. The spectrum analyzer, scalar network analyzer, and vector network analyzer can all make these measurements. Your choice of equipment will be based on accuracy, usability (which is most relevant to a fully-manual system), cost, and speed. A spectrum analyzer will only be able to make a measurement point by point, which relies on the RF source accuracy as well as the accuracy of the spectrum analyzer. Spectrum analyzers are optimized for frequency rather than amplitude, which affects the accuracy of amplitude measurements made on a spectrum analyzer vs. some other test instruments. A scalar network analyzer is broadband in its detection, and while more accurate than the spectrum analyzer, it suffers from the broadband products adding to the measurement. A vector network analyzer uses a differently designed front end to reduce broadband errors and has significant error reduction techniques built in. Using the vector network analyzer is by far the best measurement technique from a purely technical point of view, but it is also a very expensive solution.

If you have multiple signal inputs, for example, establish whether they need to be simultaneous. Your test setup can also influence the cost-effectiveness of tests. If you need to stimulate four ports sequentially, it can be done fairly easily with a single, simple device. If the four ports have to be tested simultaneously, then you will either need a multiple output device or several devices with individual outputs. Either way, simultaneous multiple outputs require much more complex test solutions and control software, particularly if there will be upgrades to the test system in the future.

Spending time with some test experts and measurement experts can often help you see other ways to do things.

Deriving Results from Other Data

This option would generally only be necessary if you are designing a test system under budget restrictions. Deriving results is usually a cumbersome process and should be avoided if possible. One exception to this, however, would be in the very early stages of product development, where changes in product design may mean that it is not practical to automate your test system until the product (and therefore the test process) is more stable. For the HF amplifier in the example above, the group delay measurement is an important test, but the cost of the vector network analyzer required is prohibitive when you consider just the amplifier itself. Depending on the value of the product the amplifier is used in and the additional benefit (ROI) you could get from the VNA in other test applications, it may make sense to purchase the equipment. However, in a manual or semi-automated system, you could derive the group delay results by calculating the first derivative of the phase difference. Thus, you use only a suitable oscilloscope and signal generator, getting more effective use from those pieces of equipment. In a fully-automated system, you would need to consider whether the cost of purchasing the vector network analyzer outweighs the development costs of the test software to derive the results using less expensive equipment. Section 5.5.3, "Derive the Result from Other Parameters," also discusses other aspects and examples of achieving this.

The derivation of results from statistical methods is often difficult to document properly; make sure that you include the additional costs for this.

4.6.2   Coverage vs. Development Time

In a high-volume environment, or where time to market is your key concern, you may have to make some trade-offs between test coverage and test development time.

If you have ten parameters to test but your project schedule (for whatever reason) only allows you time to develop tests for eight of them, you will have to make some considered choices about your test plan. Your options are the same as with cost of test vs. benefit of test with one important addition:

- Can the test be omitted?
- Can the test be done another way?
- Can the test results be derived from other data?
- Can the development of this test be outsourced?

The criteria you should consider when making development time decisions are the same as for cost vs. benefit issues above. As mentioned earlier, the third option, deriving results from other data, is cumbersome and should be avoided if possible.

Outsourcing test development can be a valid option for the same reasons that apply to outsourcing the selection of test equipment (see the tip in Section 4.2 for the major reasons for outsourcing). It is vital to specify your test requirements with precision to get delivery of a high-quality, timely result. A vague or ambiguous test description will result in your contractor taking longer to deliver a solution as they clarify your requirements, or delivering a solution which is not quite what you require.

4.7 Equipment Lists

Here are three possibilities for final equipment lists to test the HF Amplifier in Figure 4.1, which is based on the trade-off guidelines discussed above. The lists are for a manual, semi-automated, and fully-automated test system. Each version of the system will have its own degree of complexity, and test throughput will reflect this.

Manual	Semi-Automated	Fully-Automated
DC power supply x 4	Dual DC supply	Dual DC supply
RF generator	Signal network analyzer (includes RF generator)	Vector network analyzer
Power meter		Counter
Oscilloscope	Counter	Digital IO cards
	Digital IO cards	

The manual system will be slow, as the operator will be physically switching power supplies and devices, manipulating cables, and attaching them once they find the right connector. The frequency response measurement will be tedious, especially since you have to do enough points to verify that the specification is met. The oscilloscope is adequate for this frequency measurement.

The semi-automated system will be moderately fast, the major savings coming from having all the cabling now internally routed to a patch panel, whether it is through a switch or not. Instruments without bus control will still have to be set by hand and the results manually entered. You still have to connect and disconnect at the right times to the right connectors. The program will have to wait at each step for you to accomplish this. A counter is now doing the frequency measurement, as it is much faster than the oscilloscope, and has some statistical ability that may be handy.

The automated system is similar to the semi-automated one except that now the DUT is only connected to the test system once and all the switching is done behind the panels. As each test completes, the next one starts as soon as it is electrically possible. The SNA has been replaced with a VNA, as it is faster, much more accurate, and does not require any user knowledge by the operator. The VNA can also measure phase, so the manufacturer could claim an additional specification by now adding group delay and more accurate impedance vs. frequency plots. Additionally, all the stages of automation described here could have had a spectrum analyzer added for distortion measurements should they have been required.

4.8 Effective Use of the Equipment

Once you have chosen your test equipment list, allow some time to plan for getting the most effective use out of this equipment. You need not implement all decisions at this point, but if you intend to include planned upgrades in your test system project, you will benefit from planning them at this stage. Decisions such as equipment and accessory placement, wiring and cabling, and level of automation are all influenced by your future plans. By planning now for future needs, you can build your current system with anticipated changes in mind, thus avoiding some rework and increased costs later on. For example, cabling in single-layer cable trays will allow easy access for rework during your system upgrade. Test software development will also be influenced, although software development is not covered fully in this book.

Your long-term plans for the system will influence whether you use data buses or relay control lines. Depending on the required speed and complexity of stimulating data buses, you may consider several options. Simple logic using one or two lines is slow, and requires power supplies and relay control lines. With medium-density data buses, up to about 16 channels, you can still use relay control lines, but you are approaching the need for direct input/output (DIO). This, however, requires programming. High-density data buses – perhaps hundreds of lines – require either DIO or a pattern generator.

Planning for multiple user stations on one ATE, either in your original design or as a planned system upgrade, can help lower your system lifetime costs. Figure 4.5 shows the additional switching required to allow this. Part 4 of this book, "Upgrading a Test System," goes into more detail about obsolescence protection and racking upgrades.

Upgrading requires knowing the gap in capability between your current system and what you need. The test parameters matrix has to be upgraded to add capability. This also adds switches, cables, and software for control and switching.

For testing the amplifier in Figure 4.1, you have three possible upgrade paths: manual to semi-automated, manual to fully-automated, and semi- to fully-automated. Although this was a simple example, you can see how some initial planning for the first system allows easier upgrading over time to improve throughput.

Upgrading from manual to semi-automated or semi- to fully-automated involves analysis of the current position and the gap remaining to achieve what is required. The decision on what to save or what can be saved is based on ability as well as support and programmability. Generally, cables can be kept if they have not been exposed to environmental extremes. All cables should be swept on a network analyzer to ensure integrity. If the control method of the system is being changed, then the command codes for the test equipment will have to be used again. If they have been stored properly, this should not be a problem.

If the system was insufficiently documented, then upgrading the level of control means that you are really starting again on the whole test system. At this point, you need to pause and re-examine the options of upgrading vs. redesigning the system from scratch, as the software development overhead would end up being roughly the same. Under these conditions, it may

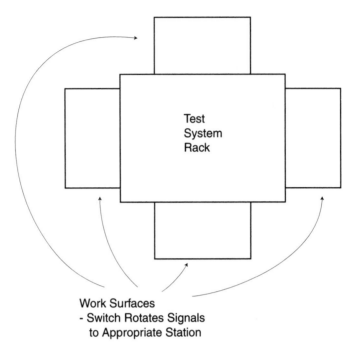

Test
System
Rack

Work Surfaces
- Switch Rotates Signals
to Appropriate Station

Figure 4.5   Switching required for multiple users on one test system.

make sense to start the design process again and gain advantages from fully updating the hardware as well as the software of the system.

Chapter 19, "Interface, Rack Layout, and Software Revision for an Upgraded Test System," covers additional approaches on replacing equipment, evaluating the existing switch interface, redesigning the rack layout, adding or updating software, and updating system documentation.

CHAPTER 5

Sourcing Test Equipment

$\mathbf{T}$his chapter deals with selecting and purchasing specific pieces of test equipment based on the equipment specifications you have decided on, and getting added value from your relationships with suppliers. We will also look at some standard and some less commonly known options that have special relevance for test system design.

The development of the test parameters matrix described in Chapter 4 (or a similar tool that allows you to establish the minimum list of test equipment required) should take place in parallel with you updating your knowledge of what test equipment is available. New products and feature upgrades are frequently released, especially in fast moving areas such as communications, and before you choose specific pieces of test equipment, you will need to know the latest capabilities that are available. You will probably also have a list of companies or suppliers with which you prefer to work.

When selecting test equipment, it can sometimes be difficult to compare performance between one manufacturer and another. Specifications can be presented differently on the equipment's datasheet, or definitions of capability can be presented differently. Some datasheets contain footnotes which specify a range of conditions for a quoted level of performance. The art of "specmanship," or experience in interpreting the nuances of technical datasheets, can become a valuable part of the test system designer's toolkit to help you sort out which information you really need from the datasheet.

You can also leverage your relationship with good vendors to make your design process more effective; for example, through selection of equipment options or through applying the supplier's expertise in certain areas of test technology. Most test equipment will come with a range of standard options; however. many companies will also have "special options" available which are not part of the standard production run setups, but which can still be ordered. A vendor who understands your test application will be able to offer valuable advice on the most suitable products and options available at the time, and will also be able to take your anticipated future needs into account.

There may also be times when commercially available test equipment does not meet your needs. Some state-of-the-art semiconductor devices, for example, have a reduced lifespan in the high-radiation environment of space unless the supplier has included radiation hardening in the manufacturing process. This is an expensive process, and as fewer manufacturers are producing this type of component, it may be difficult to source everything you need for a particular space application from commercial suppliers. Designing and manufacturing custom test equipment will always increase your costs, but the investment may be warranted if your application is critical or if the test cannot be redesigned.

Your equipment sourcing or equipment purchase plan should always take delivery and development lead times into account. In a time-critical environment, it may be important to start negotiating with suppliers well in advance of your anticipated order date, especially if you require any customization or development of equipment.

A test system must be traceable to national standards to satisfy a direct audit chain. Equipment and system calibration costs can be a significant part of a test system's lifetime support costs, but without traceability to standards, the system's test results cannot be relied upon. When examining the calibration cost portion of a test system's lifetime support cost, it is important to consider factors such as whether the equipment can be calibrated locally or must be shipped out of the country. Some pieces of test equipment have shorter calibration cycles when used under certain conditions; for example, equipment that runs under battery rather than main power.

The warranty offered by equipment and component suppliers will vary. If the conditions covered by the supplier's standard warranty do not meet your system requirements, then the supplier will either have standard terms for extended support, or should have enough support cost data available to be able to negotiate a specific support contract for your application.

KEY POINTS:

- Decide whether outsourcing equipment selection makes sense for your project.
- Evaluate both equipment and the company supplying the equipment.
- Work with good suppliers to add value to your test system solution.
- Evaluate options carefully if you cannot match your needs to a commercial item.
- Manage your order placement and contract closeout processes just as well as you manage the project itself.

5.1 Deciding Whether to Outsource Equipment Selection

Deciding whether to outsource the selection of test equipment is a business decision affected by factors within your organization and your project as a whole, as well as the availability of people with suitable knowledge in this area. As discussed in Section 4.2, there are a number of reasons why you would choose to outsource the selection of test equipment. The main factors influencing your decision are time and cost. Your time and the time of any of your staff is valuable. If a contractor with test equipment expertise can do this task at a lower cost than the value of the time that you would spend on it, then outsourcing can become a good financial decision. You may have work that is more urgent or that will provide greater benefits to your organization than if you spent that time selecting test equipment. The priority of a particular task and the benefit it brings to the organization will allow you to set relative hierarchies of work. Assuming that the necessary skills exist, high-priority, high-benefit tasks would be completed within the organization. Work that is of relatively low priority or has a relatively low benefit for the organization can be outsourced when in-house staff are occupied with other work.

The same issues that apply to the task of selecting test equipment will also apply to questions where greater resources are involved, such as the development of a specific piece of test equipment if you have an application that is not met by commercially available equipment.

Even if you decide to contract out the selection of equipment as a separate work package, it will help you evaluate your contractor's work if you are aware of the factors that influence this process. It is always important to be able to check to your own satisfaction any information provided by a contractor or vendor. You may have a contract that assigns liability, but it still wastes time and money if you have to go through rework due to a contractor's error.

5.2 Collecting Information on Available Equipment

Based on your current experience and knowledge of the test equipment industry, you will be able to decide how much extra information you need on test equipment. Market scanning may be part of your normal business routine; however, day-to-day pressures mean that many engineers will prefer to update their knowledge of test equipment as a specific need arises; for example, when they are required to build a particular test system. It is important to evaluate both the equipment and the supplying company itself. The technical specifications of a piece of equipment are important (the "minimum necessary condition" for purchasing a piece of test equipment), but factors such as the reputation and long-term stability of a supplier can also contribute to your purchase decisions.

The effort that is undertaken to source equipment should be proportional to the cost of the equipment. For example, writing a tender for the supply of connectors costing $500 is unnecessarily complex. The time and effort to prepare and evaluate the tenders is not proportional to the cost of the equipment. On the other hand, simply placing an order on the first supplier you find who makes vector network analyzers to 50 GHz is equally inappropriate, as the consequences of error when purchasing expensive, high-end test equipment are much greater.

Once a set of measurements is decided on (using the test parameters matrix described in Chapter 4 or another analysis tool which suits your work style), the next task is deciding what test equipment you need to procure. The first step is to decide on what functional type of equipment you need; for example, an oscilloscope or vector network analyzer. Then, decide which specific piece of test equipment (model and manufacturer) you need.

5.2.1   Functional Type of Equipment; Narrowing the Equipment List

You will initially be able to narrow down your consideration list based on factors such as instrument control or form factor even before you move to specific technical issues. You can eliminate a great deal of test equipment by your decision on how to control the test system, i.e., manual, semi-automated, or fully-automated control. If you decide to test manually and not upgrade in the future, then bus-controlled test equipment is not necessary; you would include bus-controlled equipment in your consideration list based on other features or advantages only. Equipment for a manual system must have front panels with full equipment control access and readout. However, if you plan a future system upgrade or are designing a fully-automated system, then you can eliminate non-bus-controlled test equipment. Equipment on your consideration list will be further limited by the system architecture you choose; for example, pure VXI or a mixed VXI and rack and stack system.

The next criterion to consider is speed of measurement. If you need high speeds, then a bed-of-nails tester may do the task, or you may need highly sophisticated test equipment.

Other factors to consider include accuracy, weight of the equipment, the power drawn by the device, other features such as rear-mounted connectors, plug-and-play drivers, calibration periods, in-country support, repair times, and equipment or system downtimes. These can generally be categorized as equipment fitness for purpose.

5.2.2   Equipment Fitness and Price

After you have determined what functional type of equipment you need to perform the measurements, a few hours spent calling major test equipment suppliers for verbal quotations and datasheets will provide you with the initial information needed to prepare a budgetary pricing list. From the datasheets, you can then start to prepare a list of technical questions that will be focused on your application.

Equipment fitness includes technical specifications, the equipment's footprint (especially if space is restricted), power requirements and heat generation (see Chapter 12 for a more detailed discussion of heat and power budgets), environmental specifications, ruggedness, MTBF or equivalent reliability data, standards used, and performance data specific to your test application.

The next stage will be to determine what manufacturer's equipment best suits your requirements. At this stage, you will quickly develop your skills in "specmanship." All manufacturers naturally specify their equipment in the best possible light, hence it is sometimes difficult to discriminate the true performance of the test equipment for your application. Do not interpret this to mean that manufacturers in any way lie about the performance of their equipment. All specifications will be correct; however, it is the usefulness or the relevance of the specification to your application that is important.

It would seem easiest to give vendors your list of specifications and then let them fight it out for your business, but this is not always the best solution. Good business relationships with your test equipment suppliers (just as with any of your organization's other suppliers) can be extremely valuable, especially when you require non-standard products, support, or delivery arrangements. There are times when regulations or other circumstances make a tender or technical "shootout" appropriate, but even then, it is important to evaluate the benefits a particular vendor provides across more than just technical features. If the best way to test a specification is a particular piece of test equipment, then also examine its speed and form factor, power requirements, and other features. A feature such as keyboard lockout, for example, may be invaluable in a varied working environment. List price for the test equipment is not always indicative of lifetime cost of ownership. The most expensive equipment may come with an effective support package that makes it ultimately worth the higher cost up front.

There is a wide range of test equipment on the market, from fundamental measurements to complex, high-speed, high-performance measurements. Cost and time drive deciding what to test and how to test it, and the next challenge is in relating your test requirements to equipment specifications. Normally there would be three main positions you would find yourself in:

1. You have a general understanding of what the figures and statements on an equipment specification sheet mean.
2. You are familiar with how the information on an equipment specification sheet relates to your test application.
3. You are a test specialist, to the extent of understanding how the design of a piece of test equipment affects its measurement technique in detail.

Depending on where you find yourself in the above, you will have to approach the selection of test equipment in different ways. A recent graduate or an engineer with a specialty unrelated to test equipment and who may be in the first category above, may find it worth considering engaging a consultant or another firm to develop the test equipment list. You may decide to expend some effort in training or researching the topic yourself or even hiring an experienced engineer off the street. All of these have advantages and disadvantages. Test equipment firms that consult for you may try to promote their own equipment rather than that of other test equipment manufacturers. This could lead to sub-optimum systems. There are a few ways to try to manage this. They include having the consultant's work verified by another expert, engaging an independent firm, having a consultant view proposals from test equipment companies on your behalf and evaluate each proposal, or passing the risk of the measurement solution to the test equipment supplier through contractual conditions.

Experienced engineers who specialize in areas other than test and measurement equipment are generally in category two above. Working with your selected vendors and making some investment in understanding any high-end technical issues will provide you with the information to select the appropriate instrument.

If you fully understand the instruments or you are simply duplicating a system, then equipment selection becomes a simpler task and your choices will focus on timing and budget issues and on how to solve any non-standard technical requirements.

There will be cases when your test requirements challenge the equipment that is commercially available. If it is possible to stay within commercially available capabilities, then your options when considering vendors remain more open, giving you greater flexibility. Try to avoid locking yourself into a single vendor with custom solutions unless you have great confidence in their ability to support your test requirements. A good supplier with custom engineering skills will be able to provide you with special test solutions (Section 5.4, "Using Vendor Options for Effective Solutions," examines some of these possibilities in more detail), but the additional costs and other factors involved warrant careful examination of other approaches.

It may be that enhanced calibration techniques need to be employed to give you the greater measurement accuracy assurance that you require. Sometimes vendors have the ability to pick a good line unit (a golden unit) with the better specifications you want; however, this is only possible if you want something close to what is commercially offered.

Sometimes test or test setup requirements will defy the laws of physics, meaning that some measurements cannot be made within a commercial budget. For example, you will not need the frequency accuracy of a hydrogen MASAR to build a mobile phone. Similarly, it is impractical to try to measure HF loss over kilometers of waveguide in a desert on a hot day to high levels of accuracy. Section 5.5, "What to Do if You Cannot Match Your Needs to a Commercial Item," discusses five different approaches to this situation.

When evaluating commercially available test equipment, you will be able to divide equipment features into those that are necessary to your application, those that provide useful additional test or user interface features, and those that do not add value to your current test application. Many models on the market offer a number of features; some are excellent – generally labor-saving or feature-based – however, completely new measurement capabilities are less common.

Sometimes measurements can be accomplished in different ways, although you may have to make trade-offs in other areas such as measurement time or overall accuracy (Section 4.6, "Evaluating the Cost-Effectiveness of Tests," discusses some of these trade-offs in more detail). A good oscilloscope will make very good frequency measurements, and some counters make good voltage measurements. Whether you can use these features depends on your measurement accuracy requirements, and it may be that you can reduce switching and/or range changes by making additional measurements while on a particular node. Frequency response measurements in high-frequency devices (GHz levels) can be accomplished using a signal generator as a source and a crystal detector and oscilloscope to monitor the output – this is a slow and tedious process, but it can be done if needed. A network analyzer can make very accurate and fast measurements on circuitry and components. All forms of signal generation or waveform generation are possible depending on your budget.

Many devices need some sort of stimulation into their working state, or once in it, to change to another state. Rather than applying multiple stimulations simultaneously, it is better and cheaper to switch the signal to the paths you need. If you need a lot of stimulation lines, you may consider multiple output devices; however, these come with a programming overhead. The more complex the signal stimulation requirement, the more likely the measurement side will be of the same high level of complexity.

Some measurement situations may be able to be simplified. In some situations, a logic probe may reveal all the information you need, rather than setting up a complete logic analysis system. Many slow-speed logic or control lines can be actuated by DC power supplies; these are often relatively inexpensive, and when not being used in other parts of the system, can be slaved to this purpose.

Determining the test equipment that best suits your requirements can become challenging. There are a few ways to make this task easier. Talk to your peers or colleagues to find out whether anyone has used this equipment for a similar application, or even completely different test applications. Expand your information search to include literature, such as magazines in your field (the Web is an excellent source of information). Look up any standards that are relevant; some will specify what the equipment must do and what features it must have to support your application. Other test equipment manufacturers may have appropriate feedback on alternative models available in the marketplace, as they may have carried out a comparative analysis. A credible supplier should be able to give you professional, well-balanced information.

If possible, have a company representative visit you with the instrument and ask him or her to show you the measurement in action. Most companies will have an applications engineer or similar expert to do this job. If appropriate, you can ask this engineer to describe the errors in the measurement and how to calculate the uncertainties involved. Remember, all instruments are not created equal, and much of what you are paying for is accuracy. Two boxes may measure the same quantity, however, their accuracies (how well they make the measurement) may be completely different. This is also a good time to have the engineer explain the specification sheet. It is sometimes too easy to get excited about pushing buttons and slick GUIs, and in the end forget to focus on the fundamental reason of why the test equipment is required, forgetting – for example – that a GUI is not used when the instrument is in remote and being driven by a computer.

Any shortcomings of the test equipment that you identify do not mean that the test equipment is not suitable for you. There may be factory options that improve the performance of the test equipment in a specific area that you require, or the equipment may offer other advantages that overcome particular points that concern you. There could be "specials" for that instrument, options that have been done for other customers that are not listed in the specification sheet. Always explain to the vendor why you have concerns about their test equipment. If a vendor does not know why you are ruling out their equipment, they cannot help you, and you are reducing your options. Good business relationships with credible and knowledgeable suppliers can allow you to work together to overcome technical or other obstacles.

The above discussions highlight some of the steps a potential buyer will go through. There are, however, some rules that should be observed by you, the buyer, in regard to how you treat a vendor.

A good vendor expects to be told the truth. No matter what that truth is, you should not offend a salesperson if you explain why you did not purchase the test equipment from them.

Vendors need to sell products to survive; they don't, however, expect to win every deal or make every sale. The more information you can supply to the vendor, the better they can help you. If you play one vendor against another simply to get the cheapest price, you will often alienate a supplier who will be less likely to go out of their way to help you in the future.

TIP:

Remember that a vendor should be able to assist you with data to build a business case for new test equipment if required. A vendor should be able to discuss the benefits the equipment was designed to deliver, and if they have sufficient business experience, will be able to discuss these benefits in terms relevant to your organization.

If you feel that a vendor's test equipment is not what you want, but you still need to get three quotations to met your organization's purchase requirements, tell them up front. Chances are they will still send you a list price quotation so that you can meet your process requirements.

The right vendors can become part of your professional team. If you find a vendor you can work well with (see Section 5.3, "Finding the Right Vendors"), then building a good business relationship will provide value to you well into the future.

TIP:

Your engineering network will most likely be a creative and valuable source of information, in addition to standard sources such as vendor materials and the World Wide Web.

5.3 Finding the Right Vendors

Good suppliers will add value to a business relationship by providing expert advice and recommendations as well as selling equipment. For a successful, long-term relationship, a company with a stable and secure future will be able to provide ongoing support and the best potential for the supply of new products and product upgrades.

5.3.1 Evaluating an Equipment Supplier

As many engineers prefer to work with a short list of trusted suppliers, evaluating the supplier's organization and products become important parts of the selection process. When evaluating the supplying company, factors to consider include the company's reputation, market share, investment in new technology and R&D, commitment to quality, and support life after obsolescence.

If you plan a long lifetime for your system, then careful selection of equipment vendors that will provide long-term support and appropriate upgrades is particularly important.

A supplier's reputation is an indication of their past behavior, and thus what their behavior is likely to be in the future. Your engineering network will be a good source of information.

What do your colleagues say about a particular equipment supplier? Are they responsive to inquiries? Do they provide good post-sales support? Is the equipment reliable? Does the supplier provide fast turn-around time for repairs and calibrations? Any company that enjoys a good reputation will not be a flash-in-the-pan organization. Their reputation will be built on their equipment and how they interact with their customers.

Market share is an indication of the size of the supplier's installed base. A large installed base or a large volume of equipment sales means that the supplier has an investment in supporting the equipment in its installed base, and that it has an incentive (future sales) to continuing to support existing and new customers.

Investment in R&D and new technologies gives an indication of how often new products and product enhancements will become available. A strong investment in R&D means that the company will tend to remain on (or close to) the leading edge of measurement technology. A large proportion of each year's sales should be equipment that has been released in the last three or four years, with a relatively small proportion of sales coming from older equipment. This shows that the company focuses on bringing new, leading-edge equipment onto the market, to the benefit of buyers.

No piece of equipment will be available forever; it will be superseded by more advanced models, or it may be discontinued because essential components are no longer available, or because demand for that type of equipment has fallen below economically viable levels (since smaller production runs push up costs and prices, thus further decreasing customer demand). If your system has a relatively short planned lifetime, or is designed with equipment interfunctionality in mind, this may not create problems for you. However, if your system will have a long lifetime or is part of a critical path, then you must have contingency plans in place. An equipment supplier will set a support life for obsolete equipment (for example, five years after obsolescence date), which will commit them to providing spare parts and support for that time. If the supplier's support life is insufficient for your planned use of the test system, then you will need to consider purchasing spare units of critical equipment if the supplier announces that it will be made obsolete.

The depth of the supplier's instrument family can tell you some things about their experience in a particular area of test. Does the vendor have a wide range of products or a focus on a particular test area? Is the product the start of a new technology direction; for example, a spectrum analyzer in a protocol analyzer instrument company? Do the product's price, form factors available, and ability to add and remove options match its specifications? None of these factors should be seen as positive or negative on their own: they should be considered in the context of all the other information you have about a particular company and its products.

The timing of any equipment deliveries may be an important factor for you, depending on your project schedule. Can the vendor deliver within the timeframes you require? Do they have a good history of timely deliveries to your company or organization? Can the delivery of equipment be held back if necessary so you do not have to store it? Special delivery requirements can often be solved through negotiation with a supplier, and it is always valuable to start these discussions as early as possible to allow more time for flexible planning.

Repair and calibration support are particularly important if system downtime is a potential issue in your test environment; for example, for high-volume applications. Can the instrument be supported by the vendor in-country? What is the projected cost of supporting this equipment for your system's projected lifetime? Do you need to be on a contract to get the latest firmware upgrades? For complex applications, does the vendor have support engineers who can provide expertise in troubleshooting problems, or provide training if necessary? Part of the purchase cost of test equipment may be allocated to maintaining a local repair and calibration center or funding local application engineers.

Knowing that test equipment meets relevant standards provides added assurance to system designers and users. Does the equipment meet international standards (where applicable – this will apply more to specialized than to general-purpose equipment) for your current test application? What EMI or EMC standards does it meet? Does the equipment meet any industry open standards relevant for your project; for example, having a plug-and-play driver?

You should also feel comfortable that the cost of any equipment or components offers appropriate value for money; this applies to high as well as to low quotations, and cost that does not match performance should be carefully considered. If you have decided to make a trade-off between test capability and equipment cost (see Section 4.6.1, "Cost of Test vs. Benefit of Test"), then lower equipment costs are of course the main benefit. If leading-edge technical capability is your top priority for the test system, then higher equipment costs are also appropriate for the additional test capability.

5.3.2   "Measurement Consultants"

Many vendors have technically skilled sales representatives or application engineers on staff who can act as measurement experts and can assist with integrating their instruments and components. If a particular vendor's expertise can save you time, it may still be cheaper overall to buy from them even if their equipment costs are higher or the vendor charges you for specific consulting services. The time saved can help you meet your deadlines and avoid other cost overruns. A company with a good reputation and highly trained staff can add value and can help you overcome resource problems by becoming part of your engineering team for specific tasks.

You can get the vendors involved with your planning so they can see for themselves if they have the products that fit your application. They may recommend other methods of taking a measurement that may help you get more effective use out of the equipment. Their solutions may be influenced by their own company's style of engineering, which is reflected in their technical training of sales representatives and that company's core skills. Good salespeople aim for a long and lucrative sales career, not a short and exciting one, and will accordingly give well-judged advice relevant to your project requirements. Less experienced salespeople may refer to their company's marketing material for a product without themselves understanding the engineering benefits of it; however, they should also have a good network of support people in their own company from whom they can get any answers you need. Good salespeople will understand when and how their product will be a good fit for your application, and can be useful engineering contacts for other work such as special options.

5.4 Using Vendor Options for Effective Solutions

There are some fairly straightforward options, as well as others that are not so commonly available, which can help you put together a more effective solution. Some relate specifically to racking your equipment, such as rear panel connectors and types of rack mount kits, while other options deal with the test solution itself. An equipment supplier with experienced staff can discuss your test system requirements with you and should be able to make suggestions that will benefit your overall design.

Options are generally classed as standard, special, or custom, although the manufacturer may have their own terms to describe these. Your supplier may also have other creative options for your test system, so working with a good supplier is always important.

5.4.1 Standard Options

Standard options are those that are part of the test equipment supplier's normal production options, and should be listed in the catalog or in the product's technical datasheet.

A common example that is useful for test systems is rear panel connectors. Rear panel connectors can save having to loop signal cables back into the test system to connect to the switch. This is an issue, especially when working at microwave frequencies, where cabling is sensitive to bending (and also expensive). This also saves having a feed-through panel that takes up room in the rack.

Other examples are frequency extensions, number of channels, localization of manuals (choice of language), rack mounting kits, connector types, cables – and many more. Standard options will cover the most common requirements for different applications, so in many instances, you will only need to select from these options.

5.4.2 Special Options

If a product's standard options do not solve your test requirements, the test equipment manufacturer may have special options that will provide what you need. Special options are those which are not part of the normal production run for that product, but for which the manufacturer has a design which can be produced if required, and which has been produced in the past. These could be options that were designed for a particular contract, so they are not standard options, but generally require a special production run or some hand tooling. However, since the manufacturer has retained the IP rights for these special options, they are also available to other   customers.

Another special option which may be available is to pay extra to select from the production line for a unit with "best band" specifications – a "star unit" – for example, a better frequency response over a certain band, or certification of tighter tolerances on one specification than are normally offered by the vendor. In any production run, you will normally get variation in the specifications of the products manufactured (this is one of the reasons for a manufacturing test in the first place). All equipment will be within the manufacturer's published specifications, but there will be some variation across units. This means that within the specified range, some equipment will perform even better than other units. By selecting for a unit with better specifications, you get a standard piece of equipment that has been tested and certified to the particular specifications you have requested.

Some special options have restricted availability; for example, government regulations may limit the countries to which a particular product may be exported.

5.4.3   Custom Options

Custom options are those which are developed specifically for your application, and have not previously been implemented by the test equipment manufacturer.

You may have to pay NRE costs for the design and development work involved, and you should also look carefully at the IP provisions in place with the supplier. Your company may have the opportunity to purchase the IP for a custom option, but this will add significantly to the cost of its development, as the supplier will have no other chances to sell that product and recover the R&D costs. If the test equipment supplier keeps ownership of the IP for the custom option, they then have the opportunity to gain revenue by selling it to other customers, and should correspondingly charge less.

If you place an order for the development and production of a custom option, it is important to specify the option or product as precisely as possible. Any ambiguities or missed areas in your specification are points at which you could potentially end up with a product that is different from what you expected. A clear, comprehensive specification is worth the extra time it takes to prepare.

> **TIP:**
>
> Always keep in mind that many manufacturers will "make a special," that is, they will modify their equipment to provide a certain specification or feature if the standard product does not meet requirements. This will incur an increase in price, but will provide the measurement benefits required for your application. Manufacturers often have a documented list of all equipment that has been modified, so an existing standard or special option may do what you want already. Even if what you need is not listed, don't forget to ask if what you need can be achieved.

5.5   What to Do if You Cannot Match Your Needs to a Commercial Item

If, after examining the marketplace and discussing your needs with test equipment manufacturers, you cannot find a piece of COTS equipment to perform your task, you are faced with a problem that merits careful consideration. There are five options available if you cannot find a commercially available item with the specifications you require:

• Design and build custom test equipment.
• Contract out the design and build of custom test equipment.
• Derive the result from other parameters or known working units.
• Redesign the DUT ("design for testability").
• Eliminate a test from your specifications.

As with most of the trade-offs you make during an engineering project, the deciding factors will be time, cost, and technical specification. A solution that is easy to implement may save you time and money at this stage; however, if less stringent technical test specifications lead to a higher failure rate of a manufactured product, then the overall cost to your process will be much higher.

5.5.1   Design and Build Custom Test Equipment

Building your own in-house test equipment is a serious issue; it can be done, but should not be undertaken lightly. Many of the issues relating to building your own test system also apply to building your own test equipment.

It is worth re-examining your test plans to consider whether the particular test capability you are after is really necessary, or whether there is some other way to handle the test. Re-examine all your options. It may be possible to alter the signal so that a piece of COTS equipment will work; for example, externally mix down a 300-GHz signal to 50 GHz and use a spectrum analyzer that is capable of operating at this frequency, instead of building a 300-GHz spectrum analyzer from the ground up.

Consider how many units you would need to build. "One-off" units usually end up being lab curiosities that have a habit of never quite living up to their goals. If, however, you need many units, more success may be possible due to the engineering effort required given a higher potential ROI. Double-check to see if any test equipment manufacturers have plans or even projects underway to build an instrument with the necessary requirements. Their timeframes may be better than those of your company.

You will have to consider your planned instrument's test methodology and how you will assure users of your instrument's ability to accurately measure the parameter you are examining. How are you calibrating the instrument? What support issues are there if you sell the instrument in a solution to another company? Will it conform to open standards such as standard commands for programmable instruments (SCPI) to control it, or will it have a unique command structure?

The cost and risk of building the instrument will need to be determined and then weighted against the benefit of making the test. Wherever possible, base any equipment you design in-house on an open standard architecture that already has communication and interface implementations in place. If you do decide to take this task on, then try to work with COTS "pieces" to again minimize risk and engineering costs. VXI development kits, for example, are available which provide all the addressing and communication functions required for compliance with the VXI standard and allow the developer to focus on the measurement task itself. This is a standard approach for test equipment manufacturers; they will purchase components from specialist suppliers and then integrate them into their design, only designing from the ground up what they really need to.

5.5.2   Contract Out the Design and Build of Custom Test Equipment

This is likely to be the best solution for a company that makes or tests products, as opposed to making test equipment. With this solution, you pass the risk on to an engineering firm that specializes in this type of work – the firm may even be an instrument manufacturer with which you already work closely. Some cellular phone test boxes, for example, were developed in this way. How far you choose to go down this path will be a company decision; you may simply specify what you want to measure and how accurately, or you may specify individual blocks that you or another firm integrate together.

Some test companies have systems divisions that are employed to do just this. They will work with the customer to build a custom piece of test equipment. It is important under these circumstances to clearly resolve questions such as how lifetime support of the test equipment will be managed, and ownership of the IP, before you and the third-party company begin work. Timeframes will need to be suitable so that they fit in with your plans.

Also consider factors such as the possible need to pay up front a certain percentage of the project if you are asking a company to carry responsibility for risk as part of the contract. If you are selling the instrument, you will need to support it through its working life, which may be beyond ten years in some circumstances. If one of your suppliers goes out of business or discontinues the components you need, you will have to find alternatives or purchase enough "supplies" to support your product for the expected lifecycle. This product support will need to address factors such as documentation, upgrades, user training, and ongoing maintenance and repairs.

See Section 1.2, "Make vs. Buy Decisions," as many of the same issues that apply to a system will apply to a piece of test equipment.

5.5.3   Derive the Result from Other Parameters

Engineering is a creative profession, and being faced with a need to think laterally about how to obtain a measurement and what other measurements relate to a situation is a perfect opportunity to experiment with a few innovations. A fundamental understanding of how electrical quantities relate to each other allows an engineer to find alternative methods for quantifying a desired measurement. If you have access to skilled metrologists in your professional network, they will generally be able to derive measurements using at least two separate (possibly even independent) methods to confirm a particular parameter; this makes them a valuable source of measurement method advice about suitable techniques or creative measurement approaches in less common test applications.

A lot of what determines your measurement technique is the accuracy you require. There are a number of different ways to measure RF field strength; for example, broadband devices such as a power meter, narrowband devices such as spectrum analyzer, or a frequency-selective device such as an RF voltmeter. All of these devices measure differently, but it is possible to derive the field strength from each measurement by conversion. Some measurement alternatives come back to something as basic as Ohm's Law; current measurements are most often done using voltage measurements across a known resistance and then converting, rather than having to use a current clamp.

Increased computing power in many instruments can also be used to good advantage. For example, a digitizer that measures output power to confirm that particular components are operational can also use a post-capture algorithm to verify a transmitter's phase error.

An engineer's measurement experience and knowledge may cover both the basic metrological high-precision methods, and also the less precise but more commonly used methods (which may be favored in some environments because of speed, cost, or other factors). Absolute RF power measurements can be made using a vector network analyzer, or by using a six-port bridge. The difference in these techniques is that the vector network analyzer can measure hundreds of points in milliseconds – and costs much more – while the six-port device can measure slightly more accurately, but each point takes minutes, making it suitable for standards laboratories, but not for a production environment.

5.5.4   Redesign the DUT ("Design for Testability")

Redesigning the DUT may be another option to consider. Again, this decision will be based on time, budget, or specification, and will be more appropriate in the early stages of your product design cycle. For example, you may have to reconsider circuit board design or module design from a "design for testability" perspective if you cannot reasonably meet your test requirements for a particular product/DUT.

Many design for testability issues can be brought down to test access issues. You may find, for example, that it is less expensive to redesign the way in which the connectors come off a circuit board than it would be to buy more expensive cables to get access to connectors which have been inconveniently located on the board. You may decide to use slide-on connectors rather than screw-on connectors to make connecting to and disconnecting from the DUT easier and quicker. You may want to have all the adjustment or connection points on one side of the board to make placement of the board easier for testing and to avoid mechanical stress on the board if it has to be awkwardly positioned to connect to the test system. Related access issues can apply to an assembled product as well.

Larger DUTs generally require larger voltages and current to drive them, due to the larger number of components involved. This means that your signal and control cables as well as power cables become more complex and more substantial. Cooling can also become an issue, which means that the orientation of the DUT with respect to other heat sources or cooling systems will become important. Your test system will re-create but should not exceed the range of working conditions (plus a margin for confidence) for which your product is specified.

As cables and looms become more substantial for more complex DUTs, you will need to decide whether it would be better to split the DUT into smaller units for testing. However, if you follow this approach, you will still need to go through some form of higher level margin testing at some stage to ensure that all of the individual unit tolerances are tight enough for the completed assembly to work to specification when you re-assemble the DUT.

5.5.5   Eliminate a Test from Your Test Plan

It may be possible to remove a test from your test plan while still maintaining full coverage of your test specifications. For example, hot mockup testing compares the DUT against a known good unit called the "golden unit." Verification of the golden unit may be a lengthy process; however, it can allow more efficient testing by comparing known and unknown units. If you stimulate two units, it is not necessary to test all aspects of the units themselves as long as the test outputs comprehensively demonstrate that the unknown DUT is working to specifications. However, if the DUT fails, you may have to drop back to more detailed performance tests if you are using a repair rather than replacement strategy for failed units. A well-designed artificial intelligence (AI) program may be able to narrow down the list of possible fault causes based on individual test results.

Depending on your operational environment, there are circumstances under which the cost of some tests may outweigh the benefits you obtain from the tests. Section 4.6.1, "Cost of Test vs. Benefit of Test," and Table 4.3 examine some of these factors, including circumstances under which you may decide not to carry out a particular test.

5.6 Placing Orders

Before placing an order, check that all the equipment and services (if you are also ordering services such as a calibration contract) you require have been formally quoted by your supplier. For services, make sure that all terms and conditions are clearly stated (for example, whether equipment adjustments are charged for separately under a calibration contract) and that they are acceptable to your company or organization. If there are any discrepancies, talk these over with the company representative. Ensure that all quotes are properly signed by a company representative, and that they contain all agreed-upon additional items such as training and delivery instructions. Lead time management is a vital part of any project. You will be able to get lead time information from your sales representative or from the supplier's formal quotation. The timing of your project will then allow you to calculate the date by which you need to place your orders for timely delivery. If your project has tight time restrictions and a supplier's lead times are too long, it may still be possible to negotiate faster delivery of equipment. The test equipment manufacturer's production planners may be able to assign an earlier manufacturing slot to your order, for example, giving you a faster delivery time.

When you are satisfied, and the order is placed, it is useful to contact your sales representative to inform him or her that the order has been placed. That person can then ensure that the order was received and processed, and that everyone in the company involved with the process is briefed for a smooth delivery cycle.

Any changes you need to make to your order or contract after it has been placed should be made in writing and also confirmed in writing by the supplier.

The sales representative should contact you if any problems arise in the delivery cycle; however, a phone call to the representative some time before the equipment is due is also recommended, just to check progress and ensure everything is on track for a timely delivery.

Inspect any delivered goods and verify any services supplied as quickly as possible. If you have any concerns with the goods or services supplied to you, it is important to take these up with the supplier quickly to resolve them.

Your closeout process for any equipment or service supply contracts should include a contract review, agreement within your organization and with the supplier that no outstanding actions remain (i.e., that all products and services have been delivered), exchange of any necessary certificates, and confirmation that any necessary title transfers have taken place. If you reach a project milestone at this point, it may also be an appropriate time to celebrate your team's achievements.

Interfacing to the DUT

This chapter describes the most common methods of connecting to the DUT and the implications of each method, particularly with regard to accuracy and reliability. It also examines the two main methods of controlling the interface to the DUT.

KEY POINTS:

- The interface to the DUT is a crucial part of both manual and automated test systems, and should allow an easily managed connection between the test system and the DUT.
- Cable management through devices such as cable harnesses and looms allows you to easily trace and address faults in the interface to the DUT and to manage signaling and power in the system.
- Good switching allows consistent and reliable signal handling, and helps to eliminate human error in test procedures. Design factors can also increase the accuracy and reliability of the system.
- Controlling the interface to the DUT can be through manual control following documented procedures or full software automation through a fixture. Signal integrity has to be maintained in whatever system you use.

The interface to the DUT should allow ease of communication for all test signals and control. Three major design factors to consider when choosing how to interface with the DUT and how to control this interface are:

1. What type of connection to the DUT is appropriate?
2. How to position all the cables in the test system for an effective and efficient design and interface to the DUT.
3. The design of the switching in your test system.

Cable management and switching become more important in the interface management of large or complex test systems; however, as with many other design decisions, these points can improve the future upgradability of your test system if taken into account at the design stage.

The interface to the DUT should provide an easily managed connection to the test system. The cost, speed, and complexity of the system will largely guide your decisions on what degree of automation to use to control the interface to the DUT.

6.1   Connection to the DUT

Two main methods used for connection to the DUT are edge connection and custom fixtures. Generally, custom fixtures are used for functional and component testing, whereas edge connections are usually used for functional testing only. Another common but less sophisticated method of interfacing to the DUT is to place the DUT on the work surface and then connect cables from it to the various items of equipment in the racks. This approach does not lend itself to speed of test and also requires a high degree of skill in the operator. Often this method is found to be unreliable over time, unless there is a high degree of constant maintenance on the cabling and connectors as well as more than usual attention to the correct use of connectors – otherwise, errors will grow to the point where the system needs to be audited and refurbished.

Edge and fixture connections give a reliable connection to the DUT if planned and constructed correctly. The key to the success of your test system is to test efficiently and quickly, with a minimum of downtime.

6.1.1   Edge Connection

Edge connection is a technique used primarily for circuit boards to perform functional testing, where signals applied and detected are verified to determine the working state of the card.

Generally, assemblies are on printed circuit boards with all the signals going on and off the board using an edge connector that allows it to be plugged into the parent assembly. This also lends itself to testing by using the same edge connector that will be the interface to the rest of the device. The card with edge connect is plugged into a fixture that provides mechanical strength to support the card as well as to isolate it from the work surface. The fixture would then interface to the test equipment via a patch panel or directly to the test equipment from the fixture.

This technique can also be applied to component-level testing. However, this involves extensive process analysis and programming to build an expert system that can choose the order of tests. The choice of which test to carry out next is based on the results of the previous tests and the probability of particular components being the cause of a fault. The expert system would assign changing probabilities of a particular component causing a fault based on past failure data and which tests return a fail result, as each test will be able to eliminate particular components of the DUT as the source of the failure. The decision to implement an expert system for component-level testing would depend on the overall cost benefit of implementing an extensive solution, including evaluating whether repair-by-replacement is a suitable alternative strategy for items which have low scrap and manufacturing costs compared with repair costs.

The tests normally performed are intended to emulate the full range of conditions under which the board will be working. The number of different signals that need to be applied and measured and the number of different actions that are taking place on the board will determine the time taken for each test. You may have to select a subset of tests and conditions that give an indication of the board's functionality if the full range of testing takes too long to be cost-effective.

Section 5.5.4, "Redesign the DUT ("Design for Testability")," also briefly examines some of the test access issues that can occur when interfacing to circuit boards.

6.1.2   Custom Fixtures

Custom fixtures are laid out to accept the DUT quickly and easily, and should be considered for use with modules or assemblies that need to be mechanically supported during testing. Connections to the DUT can be made much more easily and reliably using a fixture designed for that particular connection. The specific design of fixtures means that you will normally have a different fixture for each DUT.

Fixtures can be simple or complex – the more complex the fixture, the higher the cost of building and supporting the fixture by providing repair and maintenance. At times, the cost of the fixture can exceed the cost of the DUT, and based on your test system throughput requirements and the benefits provided by a test, you may decide to make some trade-offs in your test strategy or to combine this test stage with other test setups to lower the overall cost.

In-circuit testers that use a bed of nails to make contact with the components on a circuit board use a vacuum to hold the DUT onto the fixture, meaning that the fixture must be well-sealed. In-circuit testing may be used for repair as well as for manufacturing, particularly in military applications where the tester may accompany the parent system wherever it goes – for example, some military missile defense systems come with a support truck which contains (along with other capabilities) an in-circuit tester.

Fixturing also allows the designer to inject or measure signals by guided probe, where the operator is guided through probing the circuit card as part of the test program. Usually this is done in a mixed-signal environment; for example, analog RF and digital circuitry on the same card.

There are many situations that involve a mixed-signal environment; mobile telephones are one example. The analog signals may not be RF, but changing DC levels, beyond the voltage levels of the logic. For instance, if an analog-to-digital converter is being tested, then you will need to apply a variety of voltages to the input to verify the correct digital output for a known input state.

If you need your fixtures to be independent of your test system's connector panel (for example, if you know that your product fixtures may be changing regularly), then a large expandable switch that can connect to the panel will do all the routing to connectors for your DUT. Then your fixtures can be independent of the panel design as the signals can be routed wherever you want. This type of fixture and switch costs more initially, but does reduce the need to rebuild the interfacing regularly as your products upgrade and change.

6.2 Cable Harnesses and Looms

Good cable management will make maintenance and duplication of your test system much easier. For complex test systems in particular, the number of cables required to connect test equipment, switch matrices, and other components means that a systematic approach is required to arrange and manage cables.

Cable harnesses and looms bundle groups of cables together. A loom is generally a continuously wound device that adds stiffness to the cable bundle (see Figure 6.1) and a harness typically bundles cables at regular points, making it easier to add cables later. The cable harness or loom will allow all the individual cables to separate easily from the harness bundle so that connection to individual equipment is possible. The use of a harness will allow all cabling to be positioned along a single path, such as under the floor, down the side of the test system rack, or in a cable tray suspended from the ceiling. This method also allows the harness to be inspected for faults or tampering, and a consistent system for cable placement and tagging will make any missing cables or substitutions more easily visible.

It is important to plan the arrangement of a test system's cable harness, rather than simply gathering the cables together and tying them at intervals. Considerations include:

- Shaping cables.
- Using different types of cable in the same system.
- Using a consistent labeling system.

6.2.1   Shaping Cables

A harness should be designed to match the wiring diagram so that short cables break away from the harness in a well-sorted manner. Position shorter cables on the outside of the harness so that they can be separated out easily, and allow sufficient cable length between the harness and the connection point to take into account any cable bends required for an unstressed connection.

It is valuable to position each cable in place (if possible) so that it can be shaped before it is added to the harness. This will allow you to check the length of your cables, allow for any changes in length caused by practicalities in the physical system design, and will also allow you to position the cable bundles smoothly to prevent the completed test system from looking clumsy. Some designers will build a nail board (representing the system connection points) that will allow the cables to be shaped if they do not have access to the test system itself (see Figure 6.2).

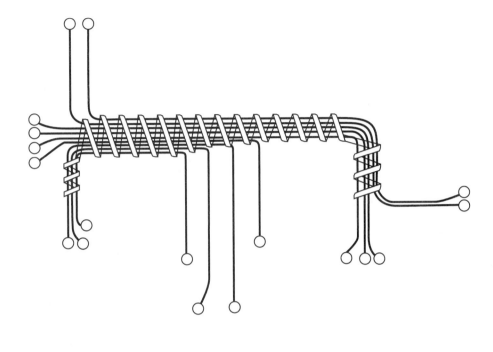

○   Terminal

Figure 6.1   A cable loom.

Some types of cables must be positioned before the test system is calibrated and then left immobile. For example, even disconnecting and refastening the cables in some sensitive microwave test systems can invalidate that test system's calibration.

TIP:

Never join two cables if you need a longer cable; buy one of the right length instead. Joins in cables introduce errors and create additional uncertainty in your measurements. Investment in the right cables is always worthwhile.

6.2.2   Using Different Types of Cable in the Same System

Additional consideration should be given to how to build a harness that is made up of different cable types; for example, twisted-pair and coaxial cables. Depending on space, it may be better to separate the different cables into individual harnesses, but run them in the same tray or side of

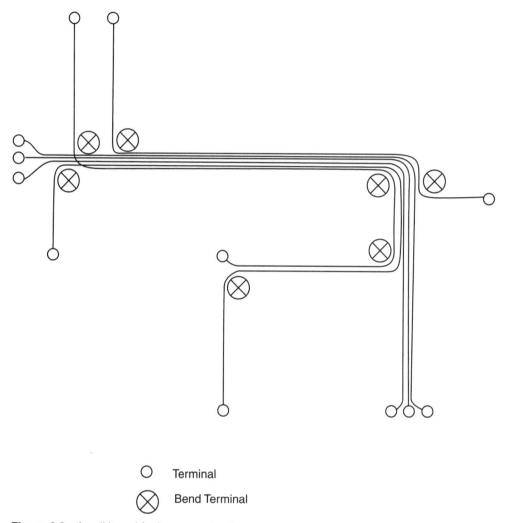

○ Terminal

⊗ Bend Terminal

Figure 6.2 A nail board for loom construction.

the test system rack. Manufacturers' recommendations can help a lot with this problem. The bending radius of solid-core or solid-shield coaxial cable may not make it suitable to be incorparated into the normal harness if that harness is mainly full of small, coaxial, easily bent cables. Cables in the tray or rack should be made secure without being over-vigorous. Some cable types can be damaged easily if fasteners are secured too tightly (see Figure 6.3).

For example, coaxial cables will suffer "dents" in them due to the dielectric being distorted if fastened too tightly. By changing the transmission characteristics of the cable, this causes an impedance mismatch, leading to less than maximum power transfer, loss of accuracy, and an increase in both errors and uncertainty in your results.

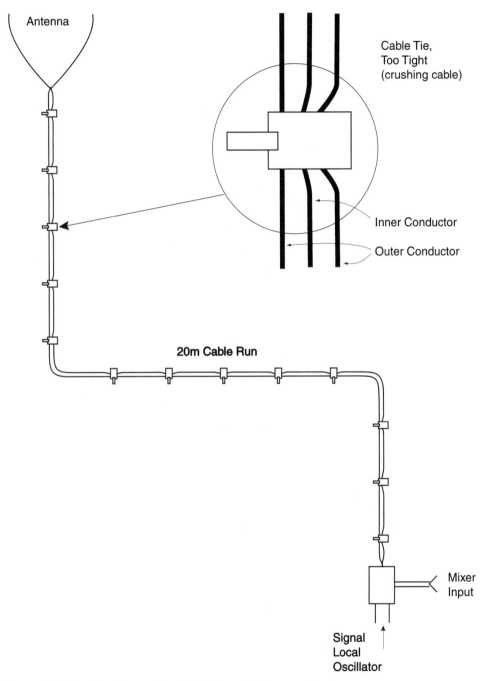

Figure 6.3 A cable strapped too tightly by cable ties, causing damage.

Twisted-pair cables should be allowed to remain twisted for as much of their distance as possible, as this is how they achieve their noise immunity. Hence, in a cable that contains a number of twisted pairs, when an individual pair is required, that pair should be allowed to remain twisted until the wires are connected to the equipment. Additionally, heat shrink should be positioned over the pair to prevent it from becoming untwisted.

6.2.3   Using a Consistent Labeling System

The labeling of harnesses and individual cables, both in the system itself and in any related documentation, is often given insufficient attention. Troubleshooting and verifying paths to check cable degradation during your calibration procedures, for example, are both greatly simplified by knowing the layout and length of individual cables. Many labeling systems exist, and in choosing one, an engineer should look for consistency and ease of application. A consistent labeling system should be used throughout the test system, and preferably throughout an organization as a whole.

6.3 Switching

Switching is the heart of a good test system. The switch reduces the number of connections made during testing, as the DUT is connected once only, and then different signals are routed to the test point by the system through the switch matrix. Generally, the switch is designed specifically for a particular system, taking into account frequency ranges, power carrying capacity, connector types, and other factors. There are many COTS switches that can be optionally configured from the manufacturer to carry out the tasks you require. For more complex switches to route high-speed signals of different types, for example some satellite payload testing applications, you may require a custom-built switch unit.

A good switch design should allow for expansion in the future, as it is inevitable that more tests or DUTs will at some stage be added to the system. Some time should be spent when doing the initial design to document your current needs and to investigate expansion at that time – before you start to build. If you choose an expandable architecture to begin with, then your task will be somewhat easier. When you investigate a card type test instrument system in particular, it is often a good idea to purchase the system the next size up from your current requirements, as this will allow you to add capability for a while before you need to increase it again.

If you intend to design and build your own switch, keep in mind that building a reliable, high-performance switch matrix is a complex task. Building a switch matrix involves much more than simply coupling switches together. Impedance matches and loss calculations through the switch paths are keys to the design of the switch. At each connection – and there are a lot in a switch – there will be reflections and losses. A consistent source of problems is that all the connections are not exactly the same; however, you can overcome much of this problem by using a high-quality connector and a torque wrench to ensure consistent and reliable joins (see Figure 6.4). Many first switch designs do not work as there is too much loss through the system.

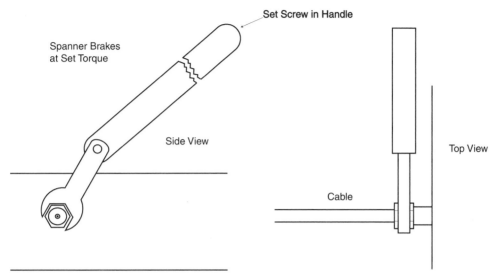

Side View

Top View

Set Screw in Handle

Spanner Brakes
at Set Torque

Cable

Figure 6.4   A connector being torqued.

If you need to design a custom switch for your test system (or if you decide to contract out the design and build of a custom switch), some of the following points may help to make the process more straightforward:

- In selecting a supplier for the switch components, choose one that can ensure supply or support for the lifetime of your test system.
- Consider whether the software design for the matrix can be used to make the matrix modular, and so reduce its size. This allows the switch to be reconfigured easily by addressing functional modules – rather than individual switches.
- Connector type and size are significant. The higher the frequency, the smaller the connector; higher frequency connectors can carry low frequencies, but not vice versa.
- A blocking switch does not allow an input to be distributed to all outputs. This is probably the most common method of switching. The switch is the cheapest option. Some switches are "semi-non-blocking," where an input can drive multiple outputs, but not all outputs. Hence, an input can be switched to an output process. If, however, another input wants that process, it will have to wait. Different inputs can be switched to different outputs.
- Non-blocking is normally referred to as a switch where one input can drive all outputs if required. It is not a splitter because the switch has an overall gain of one (0dB). Normally, these types of switches are used where one input needs to go to a number of other processes. In this case, rather than a serial process, the measurements can be in parallel. This has the potential of speeding up a test system. The decision here is whether you need a single input to go to multiple outputs.

• Check the degree of isolation required, as crosstalk could actually mask or add to your signal if signal levels are low, thus degrading the signal or masking true results. Phase noise over the frequency range, overall gain, and – at higher frequencies – return loss is important.

Good switch matrices are easy to pick out – but not from the front panel. You need to look inside to see how the matrix is mechanically laid out. If it has good access to all the parts of the matrix and is well laid out mechanically, then it will be easy to maintain and add to. Many vendors of matrices make their own hardline cables in special jigs – these vendors have learned over time what works and keeps working.

6.4 Reliability Issues

Reliability issues with regard to how you connect to and manage the connection to the DUT are often related to issues of degradation of connectors and cables, and measurement uncertainties.

An edge connect interface can suffer from stray EMC radiation from the pins within the connector, which can add to other signals and then be measured incorrectly, supposedly as part of the signals. Degradation of the mating connector in the fixture can also increase the uncertainty of your measurements.

Reliability issues for cables and cable harnesses include wear and tear on connectors, twisting of cables, and the effects of cable length.

Wear and tear and degradation of connectors may manifest itself when the connector actually falls off the cable because it is so badly damaged; however, it should be picked up in a good maintenance program at the stage when the connector does not make a good electrical connection at all frequencies. Connectors undergo a lot of stress when being mated, particularly when twisting is required for the connector type, such as Type N connectors. The torsion generated by making a connection is translated to the cable, which then gets twisted and begins to damage the cable; for example, the connection to the braiding of a coaxial cable or by the twisting of the inner conductor to the breaking point.

Added capacitance over the length of a cable affects digital signals. When extending digital cables, beware the problems of crosstalk and electrical length. You may extend so much that you affect the timing of signals, and at very high speeds, the digital signals may lose synch with each other, resulting in more errors that are not due to the DUT.

Any crushing of coaxial cable affects the characteristics of the dielectric, and sometimes the inner conductor. Many overzealous people apply too much tension when lashing coax cables and crush them with cable ties. This seriously affects their performance at microwave frequencies. A crushed coaxial cable has large reflections, and power reflects backward and forward in the cable being attenuated continuously, with very little getting through the cable.

Crosstalk is an effect caused by insufficient isolation between cables or switches. Noise or even signals can transmit into devices. A common form of crosstalk is also known as main interference, or hum. Good cabling and correct placement of switches can minimize these effects.

Check your signal levels: If you carry large signals in cables, ensure they have better than usual cabling, and improved placement may mean moving the cabling away from the general cable routing area.

Both design factors and the quality of components used in the system can improve the reliability of a test system. The degree of investment of time and money should be appropriate for the system's operating environment; however, even a small degree of investment will increase the reliability of your system and thus the effectiveness of your design.

6.5 Accuracy Considerations at RF, HF, and Microwave Frequencies

Some accuracy considerations such as wear on connectors will apply at all frequencies. As connectors are connected and disconnected many times, they will have an amount of metal-to-metal wear, and some of those metal filings end up in the connector. They may get into the threads, or anywhere in the connector body, and this buildup of filings eventually causes inconsistencies in measurement. Even if the connectors show no obvious signs of wear, it is good practice to replace them after some time. The problem with this wear and also the ingress of moisture – which is mentioned here as the effects are similar – is that the characteristics of the connector change, meaning that the connector can behave differently to what was intended and specified by the manufacturer. Often, the effect is similar to a filter, or it can just attenuate or reduce the signal strength. Regardless, at high frequencies, it will cause a change in impedance and thus cause reflections and loss of transmission. Another common problem for connectors is the physical handling or mishandling that they experience. Never turn the connector body – only turn the collett – otherwise, you risk scratching the mating surface and changing the surface impedance, thus causing unpredictable effects at different frequencies.

When using RF frequencies, there are a number of important points to remember. The first is the concept of transmission line and distributed elements (impedance). A transmission line occurs when the wavelength of the signal is smaller than the physical size of the circuit or cable. This book does not discuss transmission line theory; however, designers of test systems should be aware of transmission line theory and distributed effects and how these can impact measurements. All cables should be terminated correctly in the appropriate impedance and not left open-circuited. A common problem with new system integrators is the use of tee pieces instead of power splitters or dividers, as these do not preserve the impedance values. For example, connecting a spectrum analyzer and a frequency counter on a tee piece simply parallels two 50-ohm resistances (equivalent 25 ohms) to a system that is expecting a 50-ohm load. This will cause reflections and hence the maximum energy transfer will not be achieved, causing erroneous results.

At all frequencies, the handling and maintenance of the connections are critical. If your application makes it worthwhile to invest in a connector maintenance program, there are instruments that measure damage such as whether the pin in the connector is protruding or retarded, or the wear on the connector. There are also numerous connector designs that may impact your design. Some connectors are made for repeated connections, while others are designed for per-

Drawer Extended   Top View

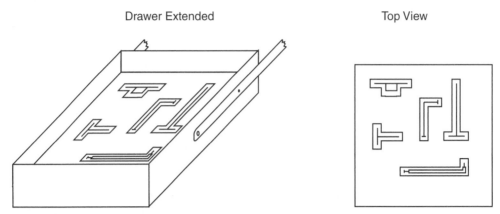

Figure 6.5   A connector drawer with cutout foam to take connectors.

manent setups and are made for just one or two connections. Be careful that your operator procedures help prevent operators or maintenance staff from incorrectly matching connector types,
and in this way, unintentional damage to one connector (usually the more expensive one) will be
avoided. For long-term care, avoid placing all connectors in a bag or drawer where they will rat-
tle around and damage each other. Instead, always place them in a padded storage compartment
or other container where they will be protected (see Figure 6.5).

You may decide to include a suitable accessories drawer in your system rack design (see
Chapter 10, "Selecting Racks and Racking Furniture," for a more detailed discussion on rack
design). Paying for high-quality connectors and maintaining them well will provide benefits to
your overall system accuracy and lifespan.

Cable runs should be kept as short as possible to avoid excessive attenuation. Cables
should be well-shielded (solid-shielded, or double-shielded as appropriate). Do not secure cables
with excessive tie-downs as this will dent the cable, altering its impedance. Take care not to
excessively bend a cable so that it becomes distorted beyond the manufacturer's stated specifications. The distortion comes from the inner conductor changing its distance from the outer conductor. This changes the impedance by changing the capacitance. In extreme cases, the outer and
inner conductors may touch, depending on the dielectric used, or worse, the strain may stretch
the inner conductor so much it breaks. Similar effects can be experienced by twisting the cable
excessively.

There are differences in connector grades; they often relate to the use of the connector,
e.g., general-purpose, precision, and metrology grade. The cost also varies greatly; for example,
metrology-grade connectors are often coated with gold to give the best repeatable connection
and reduce any resistance being introduced at the connection. Metrology connectors are not
made for everyday use and will wear very quickly. On the other hand, general-purpose connectors are quite rugged and will accept a number of connections and disconnections, but are not
recommended for high-accuracy measurements – they are simply made for a different purpose.
Choose the right connector for the task.

Some connectors must not be mated to other types even though they physically can be. This relates to SMA and APC 3.5 particularly; the center pin of SMA is larger and will damage an APC 3.5 female connector – rendering the APC connector useless, at the best it will be intermittent – an expensive way to learn this lesson.

When choosing connectors and cables, study the specification the manufacturer supplies you. If the connectors are not specified, ask for the specifications. If the supplier does not seem to realize there is a difference, shop elsewhere. Many connectors are built to standards; find out which standards and look them up. You may be degrading the benefits of very expensive test equipment by using poor connectors.

Essentially, you want your cables and connectors to look invisible electrically to your test equipment and DUT. There will always be some measurable loss and impedance effects, though. You must decide how much you can tolerate and use appropriate connectors.

6.6 Controlling the Interface to the DUT

The interface to the DUT can be controlled in several different ways, from completely manual, discussed in Section 6.6.1, to completely automated, discussed in Section 6.6.2. The purpose of the interface is to provide an easy-to-manage and thus easily controlled connection to the test system.

A test system operator will be faced with a panel that will support the DUT and allow connection to the test system. The panel may only have rows of connectors on it and signals may be switched to it from behind. Some of the connectors may have signal outputs from test equipment hardwired to them through the cable loom. You may not want all the outputs on while testing takes place, as they may add to the noise level on the signals that you are trying to measure; if your test system is manually controlled under these circumstances, then the procedure should direct that these outputs be shut off.

Using a panel brings all the connectors in front of the operator and allows easier connections and shorter leads to the signal outlet points. You may have a mass interconnect, where the fixture for the DUT is brought into contact with many points on the test system simultaneously, which saves angular wear when connecting and disconnecting to the test system. Fixtures for mass interconnect will have mating assemblies already in place according to the needs of the DUT.

To avoid having to frequently get access behind the panel to change signal connections, a large, expandable switch that can connect to the panel will do all the routing to connectors for your DUT. Then your fixtures can be independent of the panel design as the signals can be routed wherever you want. This is an expensive method to use, but it has the greatest ease of use and range of control. Control of the panel and its routing is then either manual or through the switch. If it is through the switch, then computer control or some sort of automated control panel close at hand are the available options.

6.6.1 Manual Control Following Documented Procedures

Manual control of a test system requires greater investments in detailed operating procedures and operator training. The operator must be fully trained on the functions and setup of the test equipment and the DUT. The operator should also appreciate the theory behind the measurement. In this way, results are more likely to be correct. However, whenever manual connection and manual driving of a system take place, there is the potential for errors. To minimize this as much as possible, a well-documented set of procedures should be available to the operator for every test that is to be performed. There should also be a similar document where results can be easily logged.

Manual procedures have to include all the interconnect information as well as all the control information for the equipment. The cable types and connector types have to be clearly indicated as well as the correct connection points. When calculating the signal strength at the end of the cable where it joins to the DUT, make sure that you account for cable losses and losses through adapters. Cables and connectors, adapters, and any hookup leads should be checked regularly for wear and tear and damage to cables as well as to connector surfaces.

The procedures should go into enough detail to allow the operator to hook up the DUT to all the equipment being used at each test stage, using the correct cables. The DUT should be located at a convenient height centrally to the ATE so that stress is not put on cables or their connections through having to be suspended over a long distance or at excessive angles.

Others considerations are whether the DUT needs to be disconnected and reconnected by the operator multiple times; this action will introduce errors, and to minimize these errors, operators need to be trained on proper handling of the connectors on the device, the test equipment, and the cables. Special tools, especially those for higher frequency work such as torque wrenches, should be used.

Procedures of this type will have to allow for a wider range of errors from the test system, as there are so many additive errors in the cabling and adapters alone without all the problems from wear and tear from so many connects and disconnects. Any fixtures used should also be checked regularly for deterioration.

The errors involved with manual setups are systematic in nature and need to be understood to fully appreciate the causes of error and therefore minimize them. The choice of how many operators to use depends on how many DUTs need to be tested. However, it is good organizational planning to train at least two people so that the knowledge does not reside just in one individual. The operators will need to update their training whenever new equipment or DUTs need testing. This will be an ongoing investment in your staff to ensure that best practices are used.

An important aspect of test system design is to ensure that the environment in which an operator works is suitable for the task. Occupational health and safety (OH&S) is an important issue that should not be ignored. Correct lighting, ventilation, and work surfaces need to be provided for the operators. Equipment needs to be set up so that it is easily accessed and usable without heavy lifting. Any work on dangerous items such as power supplies may require two people to be present for the testing.

In a fully-manual system, where the operator is making and changing a number of connections, the biggest potential disadvantage comes from the reliability and repeatability of each connection. If the test system procedures or setup allow any scope for improvisation, then further opportunities to introduce errors may arise. Cables used at different times may be different, in different stages of wear, have cleaner connectors, or may have been flexed less, having different losses in each case. If the operator has a large number of connections to make, then any systematic error he or she introduces will be difficult to track and to eliminate from your process. The more connections, the greater the potential for repeated error. If you have a large or an increasing number of DUTs to test, then you may decide that you have reached an appropriate time to upgrade your system to automate these tasks and make them more reliable – particularly if each DUT has a long manual connect and disconnect time.

If you can make the test system procedures straightforward and the connections and disconnections few in number, then the system operator will not require extensive training and experience. With more complex test system procedures, the operator will require greater skill to troubleshoot suspicious results. Otherwise, an inexperienced operator may not realize that his or her results are not reliable, and a day or more can be wasted on spurious testing.

To get the highest productivity in your test system environment, aim to automate your system to the extent that it can be run by the least experienced operator, and free up your best people to make them available for more skilled tasks. Unless the cost of automation is too high to be considered or the population of the DUT is too small, it is cost-effective to test in this manner.

6.6.2   Full Software Automation through a Fixture

The quickest and most reliable testing is done under full automated control using fixtures. These most often interface directly to a panel in front of a switch matrix, which brings all the signal and measurement points up to their access points on the DUT.

The fixture is mated to the test system by means of direct connect to the patch panel or by cable connect to the patch panel (for some DUTs, this is easier as they include these as part of their standard assembly). Once the DUT is connected to the test system, all measurements are taken and all devices stimulated according to the automated test procedure. As each test is completed and the signals need to be changed or rerouted, this is done by the switch matrix; the interface to the panel that connects to the DUT does not change nor does it require adjustment. The DUT may be cycled through many tests to assure proper working condition, or the test results may be analyzed as part of the test procedure to determine the next best test to run to identify the source of a fault condition.

Fully-automated control is the fastest method of connecting to your DUT and cycling through your tests at high speed. A high operator skill level is not required; the operator's main task is to handle the DUT to get it into the test position (fixture), and after testing is complete, to get it into packaging for dispatch.

The most straightforward way to track your tested assemblies is to use a system to record and track the serial number of each assembly. This has a number of advantages in addition to the obvious benefits of being able to check which items have been tested, if required. Long-term analysis of effectiveness of test can be carried out to identify whether you need to add more tests to increase test coverage. Analysis may even identify tests that can be removed from your procedures if you can demonstrate over time that no faults are found (or if failure rates over time are deemed to be within acceptable limits for your product's environment and application). If you need to identify "star" units on a complex production line, serial number tagging will also make it easy to separate these units after testing. Test batches can be tagged to time, so that if the test system develops a fault or is discovered to be out of calibration, it will be easy to identify which products must be re-tested. Long-term analysis of results can also facilitate the redesign of areas that often fail final test.

Full software automation of a fixture provides many advantages over other control methods. The first is ease of use, as the required operator skill level is reduced considerably. The software will control the system and the operator connects the DUT to the system via a fixture. The computer will not allow instruments to be connected incorrectly or to have the wrong functions engaged. The repeatability of the results is much greater and the results are normally electronically stored for further processing. The disadvantage is that the system will require investment to write the software to control the system. Hence, a company needs to determine whether the volume or complexity of the test requires or justifes the investment to develop the program.

Cabling the Rack

T his chapter explores the major issues involved with cabling up the rack, such as loss, accuracy, and cable stress. It outlines a number of good cabling techniques as well as describes how to get the best results at various frequencies. Higher frequency signals are more problematic to distribute than lower frequency signals and other issues present themselves during the design and building of a system with a mixed-signal environment. All of these issues trade off against cost – the very best cables are expensive, but it's worthwhile to always give the test system some additional flexibility and design beyond current needs.

KEY POINTS:

- Cabling through the racks should minimize cable stress and damage, and also maintain the environmental integrity of the rack.
- Different cabling, connector, and measurement considerations apply at DC, RF, and microwave frequencies. These should be planned for in the initial rack design.
- Labeling and documentation are absolutely essential despite the time and effort involved. They are key to the ongoing maintenance and support of the test system to ensure a maximum effective working life.

7.1 Cabling through the Racks

Cabling in the rack refers to all power cabling, instrumentation signal cabling, and bus cabling for interfacing purposes. The signal and bus (computer interface control) cabling will go up and down within the test system rack, and also from rack to rack if your test system uses multiple

Side View   Rear View

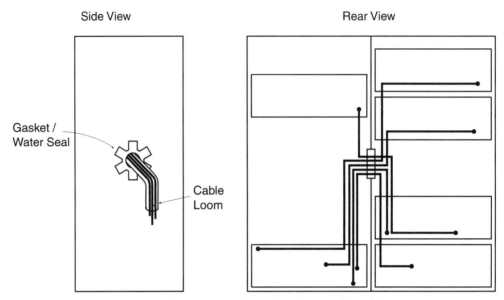

Figure 7.1   Rack cabinet wall showing properly gasketed cutout for cables.

racks, to reach the system's patch panel or to reach all the measurement and stimulation points and go back to the control computer.

7.1.1   Cabling and Racked Equipment

Cabling will generally enter the rack via the bottom of the cabinet under a false floor However, a particular test system or application layout may make it more sensible to have cabling enter via the top of the rack and through the rack walls.

It is convenient to separate the cabling functions, especially power and signal cabling, so that functionality is obvious. This will allow equipment to be added more easily at a future date. Power cabling should be kept as short as possible, leaving just enough length to allow it to be kept aside and out of the way. Always use specific-to-task cabling for power and signal cabling.

The cables going through a hole in the rack should not be subject to any stresses, such as vibration or extreme bending. Adequate measures should be taken to ensure that the cables do not cut or fray on the edges of the cutout holes between the racks. The cutout hole itself should never be used to support any cables passing through it. It should be used for access only, and not for support of any kind. The cut edge will be sharp and even when gasketed with softer material is unsuitable for serious test components support practices (see Figure 7.1).

If the cabling will be distributed via the front of the racks, then support for cables along their path is also important. Cables strung permanently at the front of the rack should be strapped in place in multiple positions to give added strength and support along their length. Many cables will compress and crush the dielectric at the support points if left to support their own weight at only one or two points along their length, causing impedance changes at different frequencies. These changes in impedance will of course instantly translate into a loss of some kind and degrade the accuracy of the test system.

Cabling leaving the rack or test system through the top or bottom should be designed to go through an area that does not affect the airflow of the rack.

Normally, a rack will be bolted or fastened somehow to the floor; hence to run cables, a hole will need to be cut in the floor – cut this hole at the back of the rack if you are running cables in the rear of the rack. If the floor tiles have shielding in them, ensure this is filed down or that a gasket or grommet is placed in the opening to protect the cables.

Once in the rack, cables should ideally be laid out in a functional manner and should be easy to access for maintenance and upgrades. Most racks can be fitted with cable trays (see Figure 7.2), which provide a convenient way to fit the cable loom. A cable tray is a long, narrow sheet of metal that is fitted inside a rack and cables are attached to it. It acts as a support for the cables to be laid flat and attached to – a loom is a set of cables lashed together so that the cables come in and out of the loom to be attached to pieces of test equipment and the DUT along the loom. The loom is normally circular, lending itself naturally to the shape of a bundled group of cables. Each cable will need to run along the cable tray and peel off to be connected to the right piece of test equipment or a connector panel. Therefore, it is best to run short cables on the inside so that minimum overlap occurs.

There are a number of useful options to secure the cables in the tray: "zap straps," wax, cotton string, and clips are all commonly used methods. The use of zap straps in particular makes the cabling process faster and simpler, but proper cable layout design and labeling is still important. All cables should be labeled clearly, showing which connectors they go to and their function. Often, false panels or boards to mock up the test system layout will be used to determine the correct length for the cable before the actual test equipment is fitted. It is also common practice to ensure that some slack is left in the cable so that future alterations are possible if required.

When ordering equipment that is intended for a racked test system, try to have all connections that will not be directly accessed by the operator mounted on the rear rather than the front of the test equipment. Some vendors offer a choice of front or rear connectors on some equipment; some vendors offer both. Test equipment manufacturers can offer these as a standard option for many pieces of equipment. This will allow your cabling to be connected at the rear of the rack, thus reducing cable length, saving money, and reducing excess bending of cables. Rear cable connections also save you from having to put feed-through panels in your test system and thus reduce the amount of room available for mounting test equipment.

The positioning of equipment in the test system rack will be a trade-off between cabling and operability (which includes weight and operator need). Chapter 11, "Weight Considerations and Equipment Placement," covers how to position equipment and system accessories in the rack.

When populating the rack, fit the cabling first if possible and then the equipment. This means that placement of equipment in the rack must be completely planned before rack assem-

Side View   Rear View

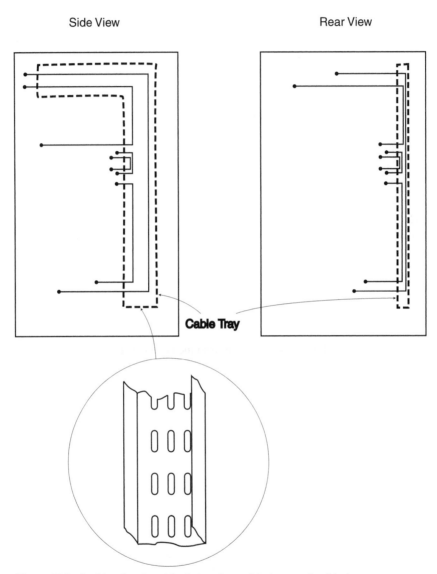

Figure 7.2   Inside of rack cabinet showing cable tray and cable loom.

bly begins, but it also allows a more methodical and systematic (and therefore neater) assembly process.

It is sometimes more convenient to remove the side panels on a rack during cabling, as this gives more room to get at and secure components. Re-install all the panels, however, when you have finished. Apart from looking better, it is easier to control the environment inside the rack.

Some pieces of test equipment in the rack will be on rack slides, which attach to the sides of the test equipment solidly, then allow the test equipment to be slid out to a fixed, supported position for easy access. Some slide kits also allow the test equipment to be rotated once it is fully extended. In addition to offering more flexible configuration of equipment, this also allows easier cabling to the rear connectors if both front and rear access to the system rack is used for re-cabling and maintenance. If rack slide mount kits are used, make sure that you also allow enough slack cable to allow the equipment to be fully slid out.

After installation, always test cable integrity, especially checking for shorts or open circuits. When you have completed the test system, you should have a fixture that can be connected to the patch panel or switch interface that allows all the signals to be switched back to verifying equipment, to ensure integrity. It is good practice to run a few spare cables for future needs or repairs to damaged cables.

The power strip will normally be secured into the rack vertically. Make sure you follow all local or international standards relevant for the power strip. The power cables can then be connected to the equipment at approximately the correct height. Some developers use an electrician to make the cables to the correct length, as most instruments will come with a 1.5- to 2- meter cable, which is not necessary in a rack. Position outlet sockets from the power strip in each rack at appropriate intervals so that the power cable from the power strip to the test equipment is kept short, while still allowing a little slack to avoid cable stress. Do not use a power strip from one rack to supply power to test equipment in another rack.

Terminate the cables with their correct connectors before installing the cables in the rack. However, if you are running cables that need to travel any significant distance, you may want to run the cables to the bottom of the rack before terminating. This will save the connectors from being damaged.

TIP:

If you are installing cables that run under floors, wear gloves, because there are often a lot of sharp objects left by builders under computer floors – not to mention the danger from edges of the steel supports. (These are words of experience from someone who has traveled under many floors.)

After all equipment is fitted and working, you may need to support the loom at the back of the equipment with a metal bar, to remove any pressure from the connectors. While working in the confined space of a rack, also ensure that the cables are not bent beyond their maximum bend radius or you will damage the cables. The loom is wound the way it is for control, not for cosmetic reasons. The loom on its own is not strong and needs to be supported if it is in the vertical plane.

7.1.2   Using Cables

When selecting cables for your test system, look for consistency and repeatability, as well as any additional rugged-ness or environmental specifications that you require for your application. Find a vendor with published specifications, and always keep a copy of these on file should you ever need to replace cables. Any special requirements that you have over and above the industry norm will attract a price premium; however, factors such as environmental conditions outside your control can make an additional investment worthwhile. If you have to deploy your solution to tropical countries or colder climates, this should be covered in your initial design terms of reference and your test objectives.

TIP:

If your test system will be deployed in an environment where cable damage from birds, for example, is possible, then armored cables are a must. Cables chewed by birds can have a catastrophic effect on radar and radome measurements in outdoor ranges. Rats are best dealt with by whatever method suits the local environment. It is important that live power cabling is kept as high as possible in the rack at all times to prevent shorts due to flooding or animal waste.

Cables normally come wrapped around a reel, hence they tend to tangle and misbehave when you are unreeling them. Spend some time untangling and straightening your cables before running them through the rack. This will save you a great deal of frustration caused by cables becoming knotted and possibly damaged. If you have time and access to setup space, lay out the cables in the required lengths for a day or so before you put them into a loom or install them on a cable tray. If the lengths are really long, use large, loose coils to store them for several days in whatever space you have.

When using a staging area for cable runs and looms, take precautions to ensure that people do not step on the cables, run trolleys of equipment over them, or do anything else that may damage the cables. If you find that your loom is getting too large and you need to split it into two looms, then you need to go through the exercise of deciding what cables are needed where. The new loom may not go beside the old one, and may go on the other side of the rack.

It seems obvious, but remember to always label your cables before you loom them or run them. This again will save you lots of frustration. Clear heat shrink over a sticky label will provide excellent protection for the label. If you have a complicated wiring loom, work from a diagram and use a highlighter pen to mark off your cables as you label and group them in preparation for laying. Develop a cable labeling system that is not onerous or illogical if your organization does not already use one – the easier it is, the more likely it will be used.

Signal cables in particular must be the best you can get that will still meet your budget. Ensure they are warranted to meet the standards you must comply with for your particular application. Cables to be used at RF frequencies should always be terminated in the correct connector type and gender to avoid the use of adapters (and the resulting increase in test result uncertainty).

At some installations, you may need to take additional measures; for example, where environmental damage can be an unexpected hazard, you will have to guard against this to keep a facility operational.

TIP:

Remember to test all cables both before and after installation! Damage can occur during the installation process, even if the cables have passed incoming inspection. For most cables, this can be a simple continuity test; for example, using a light bulb and battery.

If you want the option of making your own custom or standard cables, access to someone with high-precision soldering skills will be very valuable as the soldering will not be a trivial task. Many engineers use crimp tools and accessories to great advantage to make up cables on-site. They are simple to use, quick, and provide a very reliable connection. The equipment costs more than a soldering iron; however, its ease of use and reliability are worth the extra cost. The best way to get reliable cables for specific tasks is to have them made up by a reliable vendor, which may or may not be the cable manufacturer. Many local vendors can perform high-quality work if you are prepared to put in the time to ensure they understand your needs and performance criteria.

As you group more cables together, the overall weight of the cable bundle increases and its flexibility decreases, making the task of cabling more difficult. To avoid this, it may be necessary to run the loom in small but manageable groups rather than one large and unwieldy bundle.

Good cables are expensive, but worth the investment. They are also worth protecting, both to decrease the need for frequent replacement and for the ongoing accuracy of your test results.

Every organization that is regularly involved in test system build or maintenance should institute a policy of regular cable checking as well as a standard process of making cables.

7.1.3   Cabling Multiple Racks

The cabling between racks, if more than one rack is used to hold the test system, should go through a hole cut in the rack wall for that purpose, which should be no larger than needed. This ensures that the airflow and temperature integrity of each rack remains manageable. The hole should be gasketed (grommeted) to avoid cable damage, and also to reduce unnecessary bending of the cables. Should the cabling need to leave the rack to go to the DUT, then that should also be through a managed hole in the rack where strain is reduced.

When you have more than one test rack, the power distribution should remain common between the racks so that on every rack, there is a switch to cut off the entire system and isolate it electrically. The power cabling must not go from rack to rack; rather, it must be distributed within each rack, even if the power itself is distributed to all the racks (see Figure 7.3).

Rear View

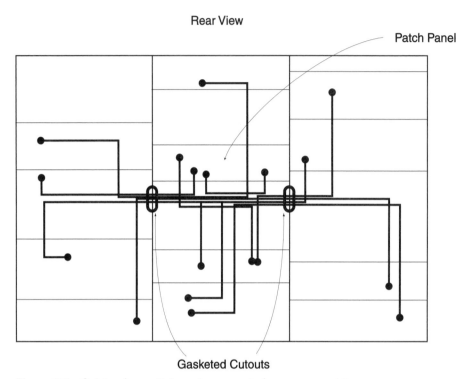

Figure 7.3   Cabling for multiple racks separate from power cabling.

7.2 Design to Minimize Cable Stress

Designing the test system cable layout to minimize cable stress will extend the life of your system and make it easier to maintain. It will also save money by reducing maintenance and failures due to damaged or faulty cables.

Methods such as using rear panel connectors and suspending cables to support their full length are excellent preventative steps to avoid cable stress. Rear panel connections, for example, reduce cable stress considerably, as you don't have to feed the cable from the front to the inside of the rack, then to the rear of the switch matrix or patch panel.

The most basic and most often repeated piece of advice when using cable ties to manage cable layouts in a test system is to take care not to apply too much tension to the ties. Crimping in a cable caused by too much pressure in the ties will degrade test system signals and cause errors in measurements. Also, be careful when attaching the cables to anchoring points within the rack, that they do not cause the cable to bend or cause it to be damaged by sharp edges. Keep signal cables away from power cables whenever possible to avoid risking exposure to 50- or 60-Hz mains hum on top of your signals.

Decide early whether any test equipment will be in a slide-mount fitting, which allows rotation of the equipment during testing and also the addition of cabling to take advantage of previously unused features on the test equipment. Slide-mount fittings also allow easier removal from the front of the rack by sliding the equipment out to its extreme position then removing it.

All cable routing in the rack itself should be laid out to avoid any movement caused by opening doors or the removal and installation of test equipment or other devices. Design your loom or cable harness so that cables come out of the loom at the correct angles to where they are needed, rather than being wrapped back around the outside of the loom (therefore causing more access problems when you need to remove or install equipment). It is also good practice to run a few spare cables in the loom just in case they are required; for example, for a minor system expansion.

The authors' top five cable management tips are listed below:

TOP CABLE MANAGEMENT TIPS:

- To minimize stress in cables, the loom must be designed to minimize bends.
- The cable connectors must never support the weight of the loom.
- The cables must not be secured overly tightly, to avoid the cables being dented.
- Keep cables located away from any sharp edges.
- All cables should be inspected for damage after installation.

Stress relief for cables is also important for test equipment on rack slides. You need to allow for the drawing out of equipment on slides, and one of the most effective ways to do this is to have a loop of signal and power cables on a spring arm or swinging hinge. In this case, it is best to lay all the cables on a cable platform that is hinged, which allows all the cables to be lashed to the tray rather than to each other. This has servicing, maintenance, and upgrade advantages. It also makes it easier to trace cabling.

It is a good idea to purchase your cables with the connectors already attached from a specialized cable manufacturer; however, this involves having a completed rack layout design and being sure of all cable lengths.

The initial investment of time and cost will pay off through the life of the system if you incorporate some cable management methods such as these at the beginning of your system layout.

7.3 DC Considerations

Accurate DC measurements and the generation of accurate DC currents and voltages are fundamental to test systems. High-quality devices give the designer a range of choices when it comes to this area. Many vendors will supply the necessary voltage dividers and additional earthing or ground terminals needed to enhance accuracy and throughput. When making very accurate DC voltage and DC current measurements, care must be taken to remove the effects of cable resistance or path loss from the measurement, or the generation of ground currents. Voltage will drop over the length of the cable as a function of the resistance of the cable. Voltage drop will also be due to heat loss caused by the resistance of the cable, as some of the voltage will be converted to heat. You will see a guard terminal on high-precision DC voltmeters, which gives a separate path to ground at a different impedance to the negative or ground terminal (a voltage divider gives isolation as well as reduction in ground currents). Using guard terminals does not negate these effects; they minimize them at best – it is impossible to avoid the physics involved, and there are no cables that are without loss.

Some DC measurements are "floated," thus removing the residual effects and losses associated with currents from loops. This is a dangerous practice and is a technique best left to experts who can do this in a controlled environment meant for this purpose. Essentially, the earth connection is disabled and the two devices concerned in the measurement, or transfer of accuracy, are allowed to come to the same potential with respect to their cases by directly connecting them together. This eliminates ground currents from being generated between each instrument and ground, which would otherwise cause a different potential between each instrument and ground, and therefore the two instruments would not be at the same conditions with respect to earth and ground. These types of measurements are usually carried out in standards laboratories. It is important to take note that this technique involves the dangerous risk of the cases floating to the full live potential of the power supply, 240VAC or 110VAC, depending on the country.

To make very high accuracy measurements in a test system, you must understand what it is you want to achieve and how to minimize the external effects on those measurements. To deliver very high-performance voltage measurements through a switch matrix and patch panel can be a significant challenge. You must be able to calibrate to the measurement plane of the test system and then be able to use a characterized fixture to interface to the DUT to maintain any kind of reliability or consistency. The cables must be kept consistent in the DC path, which includes not using different grades of cables, and using as few terminals or adapters as possible. If possible, solder the cables onto heavy lugs that can then be inserted into the switch matrix or patch panel for direct connection to the interface fixture to the DUT. Carry as many cables as necessary to get the four terminal measurements and the sense cables of DC supplies all the way to the DUT. Rear panel connectors on test equipment can be a real help in these situations. Having to take cables from the front of one piece of test equipment through the rack and to the back of another piece of equipment involves extra bending of the cables, additional distance, exposing the connector, and the extra expense (and two additional connections) of using a feedthrough panel. Rear panel connectors on equipment help to avoid these (see Figure 7.4).

When you want to measure very small signals, then external effects such as the thermal system noise of the test system become apparent and have to be reduced or removed from the measurement environment. Using measurement techniques derived from standards laboratories can improve the test system's measurement quality and throughput. A high-precision DC voltmeter with a guard terminal (see Figure 7.5), for example, reduces the effect of ground currents and lead resistance.

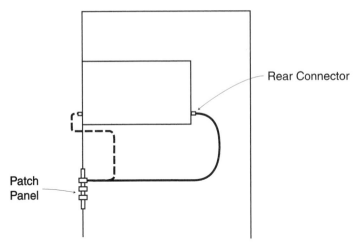

Figure 7.4 Test equipment with rear panel connectors.

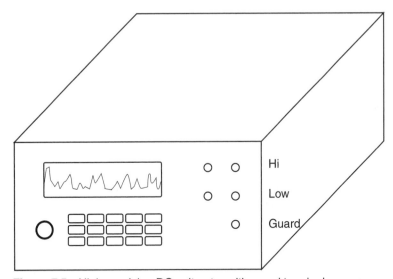

Figure 7.5 High-precision DC voltmeter with guard terminal.

When supplying a particular DC voltage or DC current to a terminal, it is good practice to check what the loss is across the length of the cable and make up for this loss by increasing the voltage to overcome it. Many precision power supplies have this feature for constant current or constant voltage sources, such as an additional set of cables that attach to the DUT where the supply cables do, and measure the voltage at that point. When using precision or even general-purpose power or current supplies in a test system, remember that the voltage or current you need is at the DUT, not at the output of the device. Thus, you must still have some accurate way to determine what exactly you have at the DUT and how to consistently get the correct value there. Generally it is better practice to measure DC voltages at the delivery point of the DC voltage, not the source. Thus, do not measure the output of a DC voltage supply at its output; instead, measure it at the end of the cables attached to its output terminals.

TIP:

Use heavy-low resistance cabling for DC voltage measurements (cabling for AC voltages is generally coaxial, to give shielding to the signal from the outside world). Buy the best cables you can afford and calculate your results to the ends of the cables for greater accuracy.

Four terminal resistance measurements are very accurate, since they supply a constant current and measure the drop across the DUT at the same point that the current is being supplied. This means all external effects, including the cable resistance, are removed from the measurement. Sometimes special voltmeter or resistance meter clips are supplied to make these measurements. Four terminal resistance measurements allow you to move the measurement from the resistance meter's terminals to some distance away.

Use the best cabling you can, particularly if your device is some distance from the DUT. Generally, you want to keep all the cable lengths and cable types from DC voltage or current sources exactly the same, as well as the cable type (you'll have a consistent, known cable resistance per meter). For special measurements, you might have special copper cables to carry the energy with minimum losses. The lugs and connector positions should also be given consideration – you want the cabling to attach with minimal electrical resistance. Good cabling for DC supplies will be heavy copper, sometimes quite stiff as you almost want a solid copper rod if you could use it (see Figure 7.6). Keep all the terminals clean, so that when cable is attached, the joins have minimal surface-to-surface resistance.

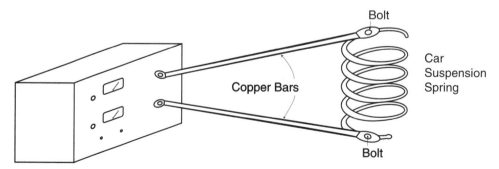

Figure 7.6 Measuring PWM on a 5V DC 1200A power supply using solid copper bars welded together to get 5 milliohms resistance.

When using copper wire, remember to clean the oxidized copper off the ends before connecting it or trying to solder it. If it is tinned, scrape the ends with a knife blade to clean them – the last thing you want is resistance across the junction of the cable to the terminal or connecting device due to oxidation or tinning of the cable. Any resistive join means that heat will be generated and energy will be lost.

7.4 RF and Microwave Considerations

At high frequencies, different effects come into play with signal generation and measurement. Different connector types are used at different frequencies, and in addition, there are several available connector types overlapping for most frequency ranges (see Figure 7.7). As frequencies get higher, very short wavelengths are difficult to contain on cables. High frequencies are normally managed by using a cable diameter that is suitable to the wavelength. Cable types at higher frequencies often determine the available range of connector types, and vice versa (some cables are very thick and heavy, so it would be almost impossible to attach some of the smaller connectors to them). Cables such as the RG-214, for example, can only use connectors like Type N, as the diameters are very similar (both are large). Connectors themselves have their own range of issues and difficulties to deal with.

When RF or microwave frequencies are being used in cables, additional considerations are required. All cables must be terminated in their characteristic impedances. Lengths must be kept as short as possible, without over-bending the cable. Particular importance must be allocated to splitting the signal if required. A true power splitter must be used (see notes in box below). A simple paralleling of devices is not recommended, as this will degrade the impedance balance of the system. When impedance mismatches are encountered, the system will not allow maximum power transfer to occur. Reflections will also occur, which can cause serious problems in measurement systems.

POWER SPLITTERS AND POWER DIVIDERS

Use power dividers when you need to get a true phase matched division of power. Splitters are normally used for leveling, where part of the signal is picked off and sampled to keep an output amplitude at a certain level. Dividers are not as good for this application, as their source match is not as good as that of a splitter. See Figure 7.8.

All RF cables in measurement systems should be of high quality, as should the connectors. RF energy can escape or radiate from the cable and cause problems in the other cables or equipment. The cables can also have stray signals ingress on them and again cause problems in the system. To avoid this, cabling that has a very good shielding should be used. For similar reasons, the connectors must also be of high quality.

RF cables require very good shielding to stop them from interfering with or from being interfered with by other equipment. They are normally a thicker, heavier, and more difficult

Type N (male)

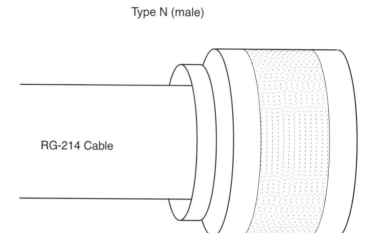

RG-214 Cable

BNC (male)

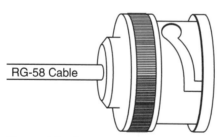

RG-58 Cable

Figure 7.7 Some cables and connector types.

cable to work with. To achieve the parameters expected of them, RF cables are also expensive, and to protect this investment, it is important to maintain the cables regularly and to use appropriate measures such as armored cables required by environmental conditions.

Care must be taken to ensure cabling is terminated in the correct connector type, and if necessary, gender. Adapters are not recommended, as they cause reflections and losses through their connections. It is difficult to establish the exact measuring plane with some connector types – for example, Type N connectors (see Figure 7.9).

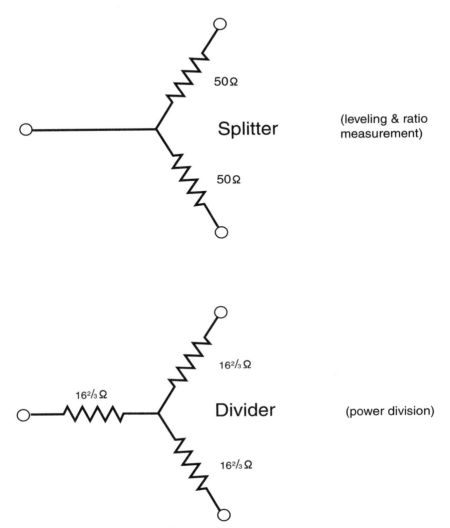

Figure 7.8 Power splitters and power dividers.

Ensure that you do not exceed the specifications of any cables for loss through the test system. RF and microwave cables that are specified to carry low signal levels without degrading them can be very expensive. This restriction also promotes the careful design of the tests so that you are not trying to route extremely low signal levels of high-frequency signals over many meters of cable, as you may not have any signal at all at the end of the cable.

Microwave cables often have a large bend radius, so plan their installation to allow enough space to accommodate any bends without exceeding the cable's specifications. These cables damage easily if forced into tight bends and the loss is no longer predictable. If you crush a

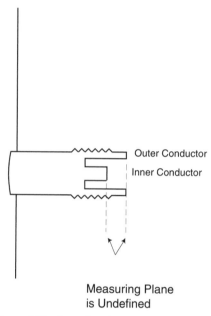

Figure 7.9   Locating the measuring plane on Type N connectors.

coaxial cable, you are changing its impedance so that now it becomes higher in path resistance and no longer has its original characteristics.

Always check that the frequencies you want to use in your cabling will not cause excessive loss. Cables are frequency selective, and appropriate cables should be used to ensure minimum losses through the cables. Also, check that the connectors are appropriate (using RG-58 cable with BNC connectors at several gigahertz, for example, will simply not allow the signal to reach the end of the cable without severe attenuation).

Make all system signal routes as short as possible. A major cause of signal loss is to have cables longer than they need to be. Try not to have too many different types of cables and connectors, as it becomes costly to keep spares and skills current for each type should you need to repair them. Adapters should be avoided wherever possible through the use of correct connectors on all cables. Adapters can be useful, but they often carry some damage through frequent use and thus cause losses in the system. Impedance mismatches cause a multitude of problems, by reflecting energy, creating standing waves, and degrading the effective return loss of the system. Energy that does not reach your instruments cannot be measured – again, causing measurement error.

Different effects can occur at different frequencies. An interesting frequency-specific effect encountered by the authors occurred while measuring a Type N connector, f-to-f barrel adapter. The device was fine at all frequencies except for a huge notch at 17GHz. After measuring several other connectors of the same type in the site workshop, it was discovered that the cleaning solvent used left behind a residue, which had resonant effects at 17GHz only.

Degradation of signals through the test system will lead to unreliable results. Be careful of having your cabling running near sources of high magnetic fields, as these have interesting effects at microwave frequencies. Many devices used in microwave wave guides are magnetic; they can be used to divide microwave fields as well as divert them. If you have large fields near microwave equipment, then you cannot predict what effects they may cause – the best practice is to avoid them.

TIP:

Have all your RF and microwave cabling made to terminate in their correct gender and type, and keep all cable lengths as short as possible.

Use well-shielded cabling so that stray signal sources or EMI cannot get into your cables and onto your signals. Gasketing materials may be used to reduce EMI effects where cables enter and leave racking assemblies. It is important for the accuracy of a test system to avoid cables acting like antennae, either receiving or transmitting RF energy. Noise levels will be increased on your signals, thus reducing the dynamic range available for your measurements. It may be so bad that your system is rendered marginal by noise and signal loss problems.

7.4.1 Connectors

The behavior of cable connectors at high frequencies in particular should be a consideration in all test system designs. Some of the more important points about high-frequency connectors to bear in mind are:

- Connectors become more expensive and complex as frequency is increased.
- They must be kept clean and be protected during storage.
- Use compressed air to remove particles, and if a solvent is required, use an appropriate one. The correct way to clean a connector is with a cotton swab.
- Before using connectors at higher frequencies, they should be tested with a connector gauge first. If the connector is mated and unmated regularly, the connector should be re-gauged periodically.
- Be very careful not to cross-thread any connectors; tighten them lightly at first to ensure that the connectors are indeed aligned correctly.
- The body of the connector should not be turned; only the connector collett should be turned during tightening. (You must never rub the measurement surfaces of connectors against each other; if they scratch, then they lose consistency and thus accuracy.)
- Torque wrenches should be used to tighten the connector to the correct degree of torque.

Remember that connectors are designed for use up to a certain frequency. In a test system, never use connectors that are not designed for that frequency.

7.5 Labeling and Documentation

It is important to label and record all cabling in a test system, and a copy of the record should be stored off-site in a secure and known place. Thorough labeling and documentation are useful for:

1. Building a copy of the same system – if you want to duplicate the system locally or on the other side of the world, if your documentation is in good order, it will be a simple process.
2. Maintaining the system, on both repair and calibration bases, and for safety when maintenance is being carried out.
3. Reconfiguring the system for new DUTs, or upgrading obsolete test equipment.
4. Ensuring that the correct cables are connected to the correct inputs and outputs.
5. Assisting with training and understanding the signal paths throughout your system.

All cables should be labeled to the common standard used throughout your organization. There are a number of cable labeling standards available, and an organization should choose one that is straightforward to administer and maintain, and can be expanded in the future. The cables should be labeled in appropriate-length segments so that operators can easily follow a cable through the system. Avoid using colored cables or wires for identification, as it may be difficult to source the same ones at a later stage for maintenance or expansion.

All the signaling and power cables should be tagged with a logical method in mind, at both ends of the cable – this makes it much easier when trying to replace a faulty cable or add a new capability by upgrading test equipment and test system ability such that cabling must also be upgraded.

Label the cables at relatively short distances (a meter or less, or every two to three feet) so that individual cables are easily identified. Labeling may include source and destination points, some information on the signal being carried (for example, whether it is HF or UHF), or it may simply be a numerical reference to a look-up table.

If you are supplying a test system to a third party, use a method that is acceptable to the customer. In addition to being an aid to repair or support, this reflects your organization's attitude toward quality. Supply the customer with what they need in an orderly fashion; many companies' manuals are similar because they tend to think about support in a similar manner. Do not go overboard in your technical content, but try to address each part of your documentation to the intended audience.

Make sure that the documentation is clearly laid out so it can be updated easily. Have some form of configuration control so when you need to audit a system, you know exactly the state of the documents by their date. This allows the user to identify a system so the correct software and tests are performed and they are of a known and documented state. To make it easier to add new modules to the test system, having a documentation boilerplate to re-use in the same format makes the quality of the process easier to manage.

Cabling documentation should include:

- A parts list of all cables, by type, length, and supplier. This information should include: whether the cable was bought to a particular specification or was built in-house or sub-contracted; what type of cable was used; what type of connector was used. If possible, have a second supply source for every cable.

- A cabling label system that covers the input and output points for each cable and the type of signal carried. The input and output portion should identify the rack, unit, and connector (including front or rear) to be really useful. There should also be cabling diagrams for signal cables and power distribution cables.

- Diagrams of all cable layouts. This should cross-reference to the parts list easily as well as to the actual wiring and cabling in the test system. There should be a schematic electrical layout as well as an installation layout, showing which cables go where as they go in and out of the looms. It should also show layouts of cable trays if these are used. The main power distribution should also be shown, including isolation transformers and other devices. (The main wiring must be done according to country rules and regulations.)

- Careful documentation of all connector types and genders, remembering that some types come in different grades, such as general-purpose, precision, and metrology grades – these are all different costs and have different characteristics accordingly. Try to use common cable assemblies and avoid exotic connections and cables. This makes it easier to repair or upgrade the test system. Should you need to refurbish the system, you will know what your starting point was.

- A signal path table, recording the signal type and bandwidth expected of each cable in the system, so that future technicians and engineers know exactly what each cable was used for and where it was laid when looking at the manual for the rack. Even standard power cables should be specified.

- An index – identify all your suppliers and the part number from each.

Related documentation should be kept commonly accessible; for example, keep the purchasing file close to the technical manual. When you have to upgrade or replace any parts of the system, this will be a good indicator of the approximate costs that will be involved. Keep all the datasheets on the cabling and connectors on file as well. If you have catalogs, photocopy relevant pages for your files. Stay on the mailing lists of your suppliers, or use other sources such as the Internet to keep up-to-date supplier, representation, and contact information available.

Using Switch Panels and Interface Panels

T his chapter discusses the use of switch panels and interface panels, to interface between the test equipment and the DUT, and how to get the best use from each method. Some test system component vendors have ready-made products such as system interfaces that have been developed based on extensive experience in this market and provide a valid alternative to having fully custom interfaces built. Data gathering about these devices is recommended before you start your own design of the interface.

KEY POINTS:

- Switch panels and interface panels are used to bring all test system signals to one panel where they can be easily accessed by the operator. This arrangement increases both measurement speed and reliability, and reduces wear on instrument connectors.
- A range of standard connector panels and other products are available to simplify this task, and can help make system design and assembly quicker.
- Auto-interconnect fixtures have the additional feature of aligning a complex DUT so that it connects with the same angle and pressure each time.
- Building your own fixturing or specifying it for a third party to build is a complex process that requires thorough specification of all signals and the accompanying control software.
- The fixture must always be considered as part of a unit together with the software to control that fixture.

The principle behind the use of switch panels and interface panels is to bring all the cabling and connectors into a fixed position that is easy to access for the operator. Switch panels and patch

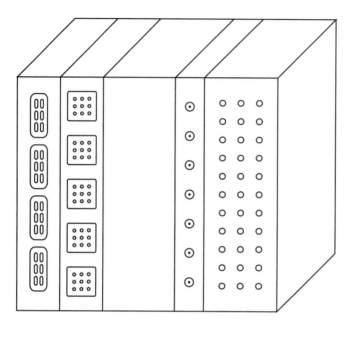

Switch Panel
Interface
to Matching
Panel with DUT
on it
(switching done
behind panel)

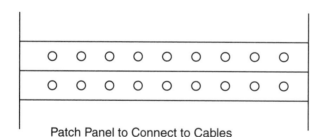

Patch Panel to Connect to Cables

Figure 8.1   Switch panel and patch panel.

panels will both be referred to as patch panels from hereon in this chapter (see Figure 8.1). Both terms refer to the method of the operator connecting to the front of panel, where all signals and connectors are brought to the same point, rather than connecting to individual signals at different points in the test system rack.

The use of a patch panel will reduce wear and tear on connectors and cables as well as reduce the time taken to make the connections between the DUT and the test system. This lends itself well to automation where speed is important, and also makes manual operation easier.

In a manual setup, the time taken to connect and reconnect cables is hundreds of times greater than the measurement speed of the test system. A voltmeter can make measurements in milliseconds, while it takes the operator a minute or so to make connections after checking for correct cabling and connector types, then double-checking the connections before starting the test again. When a patch panel is used, the operator is instructed to interconnect to certain connectors that are right in front of him or her, and then start the test process, rather than the operator searching the front panels of each piece of test equipment to find the correct connectors. Most test equipment devices have a multitude of connectors on the front and rear panels, and choosing the wrong one can have serious consequences. You may damage equipment at worst, and have to redo all your tests at best.

As all signal cables and connectors are brought to a single panel, the signaling cables can all be laid in place more or less permanently inside the rack system. This has the advantage of ensuring that you have firm knowledge and control of all the losses up to the patch panel. An additional benefit to the test system management is that the signals can now be calibrated to the connectors on the panel, rather than trying to calculate loss across the cables when your calibration is to the connectors on the test equipment (see Figure 8.2). This is very important, as you can now be assured of the condition of the signal paths by verifying them at the interface. This saves a lot of time, since cabling is now consistent, whereas previously you could not be sure which cable might be used and thus had no idea what loss might be appropriate. Under those conditions, where you are unsure of all the cables involved in the measurement, you would have to leave a wide error margin to allow for different cables at each test – which defeats the purpose of using high-performance test equipment. If you make the investment in purchasing high-performance test equipment, then using the most appropriate type and quality cables available is simply a step that protects your equipment investment. There is no point in allowing uncertainty about whether cabling has degraded the signals to decrease the surety of your measurements.

TIP:

Some test systems will incorporate a method of switching, or connecting all the generated signals back to devices in the test system that can measure and verify them. By measuring both ways, for example, you can check the measuring and generating equipment at the same time.

Set your system to generate 1V DC, then route that signal to a voltmeter and set up to measure and verify the result. If the test fails, then you know that you have at least a failed voltmeter, generator, or one of the paths. If you switch the signal to a different device, regardless of accuracy, such as an oscilloscope, and still get a wrong result, then the generator or the signal paths are suspect. By substituting a cable connection, you can remove the path effects and determine if the cable or generator is at fault.

You can generate logical test structures to verify all your componentry before you start testing. There may even be different levels of test depending on whether you are going through the daily start-up verification, or the more detailed longer testing if a fault is found in the system. When items are removed and re-installed, after calibration for example, then you must run tests after re-installing the equipment, to verify the losses and restore those as constants in your software work table.

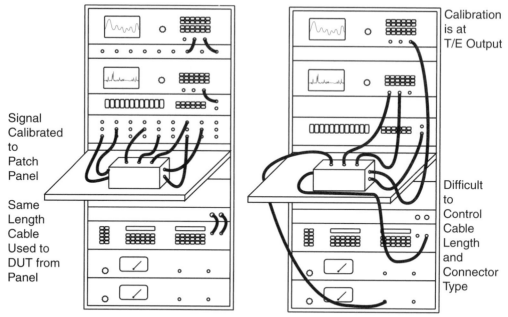

Figure 8.2 Using a patch panel in the test system allows cabling to be fixed semi-permanently in place, and allows sources of measurement uncertainty to be fully known.

8.1 Patch Panels

Patch panels are generally made up of connectors that are installed into the panel itself, with connector points on each side of the bulkhead. Bulkhead (feed-through) connectors generally have the same fitting on either side of the panel (e.g., BNC female). The bulkhead connector is designed to fit into a hole in the panel without rotating (physical locking by slot or keyway), and have cables attached to either side.

The idea is to bring all the outputs and inputs from all the test equipment in the test system to a common area that is more convenient to the operator. It also saves the operator from having to connect directly to the test equipment, which saves increased wear and tear damage on the test equipment connectors and also eliminates a systematic source of error through incorrect connection to the test equipment.

Given that there is a wide range of connectors and labeling schemes – which are often inconsistent among manufacturers – the probability of the operator making the right connection may be very high, but not perfect (that is, it is not possible to guarantee a correct connection every time). If the operator only makes an incorrect connection one percent of the time, then one thousand items from each test run of one hundred thousand items will have to be retested.

The use of patch panels can also provide a benefit in the long-term maintenance costs of the test system. The cost of the feed-through (bulkhead) connectors on the patch panel is much lower than replacing connectors on your test equipment. If you need to replace connectors on a network analyzer due to wear caused by multiple connections, for example, then replacing the front panels and connectors can cost several hundred times what a cabling connector can cost – these are precision devices and must be handled or programmed by people qualified to work with them.

Factors such as these make a patch panel an appropriate choice if a number of connections are to be made – in one sense, you could almost call them connector savers.

It is also easy to identify the connectors on the patch panel by labeling each one, which will be positioned right in front of the operator. Rather than finding the right connector on the right piece of test equipment, the operator may be instructed to connect the output of the DUT to the patch panel on R1-3, row one (from the top), connector three (always read from the left, as if you were reading English). It is best to follow a logical naming convention if possible as it makes training and documentation easier. It is also easier to articulate the benefits of ease of use to the operators and to other customers to whom you may want to sell your support solution.

If you are supplying the test system as part of another product, for example a missile system, radar system, or cell phone family, then factors such as ease of repair and ease of operation may play a major part in your customer's evaluation for purchase.

The patch panel can have any type of connector that you require for your test system and DUT. Try to reduce the number of different types of connectors if you can – the overhead in maintaining different cables and calibrations for all combinations is immense. Using the smallest number of different cables and connectors that are appropriate for your measurement accuracy requirements will simplify maintenance as well as component sourcing and documentation. When you use a particular type of connector and have decided on the grade (general-purpose, precision, or metrology – not all connector types offer all three grades), then stick to a particular manufacturer that you are happy with. Ensure the connectors are built to an industry or IEEE standard to ensure compliance with the specifications issued by vendors and demanded by your customers. Deciding to use non-standard connectors is very risky – you lose industry compatibility and you will incur higher costs as a result of having to source connectors that few other companies use. Industry-standard connectors are made in large volumes and thus the cost is kept reasonable. Everyone knows the limitations of the standards (as they are in the public domain already) and you do not have to defend your use of industry standards, whereas you may have to justify the use of non-standard connectors to a third party, such as a downstream customer.

A number of patch panels exist on the market today (see Figure 8.3). Some are very specific to the industry involved; for example, telecommunications have their own standards for signaling and audio connectors. Have a good look around the marketplace and talk to the vendors about what they have available. Naturally, the vendors may be biased by their own company's training and their market knowledge; however, it does give you good insight into why they believe their system is most suitable.

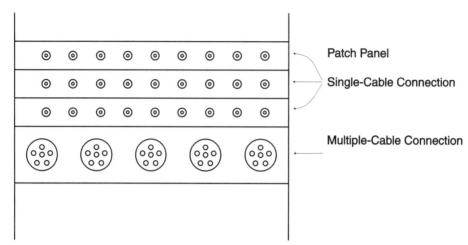

Figure 8.3   Patch panel and cable connections.

8.2 Buying Standard Panels/Rows of Connectors

Many manufacturers now sell rows of connectors mounted on standard rack-width (19") panels (see Figure 8.4). These can be particularly useful for putting together a system quickly. All cabling to or from the test equipment is interfaced to the rear of the bulkhead connectors in the rack, and then by direction, the operator hooks up the DUT connect cables to the front of the bulkhead connectors, which are visible to the operator.

Off-the-shelf panels will normally offer only one connector type. If you want a mix of connectors, then you must design and build your own, or have it built by a third party. You may decide to ask vendors to supply a mix as a specially built device just for your application. This gets expensive and pushes up the cost of your test system – not just in connector costs, but in the costs of calibrating different connectors and entering all the correct constants into any relevant software so that losses and impedance differences can be normalized out of the measurements. If

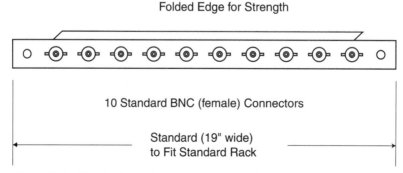

Figure 8.4   Standard panels or rows of connectors.

you have a custom inter-connect panel built for you, try wherever possible to use industry-standard connectors, and as always, be ready to invest a little extra money to buy the best that you can afford for your application.

A standard row of connectors, such as BNC (f), will be mounted on a 1-EIA-unit-high panel. One EIA unit, or 1U, is 1.75", or 44.45mm, in height. This makes it easy to design into your system as you will be using standard EIA spacing, and you will be driven by the availability of products on the market regardless of what you want. Even if you are prepared to have one-off special panels made for you, when you get the quote for the special panels, you may take the time to rethink your design decision, as the costs will be fairly high. Using non-standard, one-off panels means that you will also have the documentation requirements of drawings and material lists that you have to produce, rather than the standard documentation from the manufacturer for off-the-shelf panels, which are provided in the manuals shipped with their product.

A disadvantage of using standard panels of connectors is that you have little or no control of the quality of the connectors used. They may be the lowest grade available to the manufacturer to keep costs down to remain price-competitive on the open market. If you want a particular grade of connector, such as precision or metrology rather than general-purpose grade, then you will probably have to build them yourself or have them built for you. Generally, you should keep the same grade of connector throughout your design, or at the very least, through all your signal paths. If you mix connector grades through the signal path, then you will introduce errors if your calculations are based on the accuracy and specifications of a high-grade connector when lower grades are mixed in. Additionally, you risk damage to the high-grade connectors when mating them to lower grades that have greater tolerances to their physical specifications.

Specialized ready-built interconnect panels can save you a lot of time. The test system industry is big enough to support vendors who only build specialist componentry for test systems. This means that those vendors who have focused their time and resources on this marketplace will have spent time in there, and have a fair idea of what they are doing. It is more than reasonable to at least assess the market and what it has to offer.

Specialized interconnect panels offer a wider range of connector types and gauge. For DC voltages, particularly for heavy current carrying, you should use low-resistance connectors with large surface areas to allow as much contact as possible. This further reduces resistance at the junctions.

The panels can also offer a range of different connectors in a relatively small area, as they can be carried side by side and you have very little redundancy – this is important to keeping your rack size from becoming unwieldy through the interconnect panel becoming massive.

8.3 Virginia® Type Interconnect

Virginia® type interconnect (from Virginia Panel Corporation) is a system of transferring the signals you want to the fixtures and back to the test equipment. Even though this is a particular manufacturer's product, it is widely used in industry, is a good starting point for fixture interconnect, and is treated as a standard test system component by enough test engineers to warrant particular mention.

It consists of a series of vertical connector panels that fit into a special housing for them, meaning that you do not even have to fill the housing. Virginia® panels come in different sizes, and different signal and current carrying capabilities; their properties are in the public domain, so no more needs to be said about specifications. The system is modular and lends itself well to custom design (to a limit). This sort of system focuses on the high-speed test market, where a lot of devices need to be tested quickly, and it enables a designer to get a system running quickly.

This is a good example of one well-thought-out system for interconnecting. The system suits well to most of the software on the market today – as well as having the option of writing all your own software.

This sort of modular interconnect system allows you to focus on other parts of the test system, rather than spending energy on something that is available today. If all your system interconnect requirements are met, then you can solve this problem with a purchase order rather than engineering and design time, and focus on other engineering issues.

When you combine this type of system with all the other off-the-shelf equipment you need, then you will also reduce the amount of time spent on the system build phase of the project.

Building your own interconnect system is a task that should only be undertaken if you can justify it by production volumes and cost savings. It is also valuable to be experienced in this sort of development before quoting time to build and cost of build. It is often surprising how time-consuming it is to get a fully custom interconnect system right.

Before you try to design and build your own system, it is well worth looking at this system or other products on the market.

8.4 Auto-interconnect to Your Fixtures

Auto-interconnect refers to a method of connecting your test system to your DUT under controlled conditions (see Figures 8.5). This method is used for DUTs that have a lot of test points or require a lot of different types of signals, often simultaneously. The mass interconnect approach lends itself to high-speed testing, as measurements often only take a few milliseconds or fractions of a second to complete, then the next test can proceed as soon as conditions settle. This cannot be matched by human intervention, making automated connection of the DUT to the test system a significant technical advantage.

Fixtures can be attached to an interconnect panel at an installation point; for example, from a set of hooks. When the interconnection system is brought into play, for example by raising the handles which engage the fixture, it draws the DUT onto the interconnect panel such that all the pins connect in parallel, at the same pressure and angle every time. If you did this by hand, it would be very difficult to always get the angles exactly right every time – so repeatability and reduction of wear are achieved by an auto-interconnect system.

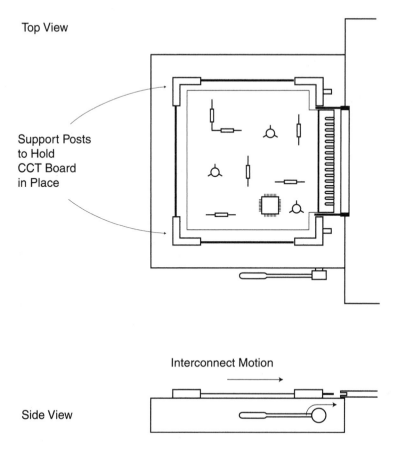

Figure 8.5   Auto-interconnect.

A mechanical engineer can be a very good ally when designing such a system; you need a combination of electrical and mechanical skills to achieve a reliable system to meet your needs.

To design this sort of system, you must put a lot of time into the design specifications and requirements of the fixture. Not just the electrical needs, but also the ergonomic and safety needs must be specified. Often, fixtures must isolate the signaling from the operator for safety reasons and also to ensure no changes can accidentally be made. For example, the operator may move a cable or lean on the work surface when they should not – it is a fact of life that mistakes will happen, and the design engineer must try to second-guess what could happen in the test environment.

There are also some very good systems on the open market from test equipment component suppliers. Many vendors of test system software or software tools will be aligned with some other fixturing and interconnect manufacturer. This gives the right match for the software vendor, as the TPS alone is not sufficient to test a DUT, and there has to be a complete package.

Mass interconnect systems of your own design and manufacture must also be supported by your organization, as do any interconnect systems you purchase. This is an additional cost and can also lead to a rising cost of test if the system is inadequate for the operational needs specified. Should you build a system or buy one for a specific task and then raise the level of usage on the system, you may find it wearing more quickly than initially anticipated. This additional load on the test system resource may lead to increased failure or downtime when the system cannot perform as it was intended. If resources allow it, over design and expect heavier use of the system right from the start.

"WAR STORY"

Most test systems get a lot more use than initially intended, as organizations realize they can test quickly and consistently.

A system designed and built for a military customer was initially built for a small number of receivers. When the system was implemented, it was quickly realized that it tested faster and more consistently than a technician on the bench could. The user started to add more and more of their equipment to the system to be tested. Very soon, they were running the system on a 24-hour basis and needed another test system. The slowest part of the system became the operator's ability to change DUTs as the system was very fast. The user then commissioned another test system to be built and at the same time increased the test specification for speed. Very soon, the second system was also overburdened and the user was still adding tests to it.

The problem in the end became that there was not enough staff to actually run the system. The solution was to outsource the entire system to a commercial organization to do all the testing for them. The user is still adding tests.

8.5 Building Your Own Fixturing

If you decide for various reasons that off-the-shelf fixturing systems will not suit you, then you may want to build your own or have custom fixturing built for you. Your fixture has to be programmed, so it cannot be built in isolation of the software in an automated system. There are experienced companies who produce these, and you may want to consider sub-contracting this work if the task will delay other tasks in your test system design project.

The reason for considering outside sources of fixture building is your resource availability. If you are just starting up your test system, then you will probably have a lot of fixtures to build, not just one. Therefore, when you look at the hours needed and materials required, you will find doing the work in parallel will take a shorter time – but require a large proportion of available resources, which it is unlikely you will have at your disposal (or you wouldn't need a test system).

To build all your fixtures serially will take a long time. If you are adding a new product to a suite of existing products, then you may have the time and resources to do the build; however, it is important to remember that it must be done in conjunction with the software. An electrical engineer needs to examine the mechanical engineer's work to ensure no electrical problems have been missed – or worse, introduced. Any new fixture needs to be de-bugged as if it were any other product you are producing, or any software. Then, when the fixture is married to the software, it needs to be debugged as a system, which it now is.

The decision to build a test system may have been justified most likely by how many devices you can test at high speed, so to delay the activation of it by waiting for fixtures may not help your plan. At the start of the system design project, you would have decided how many devices you need to test, as well as the benefits of high-speed test, plus the cost benefits of test. As part of your test plan, the number of interfaces would normally align with the number of TPSs you would require. It would be ideal if all your DUTs could be tested on one interface, and you would never need to change fixtures. This is hardly likely – unless you are a manufacturer of only one type of DUT with a single common interface, which may be possible if you are a manufacturer of VME computer cards or similar industry-standard DUTs. This assumes that all your DUTs will have the same interface to the test system – then you would only need to control all the signal levels and routing behind the interface panel.

TIP:

Generally, one TPS equals one fixture – a fixture normally being for a unique DUT.

8.6 Specifying Your Own Fixturing for Someone Else to Build

When you contract out fixturing, it must be done with the rest of your package in mind. The package consists of both the fixture and software to control that fixture. The software tells the switch where on the fixture to route the required signals.

To specify your fixture, you must get down to the intricate details, as far as testing is concerned. Too much cable length used on digital signal paths may lead to crosstalk, as well as a myriad of other problems. Depending on the speed of the signaling, the electrical parameters of the fixture may have undesired results. For example, a system seen by one of the authors had RF signals traveling on single-strand bell cable, essentially a piece of wire, so it radiated. The builder was skilled in other areas, but had little RF knowledge, so did not understand why the fixture did not work. Having access to experienced people to provide a range of expertise when working on these tasks is invaluable.

The fixture to be built needs to be specified mechanically and electrically, and your specification should include adequate self-testability as well. Building for self-testability allows you to isolate sub-sections of your fixture, and if necessary, electrically break it down into smaller functional areas to isolate any failures or problems in the fixture.

Specify any materials you want to have incorporated, and always try to get down to as much detail as you can. This will ensure that even if you have fixtures made by different vendors, they will look and perform similarly.

"WAR STORY"

One industry "war story" illustrates the value of knowledge and experience combined. A customer called to complain that the new network analyzer he had bought was not working. When the sales engineer investigated the problem, he found the output of the network analyzer, all at radio frequencies, had its precision and very expensive cable adapted into a twisted pair of cables, one meter long (suitable for lower frequencies only). This cable terminated into a bulkhead connector and the other side of it went into a 40-pin-wide ribbon computer peripheral cable. This was also one meter long and terminated into a bulkhead connector, the other side of which had just single-strand wire (30cm – 12") of light gauge up to an in-circuit test pin about 5cms (2") long – a really cool little antenna – that then was inserted into the DUT. The return path to the network analyzer was the same. No signal was seen at all at the DUT. It was all lost and radiated on the way. The reflections were immense, and no power was actually transferred through this circuit.

   RF signaling and switching is almost an art form – at HF 2-30MHz, it is still considered somewhat of a black art.

Electrical Safety of the System

This chapter deals with the safety of your test system, the immediate environment, and the most important steps you can take to help make your system safe. We examine factors such as earthing, isolation, and cutoff switches. Safety is one of the prime concerns of any engineer, and it is vital to examine all aspects of the safety of your design. It is important to consider this material in conjunction with other relevant sources of safety information and the safety strategies in place at your own worksite, including your country's mandatory safety standards and regulations.

Safety also deals with the safety of your organization as a whole. Staff training, equipment maintenance, and the level at which your work environment is maintained will all have an effect on the overall safety of your workplace.

Also bear in mind that electrical safety covers not only electric shock, but also heat-related issues of fires and burns.

KEY POINTS:

- Safety planning is a key part of any test system design. National and international safety standards can add to your own organization's knowledge of relevant safety requirements.
- Safety and cutoff switches, and isolation of parts of the test system where necessary, can increase the assurance of safety for your system operators.
- This chapter is no substitute for expert, relevant safety advice. Knowledge of relevant safety standards, access to expertise within your own organization, and expert advice will all help to create and maintain a safe working environment.

9.1 Key Safety Considerations for the Test Engineer

Your test system design must include safety planning. This will involve the test system itself and the area around the test system, such as flooring, ceiling, and a safety zone around the system. The safety zone also protects equipment from the effects of ESD (electro-static discharge), which can damage delicate circuitry very easily.

TIP:

Never place a test system rack on a carpet, as this causes a fire hazard as well as allowing an increased risk of particle ingress to the system. It is also a source of ESD. Many people can build up large voltage potentials when walking on carpets. Many carpets have a lot of man-made materials; the less natural materials, the greater the static buildup.

Your environment should be prepared for electrical safety. Many work areas have a selection of wooden poles and ropes (or other non-conductive materials) handy so that live items can be pushed or pulled off other conductors. Usually in an environment of any workshop, there will also be a range of regulation extinguishers (including non-conducting ones such as carbon dioxide), fire axes for cutting cables, and fire blankets for smothering a fire. Insulated gloves may also be useful, although these would only be used in extreme circumstances.

Safety training for staff is an important contributor to the overall safety of a working environment. Informed daily management of risk is much more effective than procedures alone. Staff with an awareness of general safety issues as well as appropriate levels of technical safety knowledge will be better equipped to identify and address potential safety issues. They will also be better able to look after each other as they work.

The importance of meeting all local safety regulations cannot be underestimated. A log of all stores will allow emergency crews, should they ever be needed, to identify materials that may be in the fire area, and any other locations where they are kept. Many regulators require special areas for storage of hazardous chemicals, such that the storage environment lends itself to reducing problems. If you store gases of any kind, they should be in an area that prohibits unauthorized access, as well as having adequate venting and audit procedures to maintain the recommended maintenance and checking of the vessels by authorized personnel.

In addition, do everything possible to ensure that your work environment is safe and that staff understand the importance of contributing to site safety. It is the responsibility of every worker to remain alert to safety issues, as well as the responsibility of the company or organization.

Safety in your organization, however large or small, should be a behavior and a culture to be encouraged. When the culture is embedded at every level and is uncompromising, then people build a confidence in their work area, and want to keep it safe. People want to do a good job, and a good, safe environment means they can get on with their jobs and not be at risk. Beware of practices to cut costs by cutting preventative maintenance, or by outsourcing so many skills that none are retained to be called on in time of need.

Actual occurrences such as a city's central business district being cut off from electrical power (when both the main and backup power cables failed) or a major explosion at a gas plant can be indicative of an environment where the safety culture has been replaced by accounting imperatives with dire results for everyone. Environments where preventative maintenance periods are stretched out or eliminated altogether, or where minor accidents are treated as one-off incidents rather than examined for underlying causes, are prone to increasingly serious problems. Any savings made are short-term and quickly replaced with huge costs and loss of reputation. Many organizations do manage costs and also manage to keep a safe environment. There is a balance to be kept, and you have to constantly strive to achieve it. Lost time in your organization from accidents costs money, as does damaged equipment. Many large organizations such as dockyards and mines keep large scoreboards up as reminders of how much time has been lost through accidents, normally expressed as time since the last incident. These organizations pride themselves on a safe workforce. People want to work where they feel safe and know that the people making the big decisions care about safety and the work environment. Workers' unions are one of the groups that have had a strong role in improving safety conditions for workers and indirectly reducing the costs to the community, but this role should be taken up at all levels of an organization.

9.2 Safety and Cutout Switches

The ability to completely cut power off from a working test system and otherwise protect your operator from potentially dangerous situations is vital. Circumstances such as using different voltages in the same rack or having the potential of exposing the operator to high current or voltage through the DUT during testing all require protective measures.

Additionally, you should have power surge protection, and also filtering if your environment has a lot of electrical noise caused by heavy machinery or electric doors putting spikes on your voltage source. Most power sources have thermal cutoffs should too much current suddenly be drawn or should any earth leakage occur.

An uninterruptable power supply (UPS) can also give a degree of protection to your system (see Figure 9.1). This can serve as a filter between the system and mains supply, and a good one may account for any unstable droops or spikes on the mains power. This is especially useful in portable situations such as a test system deployed on-board a ship, or on the back of a truck powered by generators. When generators are swapped, there may be a moment or two when the phases are matching during which power drops, and the UPS can protect the test equipment during these circumstances.

Issues related to the following topics are discussed below: the use of 110V and 240V power in the same rack; isolating high voltages and currents from the operator; cutoffs during operator operation; barring power during hookup; and master power cutouts.

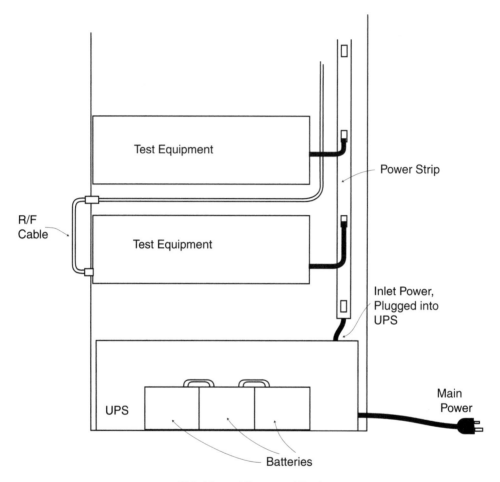

Side View of Bottom of Rack

Figure 9.1 Test system rack showing UPS wired in.

9.2.1   Using 110V and 240V in the Same Rack

You may need multiple supply voltages in the same rack if you cannot obtain all the equipment you want from manufacturers in the same supply voltage format, or if the DUTs have to be tested at several supply voltages (generally, the specified voltages plus or minus 10%). In these cases, both supply voltages can be present in the test system, and the earths of each should be common (Section 9.3 covers earthing considerations in more detail).

This requires very careful design and some rigid discipline when assembling, and also when removing items for calibration or repair, as well as during re-installation of these items.

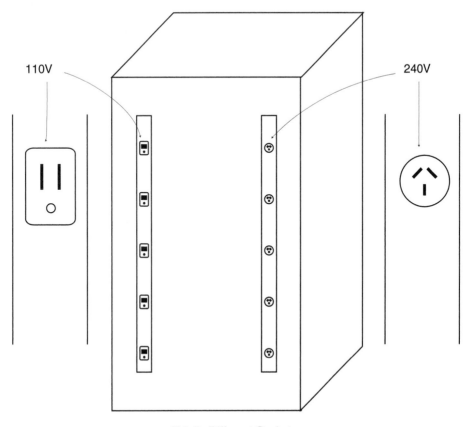

Totally Different Sockets,
Separated within Rack

Figure 9.2   Test system rack showing 110V and 240V power strips separated in the rack.

An appropriate method is to have the 110V and 240V power strips in the rack, keeping to a common in-house standard such 110V on the left, 240V on the right as you look at the rack from the rear (see Figure 9.2). Have the power strips with the correct sockets for the voltages – do not use the same sockets on both strips. This way, your 110V and 240V power cables will only fit into their correct sockets. Take care to anchor the cable to the test equipment, as many items have the same power input connector at the test equipment connection.

TIP:

Use the best quality cabling that you can get – you may even go so far as to have different-color connectors and/or cabling to identify different mains voltages. Ensure that you have strict processes to control the initial building and labeling of cables and connectors.

When using hard wiring from the power strips, beware of the problems of accidentally plugging 110V into 240V outlets. It is most likely there will be damage that will not be covered by your warranty. The use of different connectors will help manage this to some degree, but should not be relied on. You should have a process to ensure that when equipment is introduced into the workshop area, it is clearly marked at the power inlet to the equipment what its voltage is. Your processes should also include an earth screw terminal on the back panel for all equipment in a rack. If the terminal is not part of the equipment when it is purchased, ask the vendor to supply the equipment fitted with the terminal or have it done yourself by experienced personnel.

All the earths should be tied together, and additionally, all test equipment components in the rack should have their cases strapped to the common earth bar. This ensures that if there is an internal failure in a item of test equipment, then the case will not float to the mains voltage, but be shorted to earth and trip the current breaker for that electrical circuit.

It is a good practice that should be encouraged to always check the voltage selector on equipment before it is installed into the rack, regardless of the labeling or cable connections. Whenever the cables are disconnected from the equipment or the power strip, double-check them as they are reconnected to ensure compliance.

9.2.2   Isolating High Voltages and Currents from the Operator

Isolating a DUT when it needs high-bias currents or high voltages should be done anywhere the operator may come into contact with the DUT. Many fixtures for this sort of work have perspex covers so the operator can see what is happening, but should the covers be accessed in any way, then they trigger an interlock mechanism and power to the test system, or at least the fixture, is immediately cut. Often the DUT is placed in a special fixture inside an insulated box, so the operator cannot get near the DUT once the box is closed – if they open it, the interlocks are broken and power is instantly cut off (see Figure 9.3).

All high-voltage, current, or power devices should be labeled in red, indicating that they contain hazardous potential. Often a white or red lightning bolt is also part of the labeling to get peoples' attention. When the operator needs to connect devices from the rack to the DUT and the voltages or currents are high, they should always be routed through cabling adequate for the task.

High-voltage and current connectors on the patch panel or through the switch should be carried through connectors that are low in resistance to avoid heat at the joins. They should also have procedures that allow hookup and down with complete safety. (The connectors should be of a type that has as much surface area as possible to give the current as efficient a path as possible – see Figure 9.4.) There may even be a hold put on the system by the procedures or software after a test is completed to ensure that capacitors drain adequately to neutralize capacitative effects.

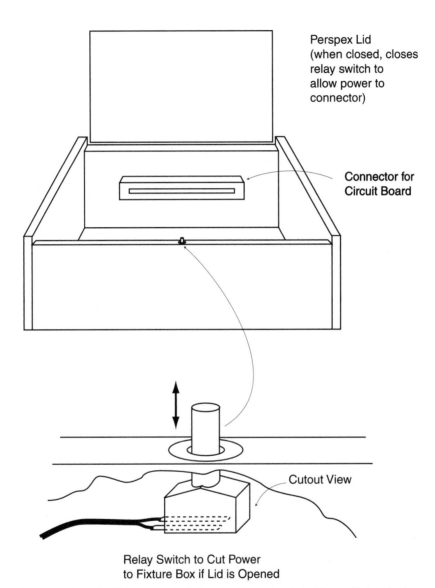

Perspex Lid
(when closed, closes
relay switch to
allow power to
connector)

Connector for
Circuit Board

Cutout View

Relay Switch to Cut Power
to Fixture Box if Lid is Opened

Figure 9.3   A DUT in a special fixture inside an insulated box with interlocks.

Procedures should protect the operator from danger while preparing the DUT for testing. This comes down to the documentation being written correctly to address the electrical knowledge of the operators. Assumptions about the level of skill in the operator can be deadly.

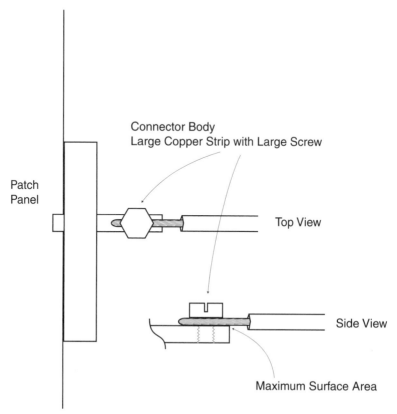

Figure 9.4   Low-resistance connectors on patch panel or switch to avoid heat at joins.

"WAR STORY"

This is a "war story" showing how easily even documented procedures can cause problems if they are not drawn up carefully and thoroughly. One of the authors was in a repair center for a large organization that prided itself on quality(but had grown complacent).

"A new engineer was repairing a computer monitor. There was no one else around; a technician and I were on the other side of the shop in a different repair area. We heard a yell and looked over to see the engineer, white-faced, staring at the monitor. We quickly went over and made sure he was OK; it seems he had been electrocuted with the full 19kV (19,000 volts with very small current) that was on the tube. We were a little perplexed about how this could have happened – so we asked him to take us through his procedure. He did this, explaining at each step how he had followed the manual procedure he had been given. When he got to the point of removing the high-voltage cable from the tube, we realized what had happened. The procedure instructed the engineer to 'remove the cable from the tube and earth it, to remove any leftover voltage.' The engineer had earthed *the cable, not the tube as he should have done*. Being straight from school, he had an engin-

> **"WAR STORY" (CONTINUED)**
>
> eering degree but no practical knowledge; he had not made the link that a CRT is like a large capacitor and will hold a voltage for a long time at the charged level, and very slowly dissipate it. The procedure was inadequate for untrained staff – the assumption the writer had made was that only experienced people would be doing this and thus the procedure's wording was ambiguous and open to misinterpretation.
>
> "Several points come out of this: lack of training in safety and basic practical electronics, and no supervision or on-the-job training. It is most likely that if we were not there and had intervened, he would have done it again. The organization felt that any electrical engineer should know better – this is in reality a very poor attitude, and a bad way for an engineer to learn such a lesson."

9.2.3   Cutoffs during Operator Intervention

Any action that could potentially lead to harm to the operator should trigger a system cutoff. Even if your operator is highly experienced, there is always the possibility that other staff will need to use the system at some stage.

Interlocks protect the integrity of the system. They are usually mechanical devices that engage when the equipment is installed into the rack. If the equipment is removed, the first few centimeters of movement will pull the switch apart and break electrical connections to the equipment. This protects the operator and also protects the equipment, now that you have changed its operating environment. This will also affect the rest of the equipment in the rack, as the rack has been designed to work with a predictable airflow and internal air pressure.

Cheating interlocks is a dangerous practice – they are there for the operator's protection. Many systems also allow the operator to make adjustments or change crystals in the system by pulling out a drawer or shelf. These should have interlocks that cut power to that shelf or drawer and restore it when the drawer or shelf is re-instated.

Interlocks may be installed on the doors of a rack to protect the operator from dangerous voltages and currents (see Figure 9.5). If you use a mainframe/cardcage system that is rear-mounted so that all the cabling is in the front of it, and need to change a connection on the system, then as you open the perspex or solid cover, the interlock should break and remove power. Naturally this is not the best practice as the test system should have been powered down already; but people do get careless and overconfident sometimes, and these safety procedures provide a good second-line backup.

There should also be a large button to set off cutout switches within easy reach of the operator. Once pushed, it should cut all power to the rack, not just to the DUT (see Figure 9.6). You may even want to put in a delay device that forces the operator to wait a certain time before they re-activate power to the rack after this sort of full cutoff. Most of these devices when pushed do not pop back out; they require another action to release them – like grasping the button, turning it a half revolution, then pulling it out.

The system cutoff button should be positioned so that it is within easy reach of the operator at all times.

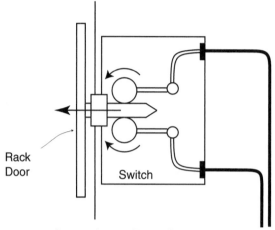

Rack
Door

Switch

Connections to Relay Cutout
(when pin is removed, roller pins
engage circuit for relay
and cut out power)

Figure 9.5   Interlocks on the door of a rack.

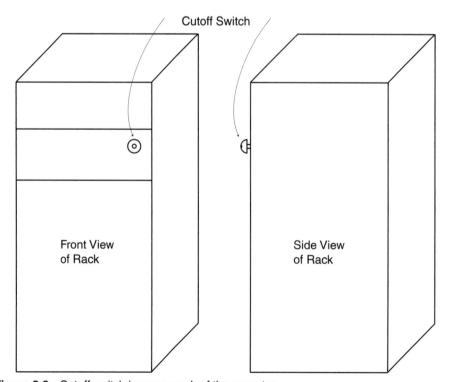

Cutoff Switch

Front View
of Rack

Side View
of Rack

Figure 9.6   Cutoff switch in easy reach of the operator.

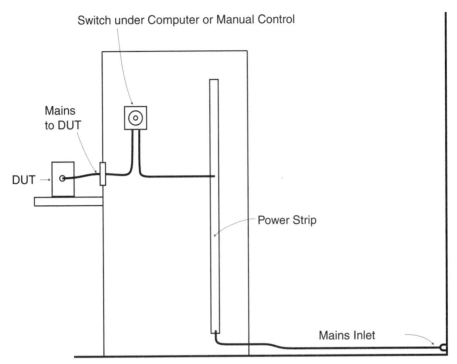

Figure 9.7   Mains to DUT being isolated by relay or mechanical switches during hookup.

9.2.4   Barring Power during Hookup

Either procedurally or by software control, the entire area where the operator is working should be isolated from all voltages and currents when each test completes, and when the DUT is removed.

During the hookup procedure, the test system and DUT should remain isolated. If the DUT is to be mains-powered, then the mains to the DUT have to be isolated by relay switching or by mechanical switches during hookup, and only energized when the operator is ready and has completed the whole hookup procedure (see Figure 9.7). Make sure you allow time for the DUT to reach operating temperature and stabilize before testing begins – this is normally called soak time.

Damage to the DUT and even the test equipment can be caused by connecting while voltage and current is present, and there is also the danger of connecting an output to an output. When you have connected the device, a visual check should be made systematically to ensure compliance with the hookup diagram or instructions.

One way to ensure power cannot be applied to the DUT during hookup is to use an interlock-controlled fixture, such that when the covers of the fixture are open, all power is cut off – and cannot be restored until the covers are closed and the interlock circuit re-instated.

Side View   Front View

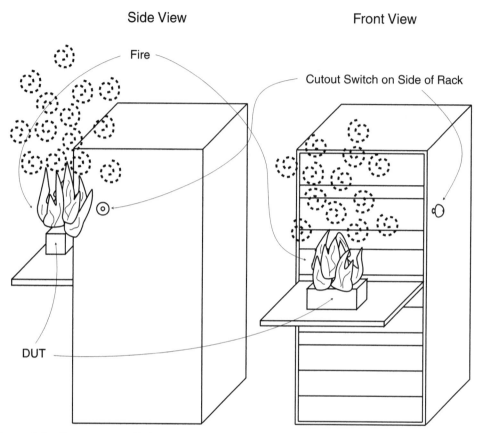

Figure 9.8   Test system with DUT on fire, and cutoff switch positioned so that it is still easy to reach.

9.2.5   Master Power Cutout

In a situation involving risk or even potential risk, it is vital for the operator to be able to shut off power to the test system with a single movement. All test systems must have a safety cutoff that completely cuts off and isolates all power from the system. Generally this will be a large red button in a position that is easy to reach and does not involve reaching across the work surface or DUT (as they may be on fire or electrically live) – see Figure 9.8.

The position of the cutoff switch is very important to the confidence of the operator, whether they are highly skilled or not. The easier the access to the cutoff, the higher the likelihood that if something should go wrong that you will reduce the damage that may occur.

Isolation from power means that the test system must be completely isolated. The active wire (110V or 240V/415V) and neutral should both be isolated, not just the active – this is good general practice to protect against the case when they have for whatever reason been inadvertently reversed. Do not rely on pulling the plug out of the wall. Not only may it take a couple of seconds to reach the power point, but also some power receptacles actually screw or lock the plug into them and it may take some time to release. During this time, someone may be hurt or equipment damaged.

TIP:

A cutoff will understandably take out the test system cooling fans as well as the rest of the equipment, so when you start up the system again, you will need to wait for thermal stability within the system before you continue testing. Most systems require at least 20 minutes.

Should a cutoff occur, you should completely investigate the cause of the cutoff before restarting the system to be assured of safe working conditions. Under no circumstances should you take shortcuts here. Remove the DUT from the test system and bring up the equipment one piece at a time. Ensure that the fans are working if the system is air-cooled, or that the pumps are working if it is water-cooled. Should the systems still fail, you may want to remove all the equipment and test it out of the system, then confirm all the cabling integrity. By following the wiring diagram, you can individually test each cable for continuity.

Do not start up the system again until you are confident that the cause of the problem has been identified and corrected.

9.3 Earthing Considerations

Earthing on a system is important for safety reasons – the most basic of which is to avoid electrocution. Earth for a system should come from a solid copper bar with holes drilled and tapped to take screws to form terminals (copper has the lowest metal resistance and is the best electrical conductor that is common; gold is the best by far, but impractical and very expensive). This is normally in the bottom of the rack where the mains power enters the rack. The earth from the mains is then taken directly to the solid copper strip or bar to form the terminal strip for system earth connections.

Earthing must be permanent; no temporary wiring may be used. It must be able to handle all possible frequencies and current levels possible in the test system.

There are noise considerations as well from poor earthing practices that can be introduced into the system. Earth loops are caused by different electrical resistance of signals to earth.

9.3.1 The Importance of True Earth

The true earth of your system is the main reference for all voltages and currents. It is from the supply socket initially, and is usually staked into the ground somewhere outside the building. You want the least resistive path to the earth grounding. The spike that goes into the ground is usually made from copper.

The earth you use for ground for your signals should not be taken from a secondary source, that is, from the earth output terminal from another device's front panel or from a pin in a connector. If you need to be sure of your earth circuit, then you should bring the earth up from the earthing strip. It is convenient to sometimes just put a jumper to the frame of the rack – however, this is not good practice for repeatable and reliable testing – ensure that the path is to the earth strip. The earth you use from such a connection is not reliable in terms of resistive path; you are adding the path resistance through the device such as a front panel terminal to your path. This can also cause additional noise in the system.

9.3.2   Checking your Building for Earthing

The installation of power and earth through your building should be done to your country's standards. You may require different circuits to distribute power to all the areas that need them, and the earth must be the same at all points. The paths from your test equipment to earth have to be of similar and as low impedance (resistance) as possible. This is within your control, the building earth is beyond your control.

Generally, the people doing the ATE installation have to rely on the authorized people employed or contracted to carry out these checks. In some countries, it is illegal for anyone other than authorized contractors to attach or connect the earthing to a building or through a building.

In general, have an authorized contractor confirm the earth to the equipment power outlet where the ATE will be connected and that they meet the necessary standards.

9.3.3   Effects of Multiple Earths

A lack of true earth or multiple earths creates a resistive path, which will affect your DC measurements. The most common problem with multiple earths is noise that is introduced into the system.

Different impedances to earth are created by the different cable types used in a system; noise is transferred from one part of the system to another. This is often very difficult to track down. There are various methods to eliminate these effects, and in extreme cases, you may have to perform extensive circuit simulation and analysis.

9.3.4   Common Earthing for the System and DUT

There are a few conditions of testing where the DUT may not have the same earth as the system, or require an earth at all. Some portable equipment that is intended to operate from batteries, or from an isolated supply, may need to be tested in isolation from system earth. There are some measurement conditions where earth is removed to reduce thermal and/or system noise to perform very sensitive measurements – these measurements and their conditions should be carried out carefully by experts or under very strict procedures. These are called floating measurements. There are also measurements that call for a voltage divider between the source and contact to reduce system-induced noise.

Mostly the DUT and the system will have the same earth; the source of voltage to power the DUT will normally carry earth with it in some form. If it is an edge-connect fixture, then the connector will have one or two pins that carry earth to the circuits. The earth in these cases is taken off a common earth strip, usually a bar of copper with screw terminals to accept earth cabling. This earth strip is usually near the bottom of the rack where power and earth come into it from the wall power outlet. The rack itself is always connected to earth.

9.4 Other Safety Considerations

There are two main areas that can affect the safety of your workplace: training of personnel and the maintenance of your work environment.

Your workplace safety training strategy should include all staff. It is valuable to document not only the training strategy itself to record what knowledge is available somewhere in the organization, but also who has had what training. This lets you know who is qualified to work under particular circumstances, and also where additional training would be of value for members of a team.

Your workplace must not only be made safe, but must also be maintained as a safe environment in changing conditions. Flooring materials, for example, should help prevent and manage the danger of moist floors or spills.

Required safety clearances from electrical equipment should be specified and maintained. The use of appropriate barricades for particular points in the system assembly process should be observed, and at times such as system maintenance or repair, the whole system may need to be barricaded off from casual staff access.

Illumination of work areas should be bright enough for easy work, even on small components, and work should only be carried out in such properly lit areas.

The use of extension cords should be discouraged if not banned altogether; permanent wiring is always preferable and is much safer than the ad hoc use of extension cords.

Documentation of any temporary changes such as temporary wiring is just as important as the documentation of permanent system upgrades. Temporary wiring or other temporary changes in the system may not be as safe as their permanent equivalents. Even where safety is assured, engineers and technicians who encounter undocumented changes will be reluctant to deal with the system any further – the risk of encountering other undocumented and potentially dangerous changes then exists. Make sure that equipment and systems are inspected regularly and document these inspections.

Static electricity is also a problem to electrical equipment, and is known as ESD. This is commonly caused when a charge builds up on a person (the operator), who then approaches the equipment and discharges the accumulated voltage into the DUT or test equipment, resulting in a failure caused by a high voltage. Many people can build up large voltages by just walking across a carpet. Most work surfaces require an operator to wear a wrist strap that is connected to earth to discharge this sort of voltage to ground before actually touching any equipment. This relies on procedures to work properly.

"WAR STORY"

One of the authors was working in a repair area, visually inspecting a circuit board that had passed final test after a repair. Another engineer walked up and was making a comment about the equipment just repaired. As he made the comment, he pointed to the board and his hand passed within 5 cms (2 inches) of the board. Both he and the author saw a spark jump from his hand to the board – sure enough, when tested, the board no longer worked properly, and after investigation, one of the integrated circuits on the boards was found to be damaged. The board had to be repaired a second time. A time-consuming way to learn a lesson!

Fire and burns are also possible risks where electrical systems are involved. Having fire safety procedures and training in place is vital in any engineering environment. First aid training of staff should also be provided and regularly updated.

If any safety-related incidents occur, it is important to make sure that the cause is clearly understood and addressed. Proper analysis of any incidents will ensure that dangerous circumstances will not be repeated.

9.4.1   Safety and Portable Test Systems

Portable systems are a serious problem for the designer and operator. You must ensure if designing a portable test system that the equipment in it is adequately earthed when it is connected to power – this is best ensured through procedures and adequate earth straps to each item in the rack as well as the DUT when it is connected.

An operator who is using portable equipment must be made aware of the risks of inadequate earthing or supplies that are not clearly earthed. Some systems in the field will even require a ground spike to be driven and connected to. You should allow some time to actually plant the spike; anything less than 2 meters (6 feet) is generally insufficient for an earth. Checking with your local power authorities is the best insurance.

9.5 Consulting the Experts

This chapter is no substitute for expert, relevant safety advice. Knowledge of relevant safety standards, access to expertise within your own organization, and expert advice will all help to create and maintain a safe working environment.

International standards are available, but more importantly, it is necessary to check what standards are required by your local authorities. Make sure that all relevant systems and products – including any modifications, upgrades, or repairs – comply with the relevant safety codes.

Get occupational health and safety advice. Understand, for example, the use of safety risk assessments that deal with possible frequency of harm occurrence as well as the likely degree of harm involved in an occurrence. This will help create an awareness of the classes of risk that may be faced if the organization does not have appropriate safety measures in place.

WORKPLACE SAFETY IS PARAMOUNT

Never guess where safety is concerned. Expert advice in this area is always worth the investment of time and money.

Selecting Racks and Racking Furniture

T his chapter discusses the selection of racks and racking furniture. This is not only important for the good presentation of your test system, but also for ease of use, maintainability (for example, protection of microwave cables), easy reconfiguration, and safe transport of your system when required. This chapter explains how to choose racks and accessories to put your system together, as well as accessories you will need to rack items of non-standard sizes and also non-standard items.

KEY POINTS:

- In addition to the size of the equipment to be mounted in the rack, a range of other aspects such as access, transportability, and environmental considerations will influence your choice of racks and racking furniture.
- Once you have decided on the size of the rack, start to design the layout of the equipment so that equipment outputs and connector locations match up.
- A range of racking accessories and racking techniques are available to put together a system, most of which will depend on the equipment and other components in the system itself.

10.1 Racks and Rack Furniture

The major factor that will drive your choice of racks and rack furniture is the size of the equipment the test system must hold. Most test equipment will be a whole number of standard rack units (RUs) high, and will be a standard width – typically 19" wide. Some half-width units are also available.

The combined height of your system's test equipment (taking into account any half-width units that are racked side by side) will give you an indication of the required height for the rack.

The environment in which the test system will be working will also determine part of the rack design, including the following questions:

- Do you need to be able to secure the system to prevent access? You may want to use perspex covers over equipment in the rack, to limit access to cabling – and also to seal the rack for airflow and temperature control reasons.

- Will you use lockable doors to limit but not prevent access? Lockable doors are most often solid material and will not allow you to even see the equipment. This may be for security reasons; for example, data that may be militarily classified. Some systems limit access to the computer keyboard so that it will slide into a lockable drawer. This means that you cannot control the system without the keys to unlock and access the keyboard.

- Do you need ruggedized rack furniture with strain relief and stress-relieving devices? This will allow the equipment to be lifted by a crane, from say the deck of a ship onto a wharf, with little likelihood of damage. You may want to transport the system by air or even by train; both cases must allow for the bumps and stresses the equipment will suffer. A common test for equipment designed for military transport is the dreaded "shunt" test, where the equipment must survive intact when the carriage it is in is hit or shunted by the complete train; the mass and inertia is enormous.

- Are there special needs for EMI/EMC qualification? For example, in an area that could be exposed to explosive devices, you do not want the risk of signal radiation from the racks setting them off. Other reasons for not emitting radiation are varied, but even in general terms, you do not want to look like a broadcast station.

- Is access to the rear of the rack a problem? If you need rear access to equipment and access to the back of the rack is not available, for example, then you need to consider the installation of slide-rail systems for your equipment so it can be drawn from the front of the rack. Otherwise, you will need to physically move the rack to get access to the rear of it.

- Will you need to take any special environmental considerations into account? For example, heating and cooling capability may both be required for a system to be transported within a range of extremes due to the different environments which may be encountered. If you intend to use your test system in a stressed environment, such as the back of a truck in the jungle, then you need to protect your equipment from all foreseeable environmental problems.

There are many types of rack systems on the market today. In particular, some racks with side panels have the advantage of the engineer being able to remove the side panels to facilitate installation of equipment and cabling. This does not mean that you should never run the racks in this condition – it is a means of easy assembly only. Your calculation of heat budgets and airflow requirements based on the rack specifications (this is discussed further in Chapter 12, "Temperature Control and Power Considerations") will be based on the assumption that the side panels are in place. It is nearly impossible to predict effects such as air pressure if the sides are removed.

10.2 Working Out What Size Rack(s) You Will Need

Once you have decided roughly how many items of test equipment you need and how many rack units high each one is, decide whether the control computer (if the test system is semi- or fully-automated) has to be installed in the rack. Then, add the work surface and you will have a rough idea of how many rack units (EIA rack units, U) you will need as a minimum for the racked system.

This gives you an immediate size for the racks, but then you also need to look at what equipment should be placed right in front of the operator, and what does not need to be within easy reach.

In addition, you will need to decide on factors such as:

- Including blank panels to allow for future additions of test equipment.
- Allowing space for the work surface.
- Allowing space for a computer monitor, if required for the display of test procedures, test results, system warnings, or other messages.
- Whether you need an extra-deep rack to accommodate very deep (or "long") pieces of test equipment.
- Managing the total weight of the test system not to exceed any weight bearing limits of the floor where the test system will be positioned (use two racks if you get close to any weight limits).
- Allowing space for a patch panel directly behind and slightly above the work surface, even if it is not part of your original design, so that it will be available for future expansion. If you have allowed space for a patch panel, allow double that for expansion, as it tends to grow rapidly.
- Including space for accessories drawers to hold spare connectors, a torque wrench if required for connecting to the DUT, and any other small items needed for the operation of the test system.

In addition, whether or not the test system must be easily transportable is important. If you are building a transportable test system, you will need to choose smaller racks (see Figure 10.1).

TIP:

For a transportable test system, use smaller racks and keep the weight of each rack below the limit for a two-person lift. Generally, allow 16Kgs or 30lbs per person to lift. Many racks are not so much heavy as awkward to lift, so even if the weight is not severe, the shape may restrict the lifting ability of the system.

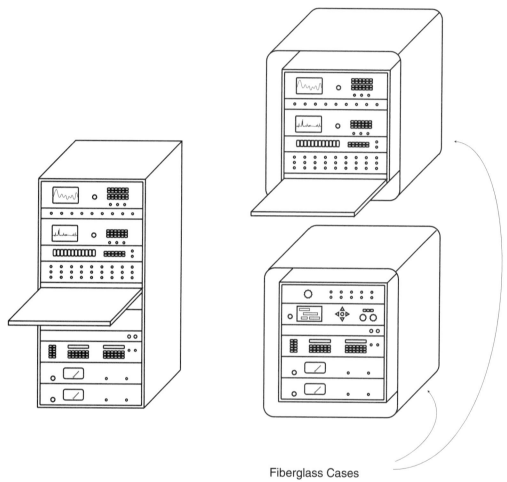

Fiberglass Cases

Figure 10.1   A test system in one large rack for permanent positioning, and the same test system in two smaller racks for the transportable version of the same system.

Once you have a rough idea of the size of the rack(s) you will be using, you can start to place equipment in your rack layout plan. Make sure you have all the heights and depths of the equipment worked out in advance in a table.

Remember that you will have to place heavy objects in the bottom of the rack to achieve the greatest stability for the rack. You will have to arrange your equipment in the rack to achieve the best balance of weight and accessibility. Do not forget airflow needs as you do this.

Either because you have included space for future additions of test equipment or because there is some space in the rack, there will be areas of your rack or racks that will be left vacant and covered with blank panels. The panels give an aesthetic finish as well as provide a convenient means of sealing the rack to ensure the airflow for cooling is not disturbed.

> **TIP:**
>
> There are many considerations to building a rack – do not be tempted to just start bolting in equipment – you will end up removing and replacing it many times.

10.3   Matching Equipment Outputs and Connector Locations

Matching test equipment outputs to the number of devices that need to connect to the DUT and connector locations can take some planning. This will ensure that cable lengths are kept to the minimum lengths needed.

First, look at where on the test equipment all the connectors are. You may have specified when ordering equipment that all the connectors be on the rear panel. This is usually the best method of ensuring that all your connections have easy accessibility to the patch panel or switch matrix, and that they do not have to have cables fed through the front of the rack, through feed-through panels or termination panels.

Test equipment that delivers or measures microwave signals should have cable lengths as short as possible to the patch or switch panel or to the DUT directly. Losses in microwave signals occur over length, so keep the paths short. Cabling for microwave is very expensive, so this is another good reason to keep those lengths as short as possible.

> **TIP:**
>
> If you cannot avoid having connectors on the front panel, you may consider some lateral thinking here, and reverse the equipment in the rack. If you have computer control, then you do not have the need to see the displays in any case. Be careful to ensure cooling is maintained at all times. If you reverse the equipment, then you may also consider racking it in the rear of the rack.

It is a good idea when planning connections to work outwards from your patch panel, or even the work surface, to place equipment. Many items of equipment like power supplies do not require close proximity to the DUT or patch panel, as they generally do not have much loss due to the heavy-duty cabling they require. Consider the weight of equipment, however. Position heavy equipment low in the rack wherever possible, and when physically racking up the system, remember to work from the bottom of the rack upwards.

To summarize, the placement of equipment is a balance of the need to be close to the DUT or patch panel and the weight of the equipment, as well as the output or input connector location.

10.4   Selecting Connector Panels

Connector panels are used in several ways. First, they are used to route cables from the test equipment back into the rack. These panels have cutouts to allow cables to pass through them, or

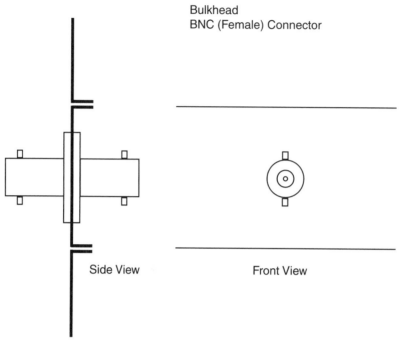

Figure 10.2   A connector panel with bulkhead connectors.

have connectors on each side (bulkhead connectors – see Figure 10.2) that allow cables to be attached to both sides.

When you are shopping for connector panels (also called termination panels), look for ones that offer the greatest ease of installation. Many vendors will supply them with folded edges, which strengthens the panel, and which is needed when you are pushing a mating connector against the middle of the row – you do not want the panel to bend or distort. Distortion in the panel will allow air to escape and thus give you cooling calculation problems.

Second, to form a termination point in front of the operator for a patch panel, usually several rows of connector panels, one above the other, above the work surface will suffice (see Figure 10.3).

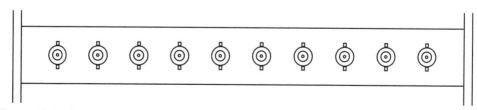

Figure 10.3   A connector panel, which can be used to form a termination point.

When you install the connector panels they form an easy and predictable position for the cables to be routed internally to the patch panel or switch matrix. From the DUT, you will need cables to connect to the panels and these should be of the same length if possible, as this makes calibration easier. When performing a system calibration, you need to be able to loop the connectors back to other connectors, such that output devices are now routed to input devices. The cable lengths are already calibrated at this point and the characteristics should be well-known.

Many vendors make connector panels, or you may decide to make your own. If you do make your own, then you will be faced with a large selection of bulkhead connectors or connector terminations from vendors. Try to be consistent with the devices you use as this will have an effect on the continuity of signal integrity.

Generally, choose connector panels that do not group the connectors so close that they inhibit connection, as you will have to connect and disconnect the cables to the panel every time you change the DUT. This will become a physical problem for the operator.

10.5   Racking Accessories

There is a multitude of accessories on the market, from cutout switches, to rails that suspend equipment, to fans to extract or inject air to the rack interior. Most rack accessories are passive, that is, merely hardware that has been designed to fulfill a particular function.

There are also racking techniques such as racking half-width units side by side or shelf mounting that can be used to put the rack together.

Some vendors can also provide ballast, which is basically shaped weights, some with 19" rack connections to keep them in a fixed position in the rack. Chapter 11, "Weight Considerations and Equipment Placement," discusses the use of ballast and other accessories for increased rack stability.

Most racking vendors will have catalogs of equipment to supplement their racks. The test system designer will have to decide how far to go to offer comfort and accessibility to the operators or to customers who are buying the system. The equipment can be expensive and there may be circumstances where it is practical and less costly to go to a furniture manufacturer or carpentry shop for particular accessories. However, commercial racking items and accessories are easy to order and are built to supplement the test system. In the interest of time, it can be a good investment to get all your racks and furniture from one or two vendors so that it all matches and is delivered consistently.

There are some accessories available on the market that may be of interest for transporting racks. These racks can be enclosed in fiberglass or some other material so that they can be sealed with removable doors and transported, limiting access to expensive test equipment and cabling. Many items are available for this purpose, including fully-military-specified devices such as ruggedized keyboards, mice, and displays – normally in a transportable system, you will use a flat display. Transportable systems can be very expensive, so only design for this if you have a need to, not just for the occasional move. Occasional moves can be carried out using large enclosures made from timber to transport the system.

10.5.1 Racking COTS Equipment

COTS equipment suppliers will often have rack-mounting devices available as accessories; ears, for instance, that secure the equipment to the front of a standard 19" wide rack. The suppliers do not offer rails unless they also offer racks, as the rails may not fit the racks that may be used, the variety is so large.

Some COTS suppliers will, however, offer slide rails; they normally have adjustable length, and the advantages of slide rails can be so attractive in a situation short on space that the user may have them specially engineered into the rack to get the greatest benefit from them. Slide rails allow equipment to be pulled from the front of the rack and rotated while being supported such that cables can be re-routed to connectors or even new cabling introduced.

During the life of a system, you may decide to take advantage of features on test equipment that you did not use on initial implementation. This will mean that as you redesign your software, you will need to route new cabling or redirect existing cabling. For instance, you may decide to introduce into your system a method of synchronizing all the equipment to a common standard such as an atomic clock (Rubidium vapor lamp or Cesium beam technology). To do this, you will have to distribute the clock's signal throughout all your system (distribution amplifiers and isolation aside); hence the need to distribute new cabling or relocate cabling that was previously used for distributing a standard that came from a stable clock from one of the items of test equipment.

COTS equipment is usually available from the manufacturer with the option of racking minima, which is normally just racking ears to hold the equipment into the front of the rack. Rack ears ensure that your equipment does not move around – for those engineers who just stack equipment one on top of another – and that it does not slide out onto the floor due to vibration in the rack. Some folks actually put in a shelf about halfway up the rack and just stack equipment, one on the other on top of that shelf – until they have their first accident and all the equipment slides out onto the floor, or even worse, onto the operator in front of the system. It would not be quite so bad if it all fell on the person who built this system – but then poetic justice is rare.

When you install equipment into racks, you must support the equipment's weight somehow. This is absolutely necessary for the mechanical integrity of your system and the overall balance. The test equipment is best supported on a rail system, usually a metal structure on each side of the interior of the rack such that the equipment can slide into the rack from the front and be supported. Rails are normally connected to the front and rear internally in the rack for exactly this purpose. Many racks lack these, and over time, the ears distort, and once removed, if possible, cannot be re-installed due to the twisting of the metal. Rack ears are not designed to support equipment, just to hold the test equipment in place.

"WAR STORY"

Some people believe the ears and rack handles have strength beyond their original purpose and design. One author witnessed a microwave synthesizer being hoisted by a crane to an antenna fixture some 20m/60' above the ground by a single rack handle. In the midst of furious arguments about the recklessness of this procedure, the handle broke. The resultant crash to the ground rendered the equipment totally useless; the manufacturer refused to even contemplating fixing it – particularly as after the repair the warranty was a serious issue.

The cast handle was built for a particular loading, which was only intended to assist moving the equipment on the bench and to assist in handling the test equipment into a rack. The equipment should never be supported entirely by the handle.

10.5.2 Front- vs. Rear-Rack Mounting and Cabling

Mounting equipment in the front of the rack is conventional; however, if the equipment has a lot of front panel connections or is heavy, then you may consider mounting to the rear of the rack. This has the advantage that the cabling may now be more reasonably managed to other connections in the rack from front-mounted connections on the test equipment. It also helps to balance the test system.

There are several disadvantages to this method that have to be overcome. The airflow of the rack is now quite different, and some channel for it has to be made in front of the rear-mounted equipment, without the flow being disturbed by the rack front being open. The front of such systems is usually sealed with a door, commonly of a transparent material such as perspex. This protects the equipment from accidental damage, the cabling being most at risk, and also being a lockable door on occasions prohibits unauthorized entry or disturbance to the cabling and test equipment.

Front-mounted equipment is traditional, but has the disadvantage of moving all the weight to the front of the rack as well. This may not be a problem if the rack will never be moved and is bolted or otherwise fixed to the floor so that it cannot move or be affected by weight distribution being awkward.

Most equipment has a mixture of front and rear connections. This is generally so that the manufacturer can put all the common connectors on the front in case they are used on the bench for most purposes. Many manufacturers offer the option of front- or rear-mounted connectors so that the equipment can be used both in a bench application where front-mounted connectors are mandatory and in an automated test system application where rear connectors are preferred. However, some test equipment is very complex and the front panel is not adequate for all the connections as well as the user interface for manual operations. The cabling for bus control or computer interface connections is rarely needed at the front panel, since it is unusual to change it once connected.

Generally, test equipment that has most of its connections on the rear panel should be front-mounted, and test equipment which has most of its connections on the front should be rear-

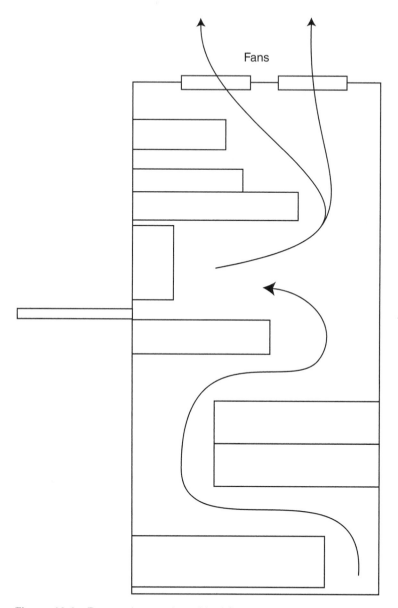

Figure 10.4   Rear-rack mounting with airflow maintained.

mounted (see Figure 10.4). The exception is mainframe-mounted equipment like VXI, VME, or similar. This tends to deliver all cabling to the front except the power connections. There are no displays, knobs, or buttons, so there is really no issue except cooling to prohibit the rear mounting of equipment.

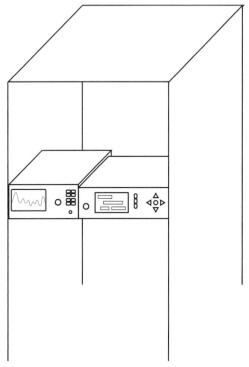

Figure 10.5 Side-by-side racking.

10.5.3 Side-by-Side Racking for Half-Width Units

If you have half-width, or even quarter- or third-width items, then they have to racked alone or on a shelf. Some manufacturers will design their equipment to lock together when used in this sort of situation. This means that you must have two or more items to make up the additional width, and you may need multiple units. These kits will negate the need for a shelf to support the devices. A racking shelf can cause problems with airflow, unless you cut it back to the exact size you need to support the test equipment. You then need to be assured it will have mechanical integrity. Some rack shelves are designed to be cut out; these shelves have a number of areas that have natural support positions and some areas around them that can be cut out, and made that way, so that airflow can be maximized once the equipment is placed and fixed in place.

If you do decide to rack devices side by side (see Figure 10.5), then take care that the units are of the same depth, otherwise you will have mechanical problems as well as environmental issues with cooling. The mechanical problems come from the support issues that will be evident when the devices are installed. The support rail system will take care of this when the devices are installed, but installation itself will be difficult and cumbersome.

When you have racked side by side as described above and the equipment is bolted together, to remove it you must remove both units together, then disassemble them from each

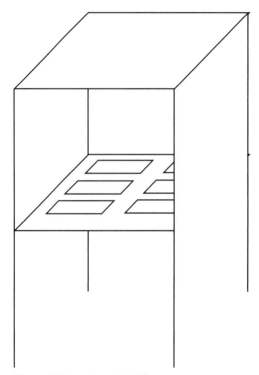

Figure 10.6   A rack shelf.

other. This calls for a written process, as most likely the system will be complicated. The strength cannot be compromised, so do not allow any of the screws or fixing plates to be removed and not re-installed when re-assembling the units.

10.5.4 Racking Special to Type and Custom Devices

Special to type and custom equipment (special to type equipment [STTE]) should all be specified to fit into a standard racking system; for example, a 19" rack. This makes the question of a racking solution a trivial one.

However, many special type items of equipment may not be made to fit into such racks, so you will need to work out a way to mount them into the rack to suit your design. There are several ways to mount non-standard equipment. Rack shelves are one possibility (see Figure 10.6), custom fittings for the rack may be another. Special fittings may include specially-made rack ears, or may be the lashing of the equipment onto a rack shelf unit. Rack shelves are commonly a flat plate with a folded side, for strengthening, to take up the weight of the device and transfer it to the rack posts. Shelves sound like an easy approach, but they have their own problems; they block airflow and cable routing if you are not careful.

STTE or custom devices may be very small or very large. You have several decisions to make under these conditions. If the equipment is small, but needs cooling, then the use of a shelf may be good mechanically but not good for cooling, especially if the device is a power amplifier – these discharge a lot of heat since they are naturally inefficient. Large devices may also be inefficient and heavy. This promotes the placing of the equipment in the lower part of the rack if you have room and boosting the cooling with intake fans at the bottom of the rack.

If you are specifying new STTE equipment, then you should always remember to specify how it will mount into the test system. Most designers will specify 19" rack or parts thereof. If you are specifying equipment, do not forget to specify how it will be cooled in your system – there is not much point in having the best piece of equipment if it causes cooling or ergonomic problems. The cost of installing poorly-designed casings can be extensive and time-consuming, and you must consider the serviceability of the equipment as well.

10.5.5 Using Sliding Rails

Sliding rails allow equipment to be withdrawn and rotated without removal to change cables.

Sliding rails are more expensive than fixed rails; however, there are some advantages to this type of system. If you are short on space, then this may be a good option to pursue. Many situations with limited space, such as warships for example, need to have a lot of equipment in a small area arranged so that operators do not interfere with each other's access. This is a situation where it is very convenient to be able to pull the equipment out from the front of the rack, and not have to support its weight yourself (see Figure 10.7). The rails will come out with the equipment to support it. The rails, if properly designed, will also have lock stages that have to be overcome (physically unlock each stage) at several points in the extraction. This saves the cabling from being stressed as well as when you pull it out, it has a lot of mass and will build up inertia – it will want to keep going. (Using several stages is a good practice to save it from hitting you in the face as well.)

Slide rails have an unusual advantage over all other racking systems in that when the test equipment is fully extended out the front of the rack, it can be rotated about a central balance point to gain access to the cables and connectors at the back of the equipment (see Figure 10.8). If you were not able to do this, then you would have to get into the back of the rack and disconnect all the cables before you pulled the test equipment out of the front.

When you decide to use a sliding rack system, do not forget that the cables will also be following the equipment out of the rack. Some systems will have all the cabling on a couple of cable trays that are hinged, and they will then freely swing out behind the equipment so there is no stress or pulling of the cables; this would damage both the cables and the connectors causing reliability issues. You could also have a large loop in the loom, if this suits other RF and loss issues, and suspend it from various points so it is not stressed. This could then unloop as the equipment is drawn out on the slide rails. Having a large loop ensures that the cabling is not coiled beyond its minimum bend diameter.

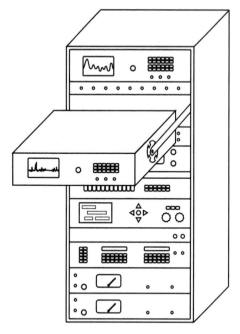

Figure 10.7 A rack with equipment extended on slide rails.

Side View

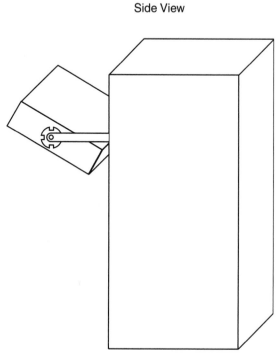

Figure 10.8 Test equipment extended and rotated so that the rear panel can be accessed without removing the equipment.

10.5.6 Racking Smaller Items and Items Not Designed for Racking

Many items that need to be in the rack are not full-width or are awkward in size, such as attenuators, mixers, or even signal splitters. These items need to be handled differently than standard test system components.

Items such as attenuators and mixers can be quite small, and it is not good practice to merely "hang" them in the rack from their connection cables – this puts stress on the cable bends and at the connectors. They will also be subject to vibration problems from all the fans and other equipment in the rack. You can use a shelf on which to mount this equipment, making sure that the shelf does not block cabling routes or airflow.

Another way to mount small devices and get away from positional problems with cabling and cooling is to cut the shelves down to the bare minimum size needed to support the devices. Many shelves are available from the manufacturer with a series of holes and slots as well as strengthening throughout the shelf; these can be cut down with a minimum of loss in strength for support.

You may need to have the devices in various places in the rack, which may require several small shelves distributed throughout the rack. Do not be tempted to tie these devices to the cases of test equipment; this will cause all sorts of removal and installation problems, even though it may save rack height. Often a shelf can be placed in the center of the rack's depth, behind a cut-out panel or the termination panels used for cable routing. These will then only be supported on the sides, and not the front or rear.

Many devices not specifically designed for racking can be adapted into blank or flush panels that are normally used to seal a rack and for retaining the cooling environment pressure. If the equipment is mounted behind a blank panel, then you can cut suitable openings in the panel to make the equipment's front panel or "power on" light visible to the operator. Sometimes devices can be strapped directly to the panel, or they can be bolted on. This does not allow for the easiest support, but can overcome a difficult installation problem.

10.5.7 Shelf-Mounting Smaller Items

You will want to mount small devices securely so as to maintain mechanical stability; in other words, you don't want devices rattling around in the rack, bumping into things, or rubbing against cables or other devices in the rack. Having devices unsecured in the rack causes a host of problems that are difficult to track down; it is also not a way to get repeatability as the effects of stress on cables and connectors are unknown. When you mount small items on a shelf, ensure that the mechanical stability of the device is not disturbed when you attach cables, or that the cables do not add abnormal stress to the setup such that strain is put on the connections. Adequate strain relief is required to ensure the stability of the setup.

You may want to put a coil or two of the cable on the shelf, strapped down, to give more relief to the devices and their connections. Make sure the coils conform to the manufacturer's minimum bend radius – or you will have phase stability problems at RF (radio frequency). Do not ever coil cabling for DC, as you will create an inductor with all its own parameters. Coiling for stress relief is only ever used with shielded cables at RF.

When mounting microwave devices, make sure that you have the correct cabling ready for them. Many devices need to have the cabling ready-made for placement before handling to cut down on problems of flexing cable into position and stressing it to fit the DUT. Microwave devices in particular have special requirements for cabling and positioning.

If you are using hard-line or semi-rigid cabling, ensure there is enough room for the cables to be installed without any further bending in the cables. Any bending beyond the cable's specifications can cause microfractures in the joins of the cable to the connectors – this causes loss and impedance changes which culminate in unrepeatable problems for your measurements. Repeatability is a major goal of a test system, and you must be able to confidently rebuild your system with all new cables and connectors, following the system's specifications, to get exactly the same result. It would be a significant problem if you were to change a cable and not get the same measurement results, within the systems limits, that you did previously – it could mean that your system has not been working properly and that you have been accepting or compensating for damaged components in your manufacturing line.

Remember to allow for cooling through the system. You may find that the mounting of small devices on shelves and cable lengths is a constant trade-off – for example, if mounting a shelf covered in components cannot be done in the middle of the rack because it blocks airflow (but is in a great position for access and short cables to the switch matrix or patch panel), then you may have to extend all your cabling to move the shelf to the bottom of the rack to get away from cooling blockages. Another way to deal with this is to break up the shelf into several smaller shelves and distribute those through the rack.

The distribution of small devices can also be dealt with by installing them all into a specially-built case for this purpose; the cabling for this case will be critical for ongoing support and any expansion for the future. The problem with this sort of case is that it is usually a one-of-a-kind building exercise, and with it comes a host of cooling and more placement problems. Mounting small devices into a system requires a lot of thought, and consideration of other factors.

10.5.8 Trays, Custom Rails, and Support Shelves

In the marketplace, there are many vendors making a variety of trays, rails, and shelves. These can all provide solutions for effective racking of your test system.

Trays are normally used for routing cables around inside the rack. They can be mounted horizontally or vertically and come in a range of sizes to accommodate varying cabling needs. Some trays can be bent into shape to properly maneuver the cabling in the rack without damaging or causing any stress to the cables or the harness if they are lashed up in that way.

Custom rails are normally used when the item to be supported is beyond the weight that can be suspended by normal rails. If you need to use custom rails, you should also have a very good look at where in the rack you intend to mount the equipment. If the equipment is heavy enough to require extra-strong mounting rails, then you may have to consider its position in the rack. One aspect to consider is that the center of gravity of the test system should remain as low as possible, and so excessively heavy equipment may need to be placed as close to the bottom of the rack as possible.

Support shelves, while they sound like the solutions to all problems – even mounting standard test equipment in a seemingly painless way – are not. The problem with support shelves is that they are usually thin metal and have inadequate cooling capability. They have an absolute weight-carrying capability, and are also sensitive to where the weight is placed on their overall surface. The inadequate cooling comes from the fact that shelves tend to be large, to try to cover a multitude of situations. If you can take a pair of tin-snips to a shelf, after you have decided how much of it you want to keep, then you may be able to recover your cooling/airflow such that your rack system does not overheat, or cause turbulence inside the racking space.

Good support shelves are actually made with a number of slots and raised sections or folds to give mechanical strength, if they are of good quality; this allows them to be cut out and still retain some mechanical integrity. If you are looking at shelves, do not just buy flat sheet-metal shelves that flex and bend as soon as you put weight on them. This is totally inadequate for a quality racking system. Good racking systems should have good weight-carrying characteristics.

10.6   Isolation Transformers

Isolation transformers are used to isolate the test equipment from the frequency effects of the mains at the general-purpose outlet (GPO) wall socket, supply, or other equipment that may radiate mains hum, or the cardinal mains frequency and its components.

Other uses of isolation transformers are to break up ground loops, since transformers provide no DC path. However, in some configurations, direct current may be required, which means that the transformer must be used in a common-rejection (choke) mode. The advantage of this is that DC can be transmitted along with differential AC signals. Some disadvantages of isolation transformers are their size, cost, frequency response, and placement in the system.

When mounting isolation transformers, try to mount them directly to the frame, either in the top or bottom of the rack, so they are securely strapped to earth (see Figure 10.9). The frame of the transformer must be strapped to the system earth connection very securely to reduce any abnormal effects, such as earthing loops.

Never remove the isolation transformer from the position the manufacturer has placed it in, or the original placement specifications that you used in the first place. This may void warranty with the manufacturer, as the system may no longer be in a supportable condition as judged by the manufacturer.

The effects of mains hum, 50 or 60 Hz (depending on the country supply) are detrimental to many items of equipment. If these frequencies are transposed onto the main equipment that is being powered in the rack, the spectral purity of the output signal may be degraded. The signal and its harmonic components may then appear transposed on all the other signals being gener-

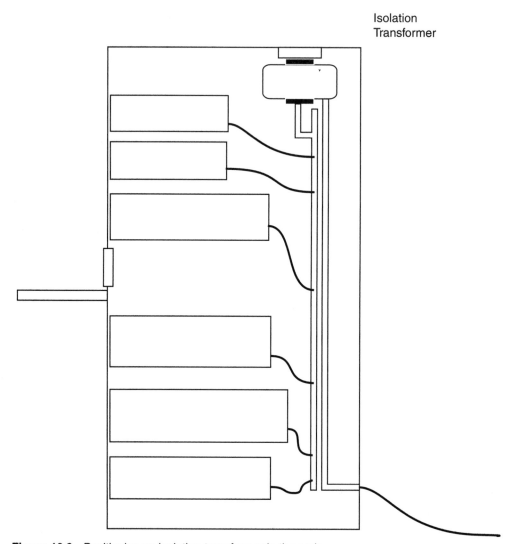

Isolation
Transformer

Figure 10.9   Positioning an isolation transformer in the rack.

ated (see Figure 10.10). This often looks like an inverted comb if looked at on a spectrum analyser. The components have energy in their content that adds to the spectral power of the signal.

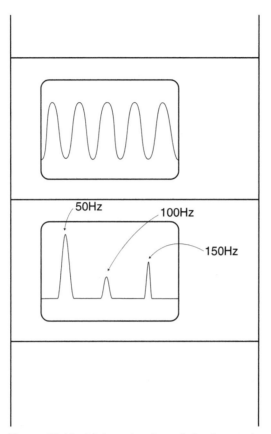

Figure 10.10 Mains signal and its harmonic components.

"WAR STORY"

An integrator bought some very expensive generators from an equipment vendor, then removed the systems, in pieces, from the original setup and integrated them into their own racking system. This involved removing the isolation transformer as well.

The system never worked again to the original specifications, and voided all warranty as the condition of the equipment could not be guaranteed. To make the situation worse, the integrator had paid for a special calibration to ensure spectral purity at certain frequencies, which was very expensive and also time-consuming. The calibration work and the system were no longer in a known or predictable state, and the original vendor would not warrant any performance, let alone the special calibration.

CHAPTER   1 1

Weight Considerations and Equipment Placement

T his chapter examines how to arrange test equipment for proper weight distribution and stability in the rack. The rack's center of gravity should be as low as possible, and balanced front to back and side to side for maximum stability. The balance of the test system should be considered both with and without the heaviest DUT for that system in position.

This chapter also discusses test system portability and ruggedness, which are important if the system will be moved around or deployed in a challenging environment.

KEY POINTS:

- Weight distribution in the rack must be arranged for maximum stability.
- The heaviest equipment in the rack should be positioned as low as possible to keep the center of gravity low.
- Using accessories such as ballast and anti-tilt feet can increase rack stability, but should not be relied on as a substitute for planning a stable rack layout.
- System portability and ruggedness are important considerations in particular for racks that will be transported or deployed to unusual locations.

11.1   Checking Overall Weight and Weight Distribution

Placement of test equipment and other components in the rack needs to be done with care. This also applies to the test system together with any DUTs, as these can change the balance of the system if they are particularly heavy.

By checking the overall weight and weight distribution of your test system both with and without the heaviest DUT on the work surface, you can consider the mechanical advantage and cantilevering effects on the test system overall under these conditions. Also consider the shock weight when the heaviest DUT is put on the work surface, as the operator may inadvertently drop it.

When you have selected your test equipment, take a look at any example or similar models even before you take delivery of the equipment you order. Both the overall weight and the internal distribution of the weight (for example, at the front or back of the unit) will be important. If you cannot find out what the weight distribution is, then the general rule of thumb is to assume the majority of the weight is at the rear of the equipment, around where the power supply is, as the transformer is probably the greatest source of weight. Most microwave equipment is also comparatively heavy due to the amount of RF shielding required to make it meet its specifications.

When racking equipment, it is important to consider the requirement for ergonomics as well as the weight and safety of the system, and hence safety of the operator. From a safety perspective, the racking of equipment is a mechanical problem where the center of gravity should be kept as low as possible. From a user perspective, the minimum amount of bending and moving when connecting DUTs is ideal. Some system developers will bolt or otherwise fasten their racks to the floor for additional stability; however, this may not be possible (or appropriate) if the rack is to be portable. Trolley-type racks used for portable test systems need to have particular attention paid to weight, as they can easily get out of control on rough surfaces or slopes, and also when wheeling over uneven levels such as into and out of elevators.

Also check the overall weight of the test system against the floor type you are expected to use. If you have to place the system on a floating computer room-type surface, make sure you have all the strong points mapped for your installation. If the weight is excessive, for example, you may get dispensation to cut a hole in the floor and put in a platform to support your test system racks (see Figure 11.1).

There are a number of general guidelines for positioning equipment in a test system rack, and a number of accessories that can be used to increase the stability or portability of a test system. Some of these are discussed in the following sections.

11.2   Positioning Equipment in the Rack

Racking up a test system in one or more cabinets makes it easier to manage and use, as well as presenting a better appearance. The fully racked test system should be well-balanced, and thus should have its center of gravity positioned as low as possible (see Figure 11.2) as well as centered as much as possible within the rack (front to back as well as side to side) for increased stability.

The rack cabinet also allows the designer to arrange test equipment for easy access by the operator, and to keep signal and power cables neatly out of the way of the operator and other personnel.

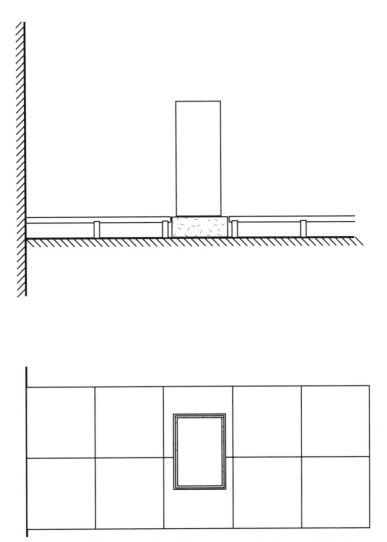

Figure 11.1   Test system located on a computer floor, with load support.

Most racks will be delivered to your workplace already built. In some rack cabinets, you may still need to attach side and rear panels and rack doors. You will also have to put support rails or rack mount kits in place for each piece of test equipment (these are often available as an option when you order the test equipment). Any handles or "ears" on the test equipment are not designed to support the weight of the equipment on its own in a rack. They can physically be used to support the equipment at the front of the rack, but are not designed to carry the full weight of the equipment (the strain in the handles is increased by the cantilevering effect that results). However, this is a very unreliable work practice that could place staff and equipment at risk if the handles break.

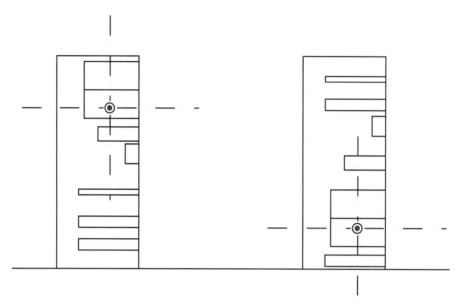

Figure 11.2 Two examples of racked test systems: the right-hand one is well balanced; the other is poorly balanced.

TIP:

Before you begin racking up a test system, buy a large bag of rack screws and the matching captive nuts for them. You should receive rack screws and nuts with each piece of equipment you purchase for the racked system; however, getting them out of bubble wrap or little plastic bags quickly becomes tedious and takes up a lot of time. There are two advantages to having a separate supply: they are easy to access and will save you time during the racking process, and they are consistent in quality and to a known finish (as they are all from one source). You can take the others out of their packaging at a later time, or assign this task to someone else!

Most racks will contain a power-isolating switch, which is normally placed at the top or bottom of the rack. The remainder of the rack will require fitting out for equipment, workspace, displays, and other system components.

Deciding on the rack layout for your system will probably require at least a couple of iterations. The first iteration will be for general positioning in the rack – high, low, or at operator height. The second will be to functionally group equipment where necessary and to arrange equipment and components if necessary according to percentage of use and access required. The following guidelines can guide your initial equipment placement decisions:

• Heavy items such as power supplies and signal generators should be marked for the lower section of the rack.

- Any equipment that the operator does not need to adjust on a regular basis should be marked for the lower or upper areas of the rack, depending on weight (see Figure 11.3).

- Any equipment that is computer-controlled can be positioned almost anywhere in the remaining rack space (as it does not require operator access).

- Any equipment that the operator is continually using by connecting to, viewing, or changing controls, and work areas such as benches, will need to be positioned in the middle section of the rack.

- Positioning of equipment at the front or rear of the rack depends on the accessories available, the overall weight of the particular piece of equipment, and whether you need to go to this length for this particular item.

- Microwave equipment in particular should have the shortest cable lengths possible – for loss reduction as well as cost reduction – as the cabling used for high frequencies can be very expensive.

- Patch panels should be positioned in the middle section of a rack such that the operator can easily reach them and also can clearly view their setup.

From an initial functional diagram, the system designer must then separate the equipment into the correct functional section. Next, they must locate each functional area where it best makes sense; for example, all the loss-sensitive equipment should be placed close to the switch or patch panel to reduce losses over the length of the cables. Supplies of lower frequency signals and DC supplies can have longer cable lengths and thus can be further away from the switch or patch panel. This minimizes long cable lengths when using equipment sensitive to loss over length.

TIP:

Always check that your cable lengths are not excessive, regardless of the signal type, to remove a possible source of error.

Related equipment such as power supplies should be grouped together. The system designer will then need to determine what equipment will need to be adjusted, viewed, or in any way be operator-interactive. If the test system has a lot of similar equipment, for example for digital simulation or analog measurement, then it may make sense to group the equipment into functional areas. This is also an option to keep in mind if you ever have the opportunity to transition from a manual to a partly- or fully-automated test system.

If the system is large, then multiple racks will need to be used. This is also an appropriate option if the test system is designed to be portable and should thus be built into smaller, more easily manageable racks.

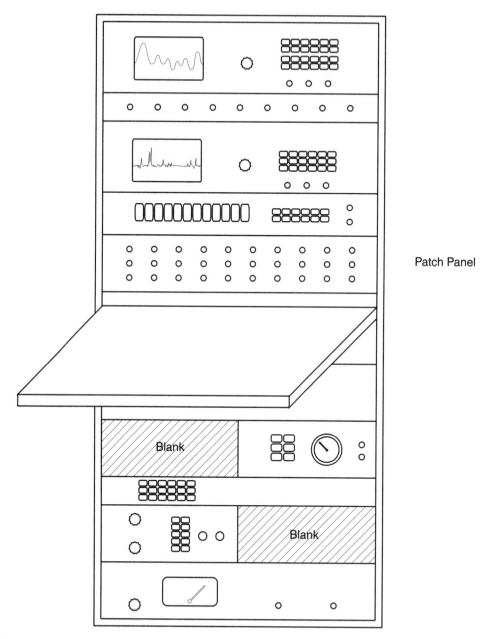

Patch Panel

Figure 11.3 Rack with infrequently adjusted items placed in lower or upper areas of the rack cabinet.

After the operator-interactive equipment is highlighted for positioning for operator access, the equipment will need to be sorted into weight and percentage of use. The final arrangement will be a compromise between these two.

Once the interactive equipment is placed, fill the bottom section of the rack with the heaviest remaining equipment (generally power supplies). The rest of the equipment can be considered for the top and middle sections of the rack.

TIP:

If you have any space in the test system rack, place blank filler panels in the top section of the rack (rather than the middle or lower part) to keep the center of gravity low.

Permanent positioning of test systems. It is good practice to plan each rack so that it physically stable in itself. Section 11.3, "Using Accessories for Rack Stability," describes the use of ballast and anti-tilt feet for this purpose. The following methods can also be used to fasten test systems permanently in place:

- Securing the rack to the floor. This is the most common method used when permanent, secured placement is required. Securing the racks to the floor is not a complicated task and can be easily accomplished with a set of dyna bolts. The installation will require a hole in the floor to run cables between racks. Most false floors are of a tile construction, so care should be used in cutting the smallest hole practical for the cables, so as not to unduly weaken the floor. If the floor's ability to support the racks or even to spread the weight load or to allow a more easily moved system is already in question, a plenum can be built from wood to fit between the racks and the floor. The racks are secured to the plenum, and the plenum is secured to the floor at strategic points, generally at the corners of the structure (see Figure 11.4).

- Securing racks together. Remember to check that this will not interfere with the ventilation and cooling of each rack and its contents. Make sure that the airflow for which the racks are designed is not disturbed, otherwise you will have to recalculate the airflow and cooling budget along more complex lines. Try to keep the racks isolated if you can; it may appear to be a good idea from a cabling and access point of view to remove the walls between racks, but it presents the most incredible problems to overcome. To get access between cabinets for cabling, use circular holes with gasketing material around them to reduce draught. This will allow you to accurately predict your airflow and cooling constants. Always position your test equipment so that it does not interfere with airflow (see Figure 11.5). Also bear in mind that some racks may need to have air conditioning pumped into them for additional cooling. If this is required for some of the test system racks, you do not want the cooled air escaping into other less critical racks.

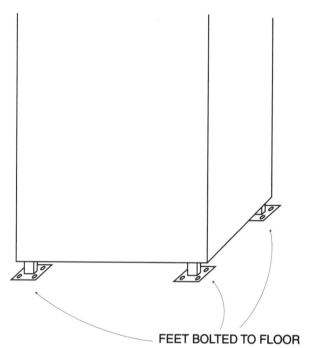

FEET BOLTED TO FLOOR

Figure 11.4   Securing a rack to the floor.

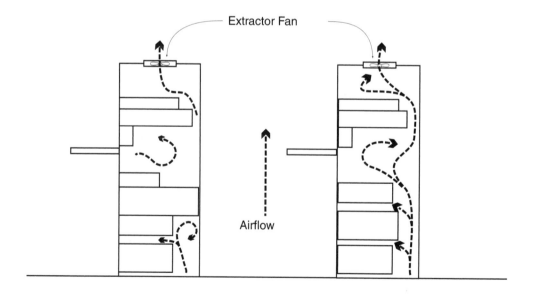

Blocked Airflow   Unblocked Airflow

Figure 11.5   Rack cabinets showing blocked and unblocked airflow.

• Securing racks to a wall from above. Remember to allow room from the wall to the rear of the rack, so that the rack door can swing and that a technician can get behind the rack to remove, install, and repair equipment. Ensure that airflow is maintained up to the cabinet and that it is not different from the racks around it. If one or more of the racks requires cooling, you may want to install an air conditioning duct at the top of the rack, keeping the airflow in the correct direction.

The most common method of securing a permanently placed test system is to fasten it to the floor. However, once the racks are secured to the floor, wall, or other racks, moving them to another position is time-consuming. If you do attach your racks to the floor, make sure they are well-labeled and that they are fully disassembled before they are moved. Even with permanently secured racks, the balance and stability of each rack is still important; the designer should at no stage be freed from these constraints. If shortcuts are taken, or the designer relies on the securing bolts to support the test system, then the system could be at risk of toppling should the bolts be drawn for the system to be moved.

When racked test systems have permanent cooling in place, some sort of fail-safe device must be installed to stop the rack from setting off the system's heat triggers after the cooling fans stop. Installing appropriate cutout switches into the test system's overall management system is one method.

TIP:

An investment in test equipment needs to be protected. This is partly achieved through a suitable maintenance and calibration program. If you are just at a preliminary pricing stage, a rough guide is to allow for about 5% of the system cost each year as the maintenance overhead to keep the test system in good operational shape.

Test systems in multiple racks.   If your system uses multiple racks, then the use of racks of the same height throughout provides a better presentation as well as simplifying logistics for your organization. The height of the rack can vary between manufacturers; for example, ranging from 12 rack units (RU) to 45 RU in height.

The smaller racks give some degree of portability and may have options to allow wheels to be fitted. The above discussion on placement of equipment and standardization of rack cabinets applies to racks for portable test systems as well.

The designer of the system may wish to select deep racks instead of shallow racks to assist with the placing of equipment and the stability of the test system (through a lower center of gravity). Generally speaking, equipment that is used by the operator is placed in the front of the rack. Equipment that is not directly used by the operator (such as equipment that is fully under computer control) can then be placed in the back of the rack. This of course will depend on the depth of the rack and the length of the equipment you wish to place in the rack. If a deeper rack is chosen, the power budget and cooling (heat) budget will need to be carefully analyzed. The positioning of the cable runs should also be carefully evaluated for possible obstructions or problems.

Test systems deployed to moving platforms. If your test system is going to be placed on a moving platform, additional parameters need to be considered. These include any sideways forces that the system may experience, such as in an aircraft or ship. If this is part of the intended operating environment of the test system, then the weight distribution in the rack must be designed to meet the relevant standard of the platform (such as the aircraft). An engineer who is experienced in these problems will normally handle this aspect of the design. Shock mounting will be a key consideration when installing on a moving platform or a platform capable of moving. An accurate assessment of the degree of shock protection needed is an important step in appropriately costing the full test system. Equipment built and guaranteed to withstand extremely rough handling will be priced accordingly. If you know that the test system will not require this degree of shock protection, then the costs can be much lower than if the requirements have been overspecified.

Fully-automated test systems. If your test system is fully automated and you only need access to the work surface and to the computer entry station, then you can generally place the equipment anywhere in the rack. The main considerations then are the system's balance and cabling needs. Any RF or microwave cabling should be kept as short as possible, so that equipment can be kept as close to the patch panel or matrix as possible.

Equipment on slide-rack mounting. If the equipment is on slide-rack mounting that allows the equipment to be slid from the rack (see Figure 11.6), this will produce a turning moment force that will need to be allowed for. This is just like a filing cabinet, where if all drawers are open, the cabinet will likely topple. Hence, be extra careful if the rack you build allows equipment to be slid out on slide-rack mount kits. Use the anti-tilt feet if supplied (see Section 11.3.2 for more information on anti-tilt feet). If they are not available, you may be able to somehow extend the baseline forward using re-inforced steel joists. Before you start, use a spirit level to make sure your rack is perfectly balanced geometrically, so all vertical forces are transmitted down the load bearing structure correctly. Most racks will have spacers that screw up or down or wedges to allow for this.

Racking procedure. When racking up a test system, the rack cabinet should be positioned correctly first, and then secured. Equipment and accessories can then be fitted, keeping in mind that cabling may need to be secured in the rack first if access will be difficult once the test equipment is in place. At this time, the anti-tilt feet should be deployed to assist in balancing the rack during the test equipment installation (see Section 11.3.2 for more information on anti-tilt feet).

The test equipment should be fitted from the bottom up, never from the top down. Each piece of equipment should be fully secured before moving to the next. If the rack topples, this prevents the equipment from sliding out.

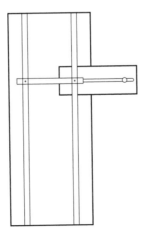

Figure 11.6 Side view of test system with test equipment on slide-rack mounts.

Generally, two people can populate a rack with little trouble. Chapter 13, "Racking the System," covers the rack installation procedure itself in more detail.

TIP:

The purchase of an electric screwdriver is invaluable during the test system racking process. Manually screwing in a number of screws or other fasteners can quickly put a strain on your wrist.

11.3 Using Accessories for Rack Stability

In addition to the designer using careful placement of equipment in the system rack to keep it physically balanced, accessories including ballast and anti-tilt feet are available to help increase the stability of a test system. There are also a number of more specialized accessories and techniques in addition to those covered here. For example, some platforms may require shock fittings in the form of coils of specially strung wire to absorb the forces along various axes. Some organizations require their equipment to be freighted on trains and a shunting test is mandatory. Most racks simply collapse during this exercise if not re-inforced for the purpose.

If the test system is to be situated in an unusual place, for example plumbed into a sensor pack at the top of a warship mast, then it is particularly important not to have the weight of the system unbalanced. Any unbalance in the racked system could then cause the crane operator or installation technician some significant problems. The crane operator would have problems bringing the load to rest if were brought in from the side, as it would be difficult to predict the pendulum-like swing length of the suspended test system. The technician would also have problems as he or she connected the cable assembly to the sensor pack as the system may move under the cable weight or strain.

When the system is to be used in a portable situation, care must be taken to accommodate any possible side movement and to protect the test system under these circumstances. Many organizations now use deployable workshops or sometimes shipping containers that have been refitted for the purpose of being used as a workshop of some type. In these cases, the test system must be solidly secured or buffered by some method that absorbs or redistributes the forces that it may be required to withstand. A railway shunting, for example, can be the equivalent of being hit by sixty tons of steel at ten kilometers per hour – a lot of mass and energy to account for. Some racks, if not suitably re-inforced, will simply disintegrate.

TIP:

If you are near a toppling test system - don't try to hold it up! It's not worth the damage to your back.

Two of the most commonly used options, ballast and anti-tilt feet, are discussed in the sections below.

11.3.1 Ballast

Ballast in the form of lead ingots or house building bricks is not uncommon in rack construction. Its function is to compensate for heavy equipment positioned high up in the rack cabinet and to lower the center of gravity for increased stability. Many companies sell large ballast weights fitted with rack mounting connections so that they can be bolted into the front or rear of the bottom of the rack. The designer should keep in mind at all times the importance of keeping the center of gravity of the test system as low as possible. It is not good practice to balance the rack by putting the ballast in the top of the rack – even if it balances out a heavy item on one side high in the rack, the ballast should in fact be placed as low as possible (see Figure 11.7).

The use of ballast will obviously increase the overall weight of the rack, so make sure that you have the appropriate load carrying capacity on the floor where the test system will be deployed. If you intend to put your rack on a computer floor or above the first level of a building, then it is appropriate to check with the architect or your organization's facilities staff to ensure that the floor will bear the load.

When using ballast, always make sure it is fixed in place sturdily and that it is not in the way of the system's cabling. Have correct labels made up and fix them securely to ensure that no one inadvertently removes or moves the ballast. Even if someone with good intentions knows that they need to leave the ballast inside the rack, they may unbalance or decrease the stability of the rack if they simply shift the ballast to another position through not understanding why it is in that particular place and must not be moved.

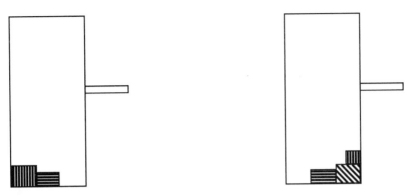

Figure 11.7   Placing ballast in the rack.

Remember, even when using ballast to even up the balance of the test system, the effect of the weight of the DUT on the work surface can still have a large effect on the cabinet's load equation. The test system may be stable in itself, and then lose that stability when the DUT is placed on the work surface.

Positioning test equipment to aid with balancing the rack cabinet.   The effects of ballast can also be accomplished or aided with the weight of some of the equipment you intend to use in the test system rack. Power supplies are an excellent example – due to their weight, the designer should always aim to position them low in the rack. Signal generators and synthesizers are also typically heavy items, and should be positioned as low as possible within any system layout constraints, such as operator access to a particular piece of equipment.

Ballast can also be managed by selecting the lightest equipment intended for the test system and ensuring that it is in the top of the rack, thus forcing heavier equipment lower. Ensure that any displays you want your operator to see are at a reasonable height, but not high enough to upset the balance of the test system.

It seems obvious, but it bears repeating, that a test system designer should always check to ensure that the area where the test system will be deployed can support the weight, and also that the path and method you will use to get the test system to that site is also capable of supporting the system's weight. If the path to the site cannot support that weight, the test system must be disassembled and transported in pieces, and then reconstructed later at its destination.

11.3.2 Anti-Tilt Feet

Anti-tilt feet extend the baseline of the rack to increase its stability (see Figure 11.8). They are most useful when assembling the test system in the rack and can also provide a degree of additional support when a heavy DUT is placed on the work surface. It is important, however, not to rely on them for the physical stability of your test system, and to use ballast and careful placement of equipment as well.

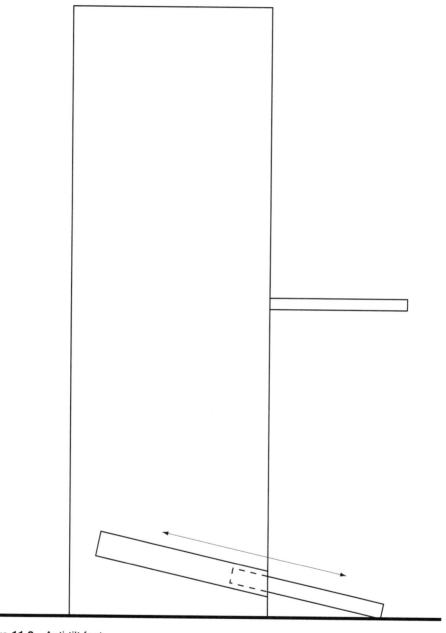

Figure 11.8   Anti-tilt feet.

Ant-tilt feet always face the front of the rack, and generally only extend a short distance from the front of the rack. If someone is installing a heavy piece of test equipment at the top of an otherwise empty rack, then even anti-tilt feet may not prevent the rack from toppling. Generally the tilt feet are fairly small and do not give a lot of mechanical advantage to the rack when weight is moved too far forward or is unbalanced in itself. The rack manufacturer cannot predict all the types or sizes of loads a test system designer may decide to place at any level in the rack. Hence, placing a heavy item at the top of an empty rack has a good chance of overwhelming the anti-tilt feet as it leaves the center of gravity high in the rack. If you fill the rack from the bottom, however, the system will maintain a low center of gravity throughout the process and has a greater chance of remaining balanced even if the same weight is placed at the top of the rack.

Anti-tilt feet are a useful option to include when you purchase a rack. However, they should essentially be used only during the test system's construction and assembly, and should not be relied upon to keep the rack upright under all conditions. They can get in the way of people's feet, and as staff turn over in your organization, people may forget why they have been used. The risk in this situation is that someone will kick the anti-tilt feet back into their stored position, and it may only be a matter of time before a heavy DUT is placed on the work surface, causing an accident when the center of gravity of the test system moves too far forward.

11.3.3 Risk Factors

Aside from the technical problem of solving an operational need with a suitable test system design, the main task of the test system designer is to ensure the safety of operators and other staff. Chapter 9, "Electrical Safety of the System," covers a number of aspects of designing for electrical safety; however, this material is no substitute for expert safety material, specialist advice where appropriate, and the skills of experienced staff.

Three of the main mechanical risk factors when assembling and using a test system are:

- Damage to equipment caused by improper use of rack mount equipment.
- The rack toppling due to the center of gravity being too high or too far forward or backward.
- Injury to personnel through poor work practices.

Damage to equipment. A common cause of damage to test equipment or system accessories is having heavy equipment positioned high in the test system and insufficiently well-fastened. The risk of equipment coming loose and falling is dangerous to the operator and also to the equipment in the test system. Damage to the test system will require expensive time-out at a repair center and as this is damage and not a normal failure, the repair center is unlikely to stock spares. Most service centers stock components, but may not stock the external panels and connectors, as these are not normally damaged in the course of electronic use and service. Additionally, since this would be damage due to poor design, it would be highly unusual for this damage to be covered under warranty or by a repair and maintenance contract. Thus, the costs to the

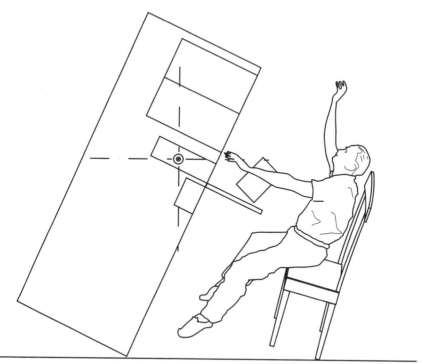

Figure 11.9   An unstable rack.

organization would include not only repair costs, but also the opportunity costs of not having the test system available.

Incorrect center of gravity.   Having the test system fall over is a serious safety issue, and exposes an organization's personnel to the risk of injury. The center of gravity of the test system should be checked not only for the system itself, but also with the heaviest DUT that will be used with the system. It does not enhance a designer's career to build a system that topples over the first time a DUT is placed on the work surface. Always allow some degree of margin rather then risk designing at the limits of a test system's stability, as a heavy DUT may be inadvertently dropped onto the work surface, increasing its unbalancing effect. Figure 11-9 shows a test system with an incorrect center of gravity.

Even if the design requirements (or the aesthetics of the system designer) call for a particular presentation of the test system when racked, for example certain displays at a particular height, do not allow these requirements to interfere with the stability and balance of the system.

Injury to staff during assembly.   The chance of injury to personnel is too important a risk to ignore either in the design or the build stage of a test system. When assembling system components in the rack, all staff should follow an agreed-upon system of work to minimize any misunderstandings about procedure or what tasks have already been completed. For example, always start from the bottom of the rack when installing equipment and other system components, as this always keeps the center of gravity as low as possible. Ensure that proper lifting techniques are always used. Test equipment can be awkward to handle, and it can also itself be badly balanced from front to back and from one side to the other.

If at all possible, never have one person assembling a test system alone. Not only does having a minimum of two people available for moving and positioning heavy equipment easily lessen the risk of strain injury, but the overall safety risks to personnel are lessened. During the commissioning stage when power is first applied and the system is being brought up, it is imperative to always have a minimum of two people present for obvious safety reasons such as electrical hazards.

TIP:

Always make sure that you leave room for safety cutouts, even if it means that you have to use more than one rack to hold the whole test system. It is never worthwhile to skimp on the safety of operators or other personnel.

11.4 System Portability and Ruggedness

If you are designing a system that will be deployed to a different site, then portability and ruggedness considerations become important. The layout design of the system should be even more carefully balanced than for one that is intended to remain stationary. Techniques such as the use of ruggedized transit cases, rack "skeletons," and castors can all increase the portability of a test system, although some changes in the rack design may need to be made.

11.4.1 Designing the Rack Layout for a Transportable Test System

The balance and center of gravity for systems in transportable racks (see Figure 11.10) are important not only to avoid damage during transportation, but also because the risks of injury to personnel will occur more often simply because the rack will be moved more often. Thus, the frequency of even a small risk is greater. If the transportable rack is designed for a two-person lift and the weight is all at the top, the carriers may be instantly overwhelmed by the imbalance and drop the system. It is safer and more professional to ensure that the center of gravity is always kept low and that the weight is even fore and aft and side to side, just as with a fixed system. If you need to pack accessories and/or manuals with your portable equipment, then they are best kept in drawers, keeping in mind balance issues. Depending on the existing weight of your transportable rack, you may choose to have the drawer in the top or bottom.

When you design a transportable racked test system, plan for the worst case and assume that it will at some time be lowered onto its side, front, or back in the course of its life. Make sure that all the equipment inside can withstand the sideways motion that will result under these circumstances and that the rack can still support the equipment in place so it does not fall out.

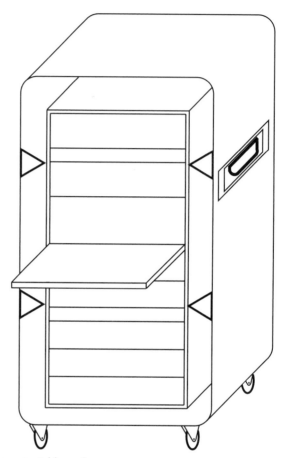

Figure 11.10   A transportable rack.

For example, the weight of the test equipment in the rack should not overcome the strength of the rack ears holding the equipment in place laterally when the rack is in its normal standing position. If you cannot ensure this for a given rack height, you may have to use more and smaller racks. Smaller racks are easier to make sturdy and to ruggedize.

Good design that will allow you to transport a system while racked can save your organization a great deal of disassembly and re-assembly work. It is far easier to transport systems in position if possible.

Smaller racks are more suitable for transportable systems, even if this requires splitting a system into two smaller racks and adding a communication bus. However, if your system needs to be lifted into areas or risks rough handling in some way, for example being lifted onto ships, some form of ruggedized rack will be required.

Rack "skeletons" can be used that are then secured inside ruggedized transit cases to further increase the strength of the test system as a whole. The skeleton is normally a very sturdy

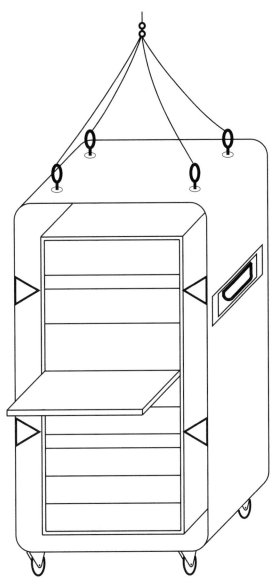

Figure 11.11   A rack being lifted.

19" rack that can be dissembled and moved around, and when assembled, is more secure and stronger than a traditional laboratory-grade rack unit. These allow full coverage of the system in a solid case and also provide lifting eyes (a term used for large bolts attached through the case to the frame of the unit; the tops of the bolts are turned back to form a ring or "eye" to allow cables or shackles to be passed through) to allow lifting cables to be attached. Cranes can then be used to lift the system (see Figure 11.11). As test system racks become larger, this approach becomes

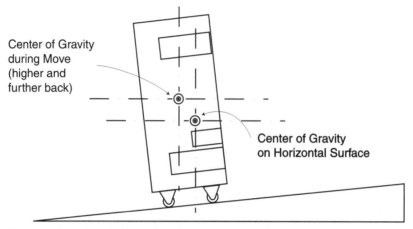

Figure 11.12   A portable rack being moved on castors up a ramp.

less useful, so as a system designer, you may need to break a large test system into smaller segments that can fit into this type of ruggedized rack so that transportation is possible. The user would then connect all the racks together to complete the test system.

When designing a test system that has to be moved periodically, castors on each cabinet can make transportation easier. The rack cabinet will be able to be moved under greater control if at least two of the castors are fixed and do not swivel. At least make sure that all four castors cannot be moved at once as you can risk getting them into a position that tilts the test system way off balance, thus causing it to fall over while you are moving it (see Figure 11.12).

TIP:

Good practice is to have at least four people move a rack that is higher than any of the people involved in the move. If it does for some reason topple, then it will be very difficult for one person to try to hold up. If the toppling rack cannot immediately be stabilized before it tilts more than a small amount, then no further attempt to hold it should be made – the risk of injury is too great.

When moving a system on concrete paths, make sure that the castors are large enough to traverse the cracks between concrete slabs.

The steepness of ramps is a potential source of risk. When moving a portable test system up a ramp, ensure that it has a gentle slope, as it can be easy to move the center of gravity too far out from the vertical and thus topple the rack. A heavy system may also roll out of control as the gravity component down the slope on a steep incline can be enough to overcome the strength of the person moving the system. In general, never move the test system on uneven flooring or up a ramp if there is some alternative. Disassembling, moving, and re-assembling the system later are far safer, both for the personnel involved and the equipment itself.

To move transportable systems up and down uneven surfaces or from, for example, a ship to shore, it is best to use pallets and forklifts, lifting eyes on the rack itself, and a crane or trolleys and lifts. At all times, try to ensure the test system is kept vertical as it was designed.

When using a crane to move the test system, make sure that you have sufficient lifting strength in the lifting eyes if fitted. Check the safe working load limit (SWL). If lifting eyes are not fitted in the rack cabinet or if the weight of the system is close to the SWL limit, then consider backing up the lift with chains or a sling.

When moving a portable test system, ensure that it is packaged as well as possible to ensure no damage results due to any poor design of the layout and the distribution of weight. Even if you are able to recover any costs from your insurance coverage, you or your customer will have to deal with the consequences of lack of access to the test system while it is being repaired or replaced, and in many circumstances, this may not be acceptable.

11.4.2 Moving Racks Not Designed for Transport in One Piece

If a rack is not built to be transported, then do not try to move it in one piece. Best practice is to take it apart, labeling all components in the process, and then move the parts and re-assemble.

This process is required because side motions and other forces on a rack when it is full of equipment are difficult to calculate when you consider a situation such as a transport truck in traffic, or a rail carriage being shunted from one track to another. The sides of the rack could bend, stress, and twist, causing the rack to collapse. Even one piece of equipment coming loose and shifting could be enough to topple the rack or to damage the rack cabinet and its contents if it were not extremely well-secured.

The processes of labeling, disassembly, and re-assembly may take some time and may also require the development of a system for labeling the system components completely. But, it still takes far less effort and time than moving the test system and risking the destruction of or damage to an undocumented system. Even if the test system is documented, the forces involved in a move are immense – more than most stable racks are designed for in their lifetimes.

The processes of disassembling the test system, labeling all components thoroughly enough to allow straightforward re-assembly, and re-assembly and power-up are complex. If you know that the system is likely to require regular repositioning during its working lifetime, then additional time and expense spent in making it portable as a complete system will be a worthwhile investment.

CHAPTER 12

Temperature Control and Power Considerations

T his chapter explains how to work out heat and power budgets for your system and make sure that your equipment will not overheat or be short of power. We examine what you can do if you need additional power, and some solutions to help get the best cooling for your system.

KEY POINTS:

- Power and heat budgets are the two key restrictions of operating test systems in racks.
- Exceeding the heat budget of the rack is the more common problem, and a number of strategies are available to help manage excess buildup of heat while the system is operating.

12.1 The Importance of Power and Heat Budgets

Power and heat budgets are important in a test system design because of the consequences of exceeding either heat or power limitations in the system rack. The system designer generally has to go to considerable efforts to maintain these budgets under controlled circumstances.

If a heat problem occurs in the system rack, the life of the equipment in it will be severely reduced. In extreme circumstances, the equipment may break down altogether or short-circuit and possibly start a fire in your lab.

Normally, the equipment specifications will tell you the amount of power required. This is a good figure to use when determining how much heat will be provided by the equipment. The simplest way to determine the overall power dissipation (heat) is to add the VA ratings of each piece of equipment in the rack. Be careful not to include the VA supplied to equipment outside the rack from power supplies located within the rack.

There are two main ways to cool a rack: natural convection and extractor fan cooling. Other cooling methods are possibile, such as forced refrigerated air. The system designer will need to manage heat buildup in the rack through the use of the above cooling methods and through careful placement of equipment in the rack to allow uninterrupted airflow through the rack to assist cooling.

The power supply feeding the rack will need to support the total of the individual equipments' power requirements – both current and voltage will be restricted by the ratings of the power supply. For example, ten amps is a common wiring standard. If your rack is wired to ten amps, then the total current draw of the equipment in the rack must not exceed ten amps.

An individual test system rack will normally be a trade-off between these parameters and the rack layout.

12.2   Calculating Power Budgets

As mentioned above, the power budget limitation is simply the addition of all the individual instruments' power requirements. However, there are some additional considerations.

The rack will be supplied by a power source that can supply only so much current, and this will normally be your limiting factor. Remember that:

$$Amperage = Total\ Power(VA)/Voltage$$

It is always a good idea to follow a conservative approach and make sure that the power used in the calculation is the worst possible case, normally the start-up power surge – or you may find that you are regularly tripping circuit breakers. If you are using a generator rather than main power, then the actual power used should be a percentage of the total rating, typically 70-80%. The authors do not recommend the use of two power supplies into the rack to overcome power budgets, as this will create a safety issue.

Some equipment form factors may introduce additional considerations. If you are using VXI technology, for example, then the situation is slightly more complex since the mainframe can only supply a rated amount of power. Normally, the specifications for each VXI card will tell you the power used by that card; however, this may not be enough as it does not tell you which voltage rails are being loaded. It is extremely important that the individual voltage rails used by each card are added, so that the cards do not load an individual rail beyond its limit. Once again, ensure that the worst-case situation is used, normally the start-up current surge.

The total power can now be calculated by summing the power requirements of the individual equipment. This power rating will need to be under that of the power supply. If it is greater, then the system will need to be separated into two or more racks with separate power supplies. Also ensure that none of the relevant technical or safety standards are broken. There is a maximum number of GPOs (general purpose outlets) that can be wired into a rack, and this figure should never be exceeded

12.3   What to Do if You Need More Three-phase Power

If you need more than one source of three-phase power, then you have very serious power needs. The solution to this is to get a qualified electrical contractor to hook up the transformers and power distribution system you need. The need for this sort of power denotes the testing of very powerful devices or that your test equipment is so extensive that it draws a large amount of current. You should take a look at your system requirements and see if you can split your test system into sections that will require less power.

Should you really need this amount of power, consider building a special test system to test the specific devices that need to draw on this power source. Generally, if you need to go to this extreme, you are trying to do too much with your system. Many military or commercial systems divide up their tests so that no individual systems needs this sort of power source.

12.4   Calculating Heat Budgets

The heat budget is an important criterion when racking equipment. The heat generated in a rack must be removed so that all environmental conditions for the equipment can be maintained. Without this control of excess heat, the equipment will prematurely fail. All instrument manufacturers will specify a maximum temperature at which their equipment will work. The cooling technique used by the system designer must ensure that the temperature inside the rack never exceeds this temperature. Hence, the cooling method must be able to remove the difference in temperature between the outside rack (ambient) temperature and the internal rack (maximum) temperature. In fact, system designers should ensure that the internal rack temperature never approaches the maximum working temperature allowed by the equipment.

There are a number of options available when selecting a cooling method. These include natural convection cooling, where the natural flow of air through the rack is used to remove the heat generated by the equipment inside the rack. Air enters the rack, usually from below the rear panel, flows through the rack, and exits via the roof of the rack (see Figure 12.1). In some cases where the rack has only a few instruments, natural conduction cooling occurs through the metal panels of the rack. However, normally both methods are considered as natural cooling. Extractor fan cooling is used to increase the airflow through the rack by the use of fans in the top of the rack (see Figure 12.2). If natural or extractor fan cooling still does not provide the necessary airflow, then replacing the ambient air with cooled or refrigerated air is possible (see Figure 12.3). This method normally requires a specialist (air-conditioning technical officer) to perform the airflow calculations and to install the system.

The method chosen is determined by the amount of heat that must be removed. Remember that this heat, caused by the power consumption of the instruments, will raise the temperature inside the rack to some temperature above ambient temperature. This amount of increase or delta temperature is what will need to be removed. Generally, the rack manufacturer will provide details or graphs outlining how much cooling is required to remove the heat (delta temperature) generated. These graphs can then be used to determine if natural, extracted, or air-conditioned cooling is required.

Vent

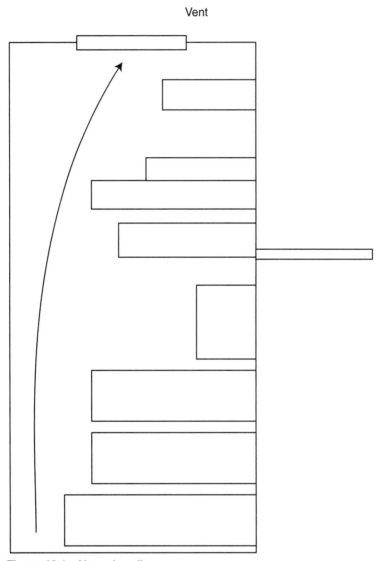

Figure 12.1   Natural cooling.

There are additional factors that will help the system designer in achieving the correct heat budget, such as the placement of equipment. Check whether each piece of test equipment has cooling holes in the chassis on the top or bottom cover. If it has, then this equipment should not be placed directly on or below another piece of equipment, since the air will not be able to efficiently escape for the instrument to remain sufficiently cool to stay within its environmental specifications (see Figure 12.4). Also, this will reduce hot air being directly blown through equipment on top of the instrument.

Fan

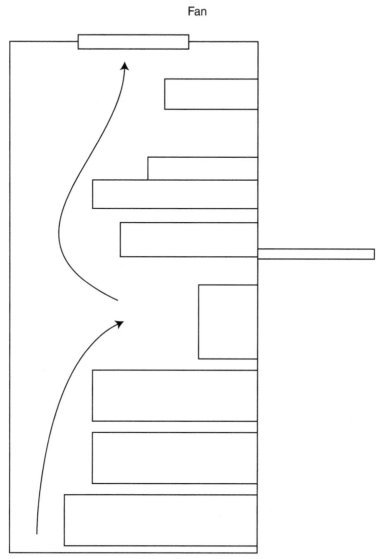

Figure 12.2 Fan cooling to extract air.

Ensure that any side holes in the equipment are not restricted by any objects of significant size that could restrict airflow. Also ensure that the fans are installed correctly and are sucking or blowing in the correct direction. It is also extremely important to check that there is an adequate flow of air around each instrument, not just in one section of the rack. A few cheap thermometers placed around the rack will provide this information and allow you to monitor the effects of the rack setup on environmental conditions within the rack. If your rack setup causes hot spots at different points within the rack, then you may have to re-arrange some of the equipment.

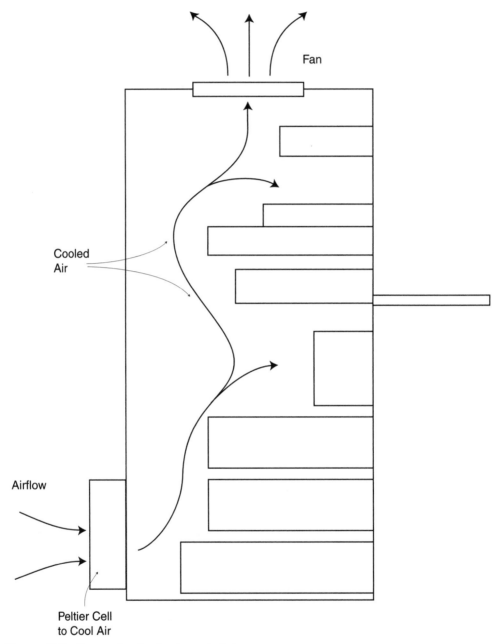

Figure 12.3   Fan cooling to pipe in cooled air.

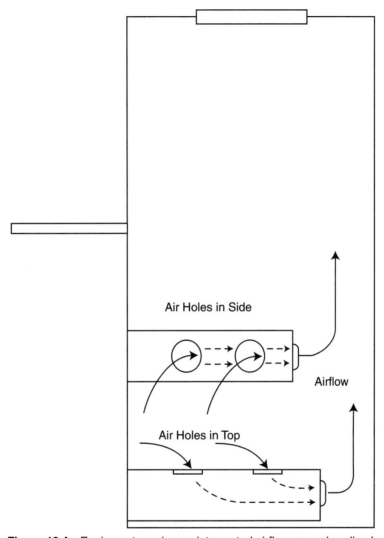

Figure 12.4 Equipment requires uninterrupted airflow around cooling holes.

To provide the best airflow possible, place the deepest instruments at the bottom of the rack and gradually fill the rack with shallower instruments. Finally, place instruments with large power output at the top of the rack and equipment with lower power ratings at the bottom of the rack. Remember, however, not to violate any other rack layout rules or guidelines when considering the above.

12.4.1 Calculating Cooling Requirements for Each Device

Calculating the cooling requirements for each device in the test system will allow you to work out how much additional cooling you need to provide to the system to stay within the test system's heat budget.

When working out the heat budget for the system itself, you may find that the numbers will not just add up simply because buildup of heat in a rack can occur over your expectations due to the way in which equipment is positioned.

As a first-pass estimate of the system heat budget, the individual equipment power requirements can be added together to provide your initial guess. This will be the amount of heat that must be removed from the system. Most instruments will provide enough cooling for themselves to prevent overheating if run on a bench; however, it is the aggregate of the total heat generated by the system in a confined space that is the problem (see Figure 12.5). However, if enough airflow is generated by forced blowing or drawing out of air, then the heated air can be removed.

Some form factors will create particular heat generation patterns. For example, remember that large VXI systems can produce a large amount of heat that will be blown out the back of the rack, which may affect instruments above them, but not instruments lower in the rack.

The easiest way to gain some expectations of how your rack will behave is to examine rack literature for heat curves. If this is not possible, then calculations using the volume of air in the rack being removed by a fan will be required. Always err on the side of providing more fans, since any heat stress will degrade the life of your equipment. If the equipment has heat sinks on it then ensures that the flow of air is not restricted around the sinks, and that the air around them can be quickly removed.

Even once you have a very good idea of how the rack will behave with respect to generation and removal of heat, it is important to monitor the actual behavior of the rack once you start it up for the first time. Positioning a few temperature sensors at various points inside the rack will give you the assurance that your test system will not experience heat buildup at any points.

To calculate the heat budget, start with the specified parameters from each vendor and draw up a table with the V times A (voltage times current needs of each piece of equipment). This will allow you to see which items need a lot of current per voltage rail. Once you have done this, you will see which items will need to dissipate the greatest amount of heat into the rack cooling space.

Compare your final calculations of necessary heat dissipation with the cooling diagram you have derived from your fans versus the environmental cooling specification. If your environment is to be stable at say 25 degrees Celsius, then you need to work out how far above that you will be when all items in your rack are at maximum rate. If it exceeds this rate, then you may want to reduce the temperature in your environment and at the same time increase the flow of air from your fans. The fans, in most cases, just extract from the system. You may want to consider an inlet fan as well, possibly in the bottom of the rack.

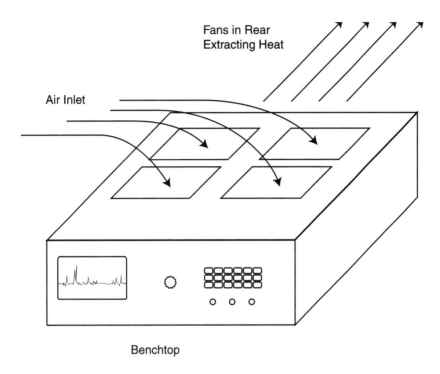

Benchtop

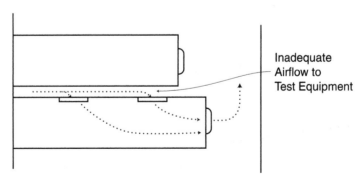

Figure 12.5 Test equipment that is adequately cooled on a bench may cause heat buildup when operating in a rack.

12.4.2 Checking If Your Rack Can Deliver Required Airflow

Calculating the overall volume of air movement required for cooling will allow you to check whether your rack can deliver this airflow. As mentioned above, you should be trying to use rack cooling graphs wherever possible, as this is the easiest way to calculate the airflow required. If you find that you will have insufficient airflow, you can install fans to add airflow to the system. If the subsequent airflow is still not enough, then forced cold airflow via an air conditioner will be required. These calculations are best performed by an air-conditioning technical officer from a company authorized to calculate and deliver such a system.

Above all, check for hot spots within the rack to ensure that airflow is reaching all areas of the system. Many engineers prefer fans on top of the rack since dirt and grit are less likely to be drawn into the rack.

It is a worthwhile exercise to test the system when the ambient air temperature rises, such as when the air conditioning fails. Some systems will shut down very quickly once the outside temperature rises; this can be a product of the internal heat sensors in various items of test equipment. If it is critical that your system remains on, then this point will need to be considered thoroughly. Additional headroom in the cooling design will need to be factored into the design.

Should it be necessary, consider intake fans at the bottom of the rack to draw in air from the surrounding environment.

12.5 Placement of Equipment to Aid Cooling

Equipment placement is important for the heat budget as well as the operation of the system.

Try not to cover the air holes of the equipment with other instruments that may impede airflow. This can mean leaving a space between instruments if the air holes are on the top or bottom of equipment. Sometimesit makes sense to leave a rack unit between equipment to help airflow (see Figure 12.6).

Fans should be placed on top of the rack when extracting or inserting air; however, air conditioning can be placed on top or through the floor. Care should be taken that the fans will not easily introduce dirt into the system, which can degrade equipment operation or even cause damage to equipment and system accessories.

If possible, high-heat-generating boxes should be placed where they influence the other equipment the least (see Figure 12.7). This, however, is not usually achievable in practice.

Always over-estimate the heat budget, or work with the worst case. Use small thermostats to check the heat in different locations of the rack to assure yourself that there will be no ongoing heat problems with operating the test system.

12.5.1 Examples of Poor Equipment Placement

Even if your heat budget numbers are correct, equipment placement can still overheat your test system or create hot spots. Devices use side, top, or bottom vents; you should take care that the airflow from one piece of test equipment is not blocked by another piece of equipment (see Figure 12.8). The authors have seen examples of racks that have had their rear panels removed because the equipment could not be cooled to the extent required for correct operation of the system.

Equipment blocking airflow in the rack can cause heat to build up in the rack as it cannot be dissipated.

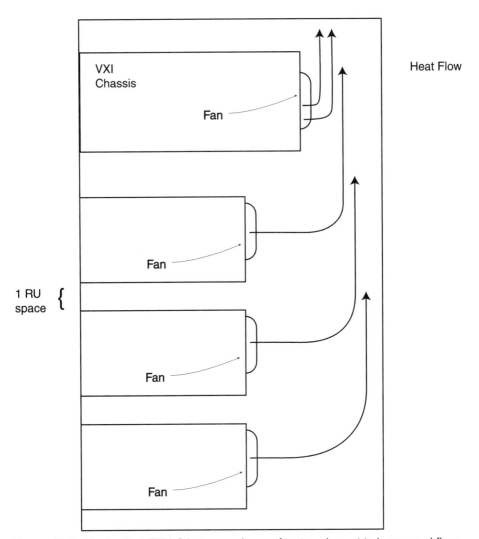

Figure 12.6   Rack with 1 RU left between pieces of test equipment to increase airflow.

Some pieces of test equipment generate high levels of heat as they operate. If high-heat generators are grouped together in the rack, they can quickly cause a localized buildup of heat.

Equipment should not be placed such that the exhaust of one item is drawn in by another item. This is common in systems that are "thrown together." A little thought should go into the equipment placement; for example, a table could be drawn up to show where exhaust and air intake takes place. Many items draw in air through the side of the equipment; also, many items draw in air through the rear and the only escape for the air is through the front panel, causing a continuous airflow into the face of the operator. If this was on a bench it would not be a problem, but in a rack, it becomes a serious issue.

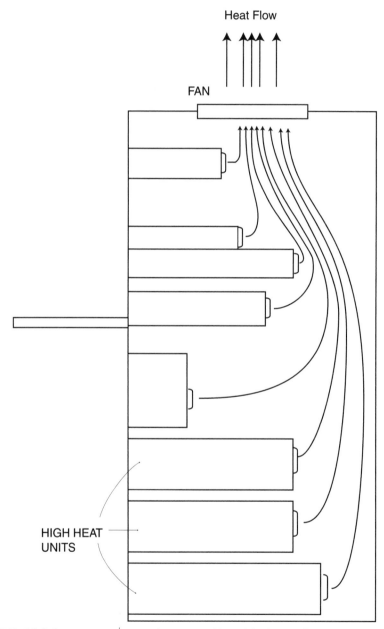

Figure 12.7 High-heat-generating equipment positioned for least effect on other equipment.

12.5.2 Avoiding Hot Spots

Some devices draw in cool air; others blow out warm air off circuit boards. It is important at all times to avoid one device drawing in exhaust air from another device. This air will already have

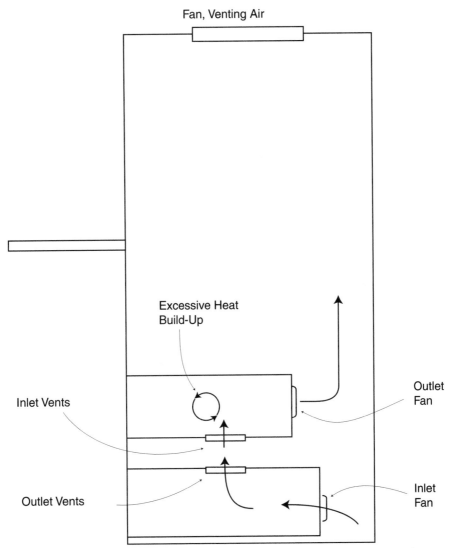

Figure 12.8   Equipment blocking airflow from another piece of equipment in the rack.

been warmed by the first piece of test equipment, and will thus prevent the second piece of
equipment from gaining any cooling benefit. Another point to remember is that an extractor fan
system will be coolest at the top and bottom of the rack, and warmest in the middle. The system
designer should try to work the system layout with this rule in mind. Additionally, some equipment will provide a concentrated heat exhaust, rather than a broad, warm heat exhaust, simply
because of its internal layout. Equipment that does this should be identified on the bench and
positioned in the rack where it will have the least impact on other equipment. Remember to

TopView   Side View

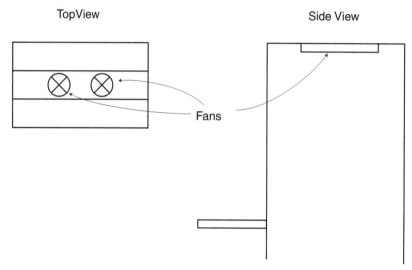

Fans

Figure 12.9   Fan extractors in the rack.

ensure that the cable looms do not restrict airflow through any vents or this will impact the cooling efficiency as well.

Some causes of hot spots are merely that the equipment will run hot regardless of where it is in the rack; these items run at the edge of what is allowable legally for power consumption. Generally, certain items run "hot." Analog-to-digital converters and power amplifiers, for example, run "hot"; it is inherent in their design that they are inefficient in converting power into usable output.

12.5.3 Using Fan Extractors in the Rack

When using extractor fans in a rack, the designer must ensure that headroom for the fan extractors at the top of the rack is included in the design (see Figure 12.9). Fan units are available in two-, four-, and six-fan arrangements. Some factors to consider when selecting fans include the power, size, weight, and noise specifications of the fans. The important specification will, however, be the airflow rating of the unit.The higher the airflow rating, the larger the potential to cool the system. Also remember that the fan unit requires power, hence one GPO will be removed from the system to power the fan. Be careful not to have the fans directly beneath an air-conditioning outlet. When you have warm air directly flowing into cold air, you could create precipitation, or at least have a high degree of moisture forming, if the air from the air conditioner is not cleaned of water beforehand.

12.6 Cooling with Water or Other Liquids

Under some circumstances, you may not have access to cool air to provide cooling for the test system. For example, your test system may be deployed on a ship or submarine in a very

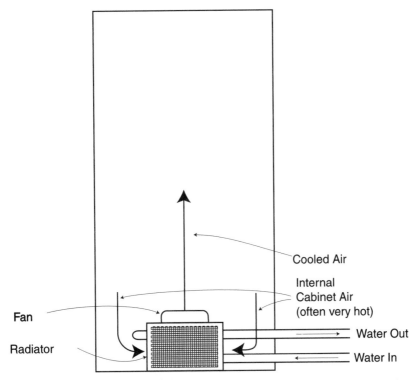

Fan

Radiator

Cooled Air

Internal
Cabinet Air
(often very hot)

Water Out

Water In

Figure 12.10   A water-cooled test system.

restricted space. If air cooling is not a practical option, then you will need to find an alternative – water cooling is one example (see Figure 12.10).

When you are setting up equipment in an environment that cannot possibly cool the air and the ambient air in the chamber is quite hot to begin with, then water cooling or some sort of liquid cooling may be the best option. Some very fast computers, Crays for instance, run extremely hot and there is no way that an ordinary cooling system will suffice.

When you do run water into a system for cooling, then the way to accomplish the actual cooling is by a heat exchange system. Heat exchangers work by transferring the heat to the cooling system for extraction. There are many variants of this – but generally, they are used when there is no alternative. Rather than cooling the air, they work by absorbing heat from the air; the difference is best understood by looking at the way a conventional home refrigerator works – it does not radiate cold, rather, it absorbs heat.

When you do decide to run a system this way, be sure that you have adequate safety meaures available to deal with any emergency, such as a coolant leak. Some coolants are dangerous, such as nitrogen cooling. Nitrogen gas cooling, or a liquid when it is under pressure, is very efficient, but difficult to maintain; there are few people who are qualified to deal with it or with the leaks, so you will have a considerable overhead expense when you have a problem.

Water cooling has its own problems with corrosion. Water moving through the system in the presence of various voltages will have a degrading effect on other metals, even though all the plumbing should be at earth potential. Earth in a ship, for instance, is through the hull, then into salt water, then to earth. The earth is not the same as driving a copper stake into 6' or 2m of ground to get a good connection. Thus, you will have dissimilar metal corrosion and need sacrificial anodes to protect, for a start, the pipes.

Racking Up

Once you have a working technical design for the test system, racking it up will increase the ease of use and improve the appearance of the system. Racking allows you to control the electrical, temperature, and EMI environments of the system and create a consistent test environment and thus increase the reliability and repeatability of the system.

Racking requires significant planning to avoid rework. The old carpentry adage of "measure twice, cut once" applies equally here.

Racking the System

This chapter describes the physical process of racking up the test system, including positioning all the components for ease of use for your operator and tips on putting everything together. This chapter also includes tips on racking an existing test solution that is currently spread across a benchtop.

KEY POINTS:

- Positioning user interface components is important for ease of use of the system, and will also depend on the degree of automation in the system.
- Position patch panels to allow maximum connectivity in the test system, and then position equipment in your racking plan. Also plan to include safety features and cabling for ease of use at this stage in your layout.
- Always test weight distribution before starting to rack up the system, and update any changes in equipment or cabling layout in your system documentation.
- Transportable test systems will require some additional features.

13.1 Positioning User Interface Components

Positioning the work surface, computer display, keyboard, and mouse in front of the operator is a matter of providing ergonomically suitable access to the components and connectors that the operator will use. First of all, the system designer will need to decide where the operator position is. This will partly depend on the degree of automation in the system.

If the test system is a fully-manual one, then the operator is normally standing for most of the time. This allows easier and more convenient access to all the equipment that the operator

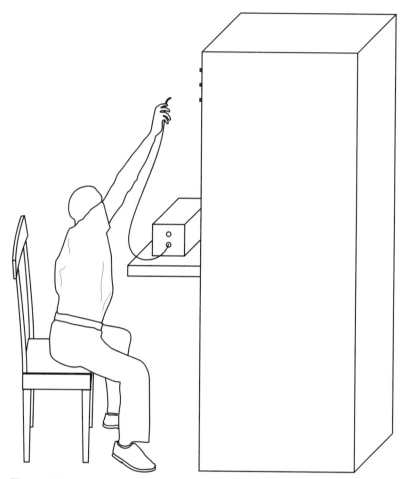

Figure 13.1   An operator seated at a manual system may have to strain awkwardly to reach connectors – poor ergonomic practice.

needs to connect cabling to. If the operator sits in a low position, then they may have to lean over or lean sideways to connect cabling and could easily overbalance or misconnect cabling. These actions also place a physical strain on the operator (see Figure 13.1).

It is also not good for the operator to be getting in and out of a low sitting position. Apart from the potential of physical strain, sooner or later they will try to connect from the sitting position and risk damage to connectors or personal injury. The goal of positioning user interface components is to make access easy rather than difficult.

There may be a high stool available so that the operator can rest while tests are run; one on castors makes it easier for it to be wheeled out of the way when it is not needed.

The work surface is normally placed at waist height, so that the operator can access the DUT without leaning over or reaching up. The work surface should extend out far enough so

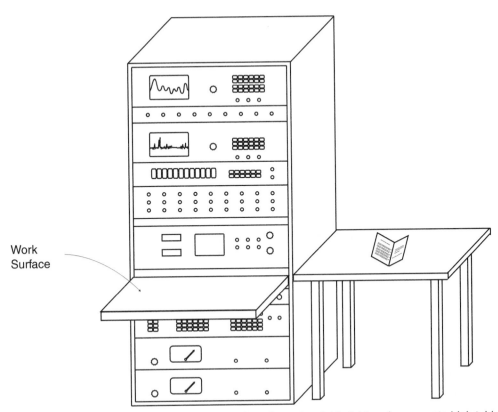

Work
Surface

Figure 13.2 A manual test system with a work surface at waist height and a separate high table or trolley for recording results.

that when sitting near the DUT to probe the device, the operator is far enough away from the test system that they cannot accidentally kick off switches or catch cables with their feet.

Ensure a reasonable position for manual procedures and result log sheets – it may be easier to have a separate table or a trolley on wheels, high enough to be easily accessible, but not in the way of cable connection points (see Figure 13.2). With a manual system, the operator will be almost constantly busy. The test equipment does not take long to make measurements, so most of the time is spent changing connections, setting up equipment, and recording results.

A semi-automated system with patch panels can be arranged so the operator is sitting in a high or low position (the low sitting position is not very common). This allows easy access to the connection points. Once again, any connection points required for the manual test portions of test procedures should be positioned to be easily accessible to the operator for recording results and reading test setups and connections.

If the system uses a computer for operator guidance through a step-by-step presentation of SOPs and recording of results, then that display should be placed so that it can be easily seen by the operator. The interface devices such as the keyboard, mouse, or light pen should be accessi-

Top View

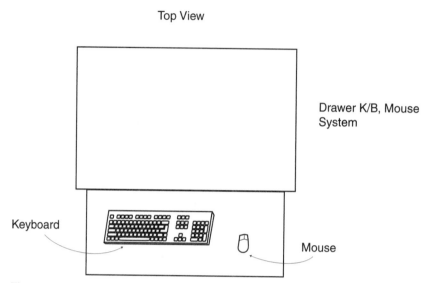

Drawer K/B, Mouse
System

Keyboard

Mouse

Figure 13.3 Display, keyboard, and mouse on a swing-out shelf.

ble, but not on the same surface as the DUT – you do not want to clutter the work area. Many devices are available for keyboards such as floating-arm-type devices, with the monitor attached. A floating-arm device is a series of hinged struts that allow the monitor and/or keyboard to be moved to whatever position is convenient (see Figure 13.3).

Many systems have the computer on a desk beside the system rack where the operator sits while the tests run and from which he or she is prompted to change connections and setups (particularly with manual test equipment where there is no computer bus) under direction of procedures on the computer display.

A fully-automated test system will have the connect device for the fixture at a reasonable level, generally around chest height or slightly lower. It should be positioned so that it is easy to lift the DUT up to the connect device. The connect fixture may be horizontal and on the work surface, so that the DUT is placed into it (see Figure 13.4). Even if you use the vertical-type fixture connection, you should also have a work surface to rest the DUT on before or after connection to the fixture (see Figure 13.5). This is because the DUT may be heavy or awkward to handle.

Displays that need to be seen by the operator should be placed at eye level or above for operator comfort (see Figure 13.6). Note, however, that this placement is not best practice in an automated system. If the system is under automatic control, then it is best practice for the displays to be covered, as they can distract the operator from what he or she is doing. An inexperienced operator may even get the wrong idea about what is going on; for example, they may see that a test is finished according to the computer, even though the display is still showing the previous test results, and decide the system is in error – the reality may be that the device does not show the next result for some time, as the test equipment's resources are being

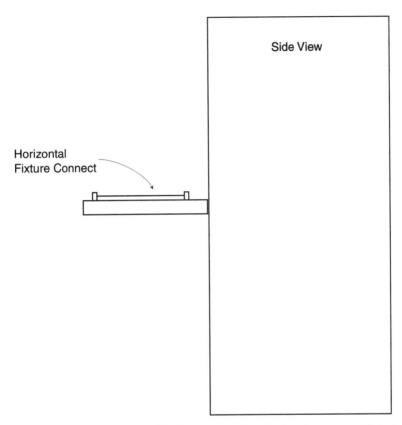

Figure 13.4 An automated test system with a horizontal connect fixture and on the work surface.

dedicated to set up, measure, and then return results to the computer before releasing the equipment to do something else. Then the test equipment may update the display, as it is now free, and display the previous results of a test – because that is what is in its display buffer. Modern test equipment is very sophisticated and can do many more measurements than it can display. Another example is that the equipment is making a frequency response measurement across 1600 points, but only displays 400; that's because if it did display 1600 points, it would take longer and may not reveal any more detail to the human eye. Again, the inexperienced operator may think there is a problem.

The primary reason, though, is to stop anyone from actually interfering with the equipment – for example, they may inadvertently push the "local" key and disconnect the equipment from computer control.

Fully-automated test systems will not need to have test results or setups monitored by the operator (as everything is managed by the operating system), so the visibility of displays does not need to be a factor in deciding where to place the equipment. Some equipment designed for

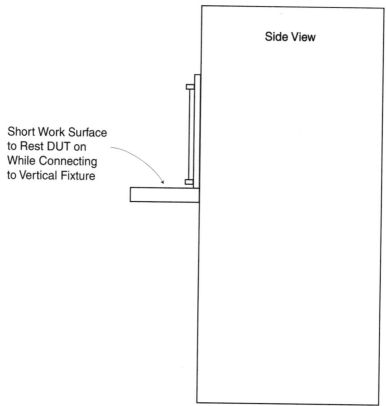

Side View

Short Work Surface
to Rest DUT on
While Connecting
to Vertical Fixture

Figure 13.5 An automated test system with a vertical connect fixture, but also a work surface on which to rest the DUT.

a fully-automated test system, such as equipment in the VXI form factor, will not come with a built-in display, in any case.

13.2   Positioning Switch Panels and Patch Panels

The patch panel will normally be above the work surface but around 6" (15 cms) higher (see Figure 13.7) so that cables are connected above and over the DUT and not behind it where they could become tangled or disconnected. This also allows the operator to visualize the system, to ensure that everything is where it should be.

Switch panels and quick-connect-type fixturing should be above waist height and in a position that the operator can easily lift the DUT to the supporting hooks, before locking the device to fix the DUT in place.

The position of the panels needs to be placed such that there is no strain on the cabling or connectors. Keep the cable lengths as short as possible, but still long enough to be convenient. If the system is an odd number of racks, then generally the panel will always be in the middle, as

Front View

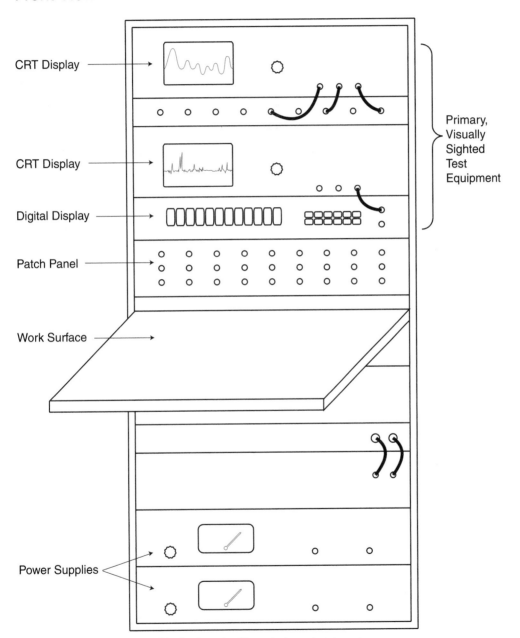

CRT Display

CRT Display

Digital Display

Patch Panel

Work Surface

Power Supplies

Primary, Visually Sighted Test Equipment

Figure 13.6   Test system with displays positioned at eye level or above.

Side View

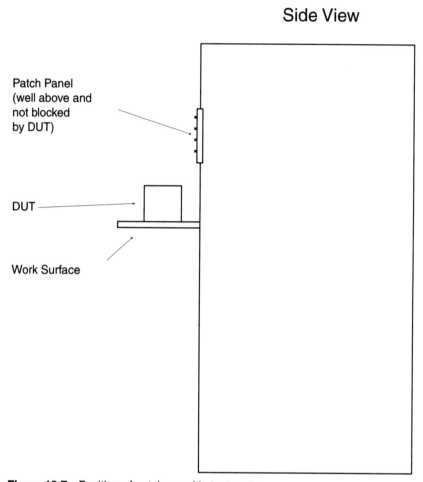

Patch Panel
(well above and
not blocked
by DUT)

DUT

Work Surface

Figure 13.7   Position of patch panel in test system.

this allows the easiest cabling solution. If the racks are an even number, then the general rule of thumb is to keep the panels to the right, and the computer or procedures book to the left. This is arbitrary, though; it also depends on what is available in the way of space and access. Figure 13.8 shows a rack layout which includes a switch and quick-connect-type fixturing.

13.3   Positioning Test Equipment in the Rack

To size up a rack for test equipment, you can use the heights of each of the items in the system to count out how many rack units of height each item needs. Another way to do this is to use a cardboard cutout of the height of the item, then tape those to the side of the rack – this will ensure that you do not miscount and will also force you to consider where to put the cable routing panels. Cable routing panels are required to feed cables back into the rack from all the equip-

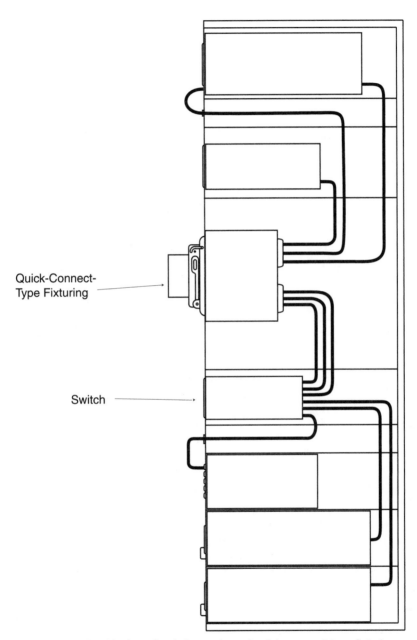

Figure 13.8   Positioning of switch panels and quick-connect-type fixturing.

ment with connections that are on the front panel of the equipment (see Figure 13.9). Unless you have had to re-use whatever existing equipment was available for the system, this should only happen with equipment where an option for rear connectors is not available. Generally, for a test system, it is easier to order test equipment with rear rather than front panel connectors.

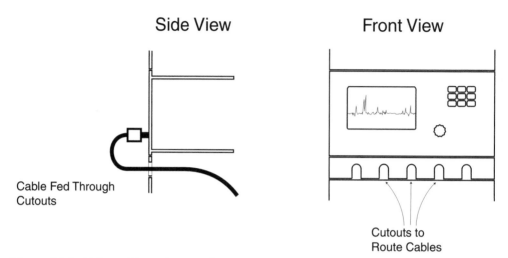

Figure 13.9   Using cable routing panels.

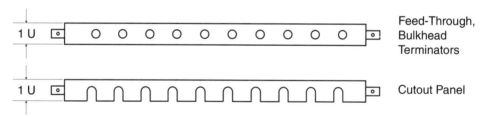

Figure 13.10   1U panels – cutout and bulkhead terminators.

Leave spaces between devices for cable routing if required, either at this stage or to allow potential for future upgrades in the life of the test system. Use 1U (one rack unit) panels with cutouts for the cables that you want to route to the switch or patch panel without joining cables (see Figure 13.10). If you are using joins, then use a 1U panel with bulkhead connectors on each side, which is additional work, but sometimes necessary. Some companies will supply the panels; however, a machine shop will punch the required holes for you in any position you want. The bulkhead connectors can then be secured and the cables connected. The length of cable from the test equipment to the connector should be as short as possible, so that it does not catch on anything or get in the way of access to equipment.

Route all cabling to the switch matrix and then to the patch/interconnect panel. Test equipment that needs short cabling, such as microwave devices, should be placed as close to the work surface, patch panel, or switch interface as possible. Heavy devices go low in the rack, the heaviest in the bottom, where they act as ballast and at the least do not counter any ballast in the rack.

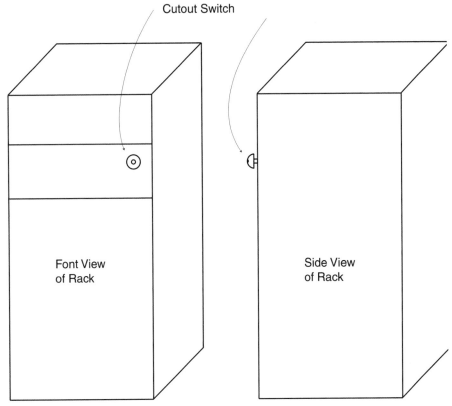

Cutout Switch

Font View
of Rack

Side View
of Rack

Figure 13.11   Positioning of safety switch.

13.4   Safety Features

The primary safety device in any test system is the power cutout switch. The power cutout device should be in the rack with the cutout pad within easy reach of the operator. It should be in a position that is not blocked by the DUT or the cabling.

Generally, the switch is placed directly above the work surface, clear of cabling if a manual system, above the patch panel or the fixture interface. A common practice is to put it toward the right-hand side of the rack, not in the middle, as this allows other people easy access to it as well (see Figure 13.11). However, the switch can be positioned in any suitable location. As part of the system training and general OH&S, all staff who work in that area should be made aware of where the safety mechanisms are.

Chapter 9, "Electrical Safety of the System," discusses safety features in more detail. It covers key safety considerations, cutout switches, using different supply voltages in the same rack, isolating high voltages and currents from the operator, cutoffs during operator intervention, barring power, earthing considerations, and safety training for personnel.

The material in this book is no substitute for a high level of safety training within your organization and the development of a strong safety culture. Take advice from safety experts wherever relevant and refer to the relevant national and international safety standards for your application.

13.5   Cabling for Ease of Use

There are a number of cabling practices that can increase the accuracy of your system, decrease the chance of component wear, and make maintenance and system upgrades easier.

13.5.1   Using the Correct Cables

The most important point is to make sure that you use the correct cables for each component of the test system. Use your wiring diagram to ensure that your cables adequately cover the frequency ranges of the signals that they will carry. Buying the best cables you can afford is an investment in the quality of your test results, as varying cable standards can also have an effect on the quality of the signals carried.

13.5.2   Using the Correct Connectors

Always have your cables made up with the correct connectors at each end so that adapters (which degrade signals and are a possible source of connector wear) do not need to be used. If you need to have different connectors at each end of the cables, have them made to your specifications. It may seem easier to buy off-the-shelf cables and use adapters – however, this is not good practice, as the convenience soon gives way to problems with loss. Most general-purpose adapters have much higher losses than precision connectors and, as such, when used on precision connectors, transfer their poorer performance to the connection. The poorer performance then becomes the specification for that connection. Another consideration is that since the mechanical workmanship of general-purpose adapters is not as precise as in precision connectors, the adapter can cause damage to the precision connector when mated to it.

> **TIP:**
>
> Precision adaptors are available from manufacturers and should be used when instruments with precision connectors need to be connected to devices that have low-cost connectors on them (such as SMA connectors). The adapter then bears the brunt of the damage, rather than the precision connector on the instrument itself, thus protecting your instrument.

13.5.3   Avoiding Damage to Cables

Building strain relief into your test system cabling can help protect both the cables themselves and also the connectors on the test equipment in the rack. Make sure that cables are supported at

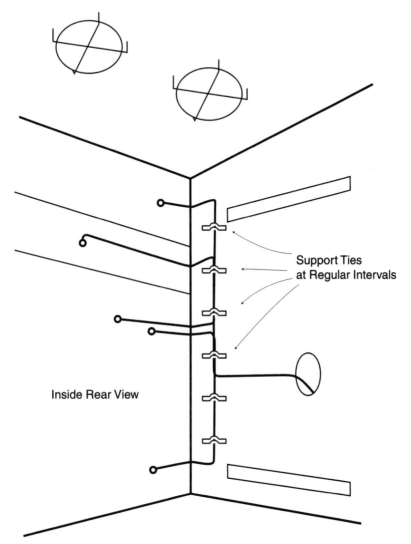

Figure 13.12 Cables supported at regular intervals and not fastened too tightly (to avoid damage).

regular points within the rack cabinet so that the weight of the cables is not borne by the connector into the test equipment (see Figure 13.12).

Some cables can also be damaged by incorrect handling, and should be carefully fastened within the rack. For example, coaxial cable can become crimped and damaged if fastened too tightly. If the dielectric is crushed, signal degradation will occur, decreasing the accuracy of the test system. Cables should be fastened securely, but not overly tightly.

Some equipment in the rack may be mounted on rack slide kits so that it can be slid out of the rack and even rotated while still remaining connected to the test system. This will require additional cable lengths to allow for the equipment to be slid out on its rails. Using a loop of signal and power cables on a spring arm or a swinging hinge will allow the equipment to be safely extended and rotated.

13.5.4 Labeling the Cables

When selecting cables, make sure that your labeling has both ends of the cable identified to avoid confusion once you start racking up the system. This will also make maintenance and system upgrades much easier, as engineering staff will be able to quickly identify relevant cables without having to trace them through the whole system. The labeling system can be as simple as a tag with a reference to a look-up table, or full signal type, connection, and purpose.

Chapter 7, "Cabling the Rack," covers many aspects of the use of cables in the test system.

13.6   Testing Weight Distribution

You should take some time to check the proposed layout of your test system on paper rather than simply starting to rack the system with a plan to move things around if the rack falls over. Some fine tuning may need to take place at the end of the racking process; however, you will be able to get the layout either completely or mostly correct during the layout planning phase.

Once you have decided where user interface components, switch panels, and other key items will go, you can start to place other equipment in your rack layout plan. A drawing of the rack from a side view showing the depth of all the equipment in the rack is invaluable when analyzing weight distribution. You will know the weight of all the equipment and the depth from the datasheet specifications. The drawing will show how much of the equipment is in front or behind the center of the rack, if you draw a line right down the middle (see Figure 13.13). If all your equipment is in front of this line, you will know immediately that you have all your equipment weight too far forward and the rack will be badly balanced.

Once your test system rack appears to be roughly well-balanced, just on a visual basis, write in the weight of each unit in the rack on your proposed rack diagram. Bearing in mind any system-specific restrictions you have with the system, you should have lighter items at the top of the rack and the heaviest in the bottom to increase the stability of the rack.

Once you have positioned heavier equipment low in the rack wherever possible, you may also decide to position some components at the back of the rack rather than the front of the rack to help balance the center of gravity in the rack.

The test system must also remain stable once the DUT is placed on the work surface. The effect of the increased impact shock of the DUT being dropped onto the work surface should also be considered in your layout plan.

If the system looks relatively well-balanced on paper but you are still have some degree of doubt as to whether it may be on the borderline of instability, you can go a step further and calculate the moment arms for each component in the system to get a very good idea of the rack's

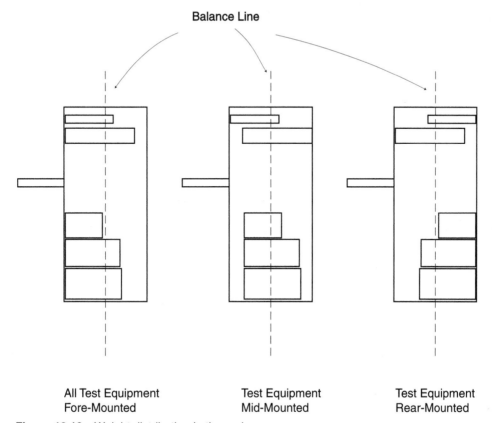

Balance Line

All Test Equipment
Fore-Mounted

Test Equipment
Mid-Mounted

Test Equipment
Rear-Mounted

Figure 13.13 Weight distribution in the rack.

stability. It is, however, inadvisable to use a racking design that does not include a significant margin of stability. You must allow for the possibility that a piece of equipment may be removed from the rack during system maintenance or a system upgrade, and if the rack is too finely balanced, it could topple when this is done. A finely-balanced test system rack also has the risk of toppling if a much heavier than normal DUT is placed on the system's work surface.

If the system itself or the system with the heaviest planned DUT is at the risk of being unstable, then the use of ballast in the bottom of the rack can increase the stability of the system and increase your margin of safety (see Figure 13.14).

Once you start racking up the system, work from the bottom of the rack cabinet upward and monitor the system for any signs of instability. Using anti-tilt feet for the rack during the racking up process can help keep the system stay stable even when partially racked.

Chapter 11, "Weight Considerations and Equipment Placement," contains more information on this topic.

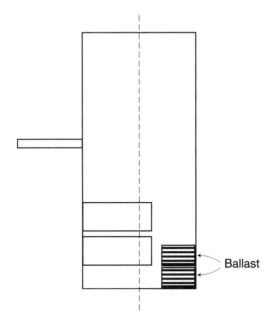

Figure 13.14   Positioning of ballast in the rack.

13.7   Mounting Heavy Equipment Safely

When handling heavy equipment, always have two people present to lift and position the equipment. When you are inserting equipment onto the rails, it can be quite awkward to manage, and there can be risk of damage to the equipment, the rack, cabling, or personal injury if the equipment is dropped. There is often very little room for error if other equipment is already in the rack and the equipment must be inserted directly and not at any time be at an angle to the straight path of insertion.

Heavy equipment that for particular reasons should be placed high in the rack should be handled with particular care. Overhead work or above-waist work is very demanding with heavy loads. One useful tip is to use an electric screwdriver to assist with the securing of the instrument or load. Another is to secure a single blank panel in the rack below where the load is to be placed and then use this as a support while securing the load. A third person in the back of the rack may help to hold the load while positioning it in the rack.

Finally, a shelf for the instrument to rest on may be the most appropriate way to position the instrument before securing. Try to avoid resting the instrument on other equipment as this may damage the equipment or the rack mounts, causing the other instrument to fall.

13.8   Connector Care

There are a number of handling practices that can increase the useful lifespan of connectors, or at least prevent them from being damaged or worn down prematurely. Some of the more common points are covered below; however, most equipment manufacturers will be able to supply detailed recommendations on connector care and use.

When handling connectors, particularly microwave connectors, take care that they do not become dirty or dusty. This can have serious consequences as the properties of the connector may change in an unpredictable way. A bag of rubber connector covers is a good investment to keep connectors safe.

Operators should not touch the actual mating surfaces of the connectors, as this transfers natural skin oils that can hold dirt. The operator should wear a grounded wrist strap to prevent ESD. This discharge can damage equipment that the connector is connected to. For example, any ESD on the center pin of an N Type connector on a low-noise amplifier can cause major damage to the internals of the amplifier. All connectors should be visually inspected for damage before use.

If your operator is not aware of the ways to protect connectors or the reasons why this is important, then a short course on connector care combined with some information on the cost of these items may be helpful. Often operators are not aware of the cost and may be more careful when they know what the cost penalty is to the organization.

13.9 Adapters

Adapters should not be used at all if possible, unless they are precision adapters used to protect an instrument's input connector from damage (such as in the case of a network analyzer). They create problems for the user in the form of signal loss, mismatch of impedance, and possible damage if used incorrectly. For example, mating an SMA(m) connector with an APC 3.5mm (f) connector creates permanent damage to the APC 3.5mm (f) connector.

The design phase of the test system development project should allow you to order all your cables at the correct lengths and with the correct connector types.

Avoid joining shorter lengths of cable with adapters to create a longer cable. The same problems of signal loss occur through the use of unnecessary connectors. The test system will have better signal quality if you have your cables made up to the correct length.

An adapter's electrical performance will be transferred to your system when used in connections. Since general-purpose adapters have poorer performance than precision connectors, the overall system will be degraded. Also, the accuracy that you can claim on your measurement is degraded. It makes no sense to purchase high-quality, precision cable connectors and then connect a cheap adapter to them. Remember that both the measured result and the accuracy you can claim for the test will be reduced when adapters are used.

Avoid adapting to a different connector so that you can use a cable, then adapting back to the original connector type. Get the right cable in the first place.

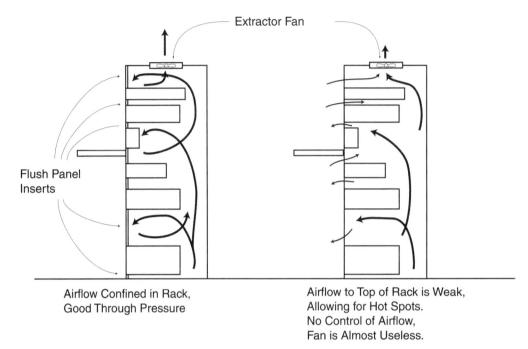

Figure 13.15   The effect of panels on rack airflow.

13.10   Cover Panels

Cover panels should be used to cover any holes in the rack to ensure correct airflow and temperature control. Holes in the rack will make your fans useless when they rely on a constant pressure within the rack to perform their task (see Figure 13.15).

Cover panels also have an aesthetic purpose in giving the test system rack a more professional appearance as they cover any gaps in the system.

Cover panels can also be used for mounting small devices. Generally they are attached to the back of the panel to protect them from straining cable or connector joins and any problems with vibration in the rack. Vibration comes from all the fans in the rack, as well as from air turbulence.

13.11   Putting Everything Together

Before you start the physical racking process, check the overall weight and weight distribution of the rack one last time. Also check that the correct weight of each piece of test equipment has been used in the design of the rack balance and layout.

Documentation of the physical design and cabling layout should also be checked for a final time against the rack, counting all the rack units off the diagram and comparing this to the rack itself. The cabling diagram should also be handy so you can check installation of the cabling as you go.

The racking up process starts from the bottom of the rack, and you may want to put all your cable looms in first if you are using looms to distribute and manage cables. If you are using them, lay all the cable trays in place, screw them down, and then install all the cabling. Keep checking your diagram to ensure the cables are ending where you need them to be when the test equipment is installed.

Place your captive-nuts in place in the holes in the front of the rack, at the sides where the rack ears will be screwed in place. If you have enough, put captive-nuts in all of the holes; this saves a lot of time later should you need to move anything around for whatever reason. If you need to move things much later, then you do not need to go searching for captive-nuts or trying to move them. Moving captive-nuts can be difficult – always use tools, never your fingernails.

Hang mounting rails and equipment from the bottom of the rack upward. This keeps the center of gravity of the rack as low as possible at all times, and helps maintain the stability of the rack as it is filled.

Size the equipment in as you go and leave space for termination or feed-through panels. Sizing the equipment means that if your equipment is 5U high, measure it out, put a pencil or grease mark, then measure the next one from there.

Keep in mind a safe working approach when mounting heavy equipment. Section 13.7 has some tips for keeping both staff and the rest of the equipment in the rack in one piece.

Double-check each piece of power and signal cabling as you connect it to the instrument. If you have laid out all the cabling in the rack first and checked it at that time, then connecting each piece of equipment should be relatively straightforward. Remember that you are installing into the rear of the rack and everything is reversed at the front of the rack – do not get mixed up!

Connect any accessories such as extractor fans and install accessories drawers.

Finish by placing any panels in position to cover gaps in the rack and maintain airflow integrity throughout the rack.

Power up the rack, then start up each item of test equipment one at a time, starting from the bottom (left, if more than one rack). Check temperature buildup over time.

Do some verification tests after about half an hour – take a signal from one device and connect it to a measuring device, or you may want to do this through the patch panel. Develop some tests to ensure integrity of all paths and to ensure none are in the wrong position. Always beware of connecting an output to an output.

13.12 Documentation of Physical Design and Cabling

Documentation of the physical rack design and cabling layout is just as important as documenting the development of the test system itself. The documentation of your design process and how the system will achieve each of its test objectives will allow another person to understand and duplicate this process if necessary, and to design a system upgrade without having to reverse-engineer the system or start a new design from scratch. The documentation of the physical build of the test system and the cable layout will allow another person to safely and efficiently integrate a system upgrade into the existing system, or carry out maintenance on the system.

Without adequate physical layout documentation it will be difficult and may become potentially dangerous for people to work on the test system.

Your documentation for the build must be kept up-to-date during the system build. If you change any of the components, or change a cable position, then you need to record that change immediately. If engineering or technical staff working on the system find one undocumented change to the system, then the rest of the layout will also become suspect.

It is also part of the whole documentation process to ensure that any changes to cabling that need to be made will align with the cable labeling system.

Chapter 14, "Documentation," discusses many aspects of the documentation process in more detail. It discusses documentation standards, documentation and system lifetime costs, intellectual property, version tracking, and configuration control.

Good documentation is vital to effective system support. Without it, maintenance staff will spend a disproportionate amount of time trying to understand the system before they are able to safely begin work on it.

13.13   Tips for Racking an Existing Benchtop System

There may be an existing manual test system that has been built up over time and is currently laid out on a bench. In this case, you will have an existing range of equipment to rack up. Some of the equipment may have to be modified, and you will need a range of system accessories to rack up the system.

The first step is to draw up a table of the items or upgrades that are required to make the equipment compatible for racking, and also to identify what connectors must be accessed. If the equipment has only front panel connector access, then you will need to use feed-through or bulkhead connectors to route cabling into the switch.

Another consideration to include in the table is whether the equipment has the ability to be controlled by a computer, and if it does have this capability, what type of interface it uses, for example IEEE 488, RS-232, or Ethernet. Decide whether you will use computer control of all these instruments for full automation or only some of them for semi-automation. You may decide to replace some of the old equipment with more compatible instruments for a system with some automation. If you want to automate and a piece of equipment has no bus capability, then you will definitely need to replace it or retrofit bus capability if this option is available.

Additional points to watch out for if you're racking up an existing benchtop system include contacting the manufacturers for all the equipment to see whether they have the rack ears and rack mount kits available for bolting the equipment into the racks. This will save you from having to have your own rack ears made up, and they will also have the correct screws to take the rack ears.

If you intend to still run the system manually but you are racking it to recover real estate (the space on your benchtop), then you only have to make sure you have all the necessary mounting equipment, and that you can route the cables in a reasonable manner. This is, however, an appropriate point at which to consider whether the system will be automated at some time in the future. If you want to plan for possible future automation, you can carry out some preparation now such as retrofitting bus capability into equipment, or leaving space in the rack to install patch panels in the future.

If the system will be upgraded to semi-automated control or full automation, then the bus issues become much more important. Section 3.5, "Making Future Control Upgrades Easier," discusses some of the factors that can make upgrading the automation of a test system worthwhile.

Cooling of the racked test system is still a vital consideration. Equipment that worked well in a benchtop environment can overheat and be damaged if it is poorly racked and heat buildup occurs within the rack cabinet. You still need to go through the exercise of positioning equipment so that it will be cooled properly during operation. Chapter 12, "Temperature Control and Power Considerations," covers how to calculate heat budgets and measures that can be taken to prevent heat buildup in the rack.

You will need to have cables made up of correct lengths and with the correct connector types if these do not already exist. The layout of cables in the rack is important for a professional finish and to avoid interference between cables. Chapter 7, "Cabling the Rack," covers cabling through the rack, designing to minimize cable stress, signal conditioning considerations, and documentation.

Table 13.1 summarizes the major considerations to take into account when racking a benchtop system.

Table 13.1   Summary of Considerations for Racking a Benchtop System

Are the correct rack ears available to rack mount the equipment?

Are the correct rack mount kits available to rack mount the equipment?

For systems that will be automated now or at some point in the future, are bus control retrofit kits available?

Will the rack's heat and power budgets be maintained?

Can the screen be seen easily?

Can the operator push all buttons required in the test procedures?

Can the operator connect cables without damaging the connectors or their knuckles?

13.14 Special Procedures for a Transportable System

Some systems must be designed to be readily transportable, as they will need to be set up quickly at different sites and under varying conditions. Different procedures apply under these circumstances as the transportation requirements can vary.

Constraints can include:

- The rack cabinet should be able to be moved by two people at the most. Make certain that it is labeled on all sides (six normally) in large letters that it is a two-person or greater lift. Put a "bend the knees" diagram on if you want to be really sure no one gets hurt.

• If the rack should be able to be lifted by a crane, requiring eyes and pulleys to be fitted, make sure the lifting eyes are sufficient for the rack when it is full of equipment and then allow a 50% overload to be sure. This will allow for those crane operators who, when lowering the system, bring it to a stop too quickly.

• The rack must be able to withstand high acceleration and stresses during transport. Some racks may require transportation by road or railroad – railroad is possibly the worst case for this. When trains are shunting carriages, they tend to hit the carriage fairly hard, and do not slow down due to the weight of the carriage; most train engines weigh over 30 tons and have a great deal of inertia when they get moving.

• Cooling and dust ingress may require that the rack be sealed anywhere air can get in, except where you want it to get in, via filtering.

• Balance is an absolute must for a transportable system. You may have to design your system with a lot of equipment in the back of the rack (rear) so it maintains balance. Some system designers ignore this for the sake of easy racking and when people have to lift it, the unexpected weight at the front catches them off-guard and they drop it.

• Modularity is essential if the system is to be transported by commercial airlines – some of which have load limits on individual components. (One of the authors has spent hours breaking equipment down to meet this requirement, on the floor of an airport terminal, to the point of actually splitting a microwave synthesizer in half diagonally.)

• Label everything very well, such as voltage, fan direction (blowing in or out), and which way is up – you never know what level of skill may be available where you are sending equipment. For fans, also label how much space is needed around them for them to work efficiently.

• The rack must have additional environmental protection to withstand being deployed outdoors. Fans may have to go in the sides rather than the top of the rack to be more efficient and to retain strength in the top of the rack.

When all test equipment and software is designed, the system must be broken up into easily manageable and transportable chunks. This will generally mean using smaller rack cabinets than would be normal for a fixed-position test system, as each rack cabinet should be within the weight limits for a two-person lift.

Select appropriate operating cases to contain all equipment and switches. If the system will be deployed outdoors, for example a portable antenna range, or will be regularly transported outdoors, such as a remote-controlled HF surveillance system, then sealed cabinets with additional environmental protection will be required.

Carefully lay out the test equipment so that operating cases are of roughly equal weight and the cases are balanced from front to back. Within each case, all the requirements of power and heat budgets and good labeling and documentation practices still apply. Do not stack more than three operating cases high if the cases are "square."

Allow drawers in the cases for cabling and accessories storage, as the system may need to be fully self-contained in a number of different locations. Use separate cases for the switch interfaces, as this allows easy troubleshooting in case there are any problems during setup or operation. It also allows the system to be split into functional components more easily.

Documentation

This chapter looks at the importance of documentation for your test system, including documentation standards, version tracking, and configuration control. Good documentation impacts system lifetime costs such as support and upgrade costs, and is particularly important if you want to duplicate an existing system (for example, if another company or department has purchased a copy of your system). As with all aspects of test system design and operation, it is important to make your documentation processes repeatable and controllable.

KEY POINTS:

- Documentation standards vary, and it is important to choose a standard that is appropriate for the test system application and environment.
- You may decide to outsource the generation of system documentation; however, this still requires planning early in the project and ongoing involvement.
- Good documentation will lower system lifetime costs by lowering system support costs.
- Good documentation is also a way to gain access to the designer's plans and thought processes, and allows you to transfer that knowledge within the organization or to your organization's clients. It also helps protect and maintain the IP generated in the system design.
- Processes for version tracking and configuration control can simplify the management of the system and system documentation.

14.1   Documentation Standards

Documentation is a way to capture the design, plans, and system knowledge of the test system designer(s). Without documentation, you are forced to rely on the presence of the designers to gain access to the knowledge they put into the system. If you need to upgrade the system or locate a fault and the original designer is unavailable, the costs and time involved will be immense.

Good documentation will make it easier for you to sell a test system to another organization, and maintains knowledge and understanding of the system even when the original designer has moved to another role.

Good documentation is also an important aspect of delivering a professionally presented product, and is the mark of a skilled engineer.

If you decide to contract out the provision of documentation, or you have bought a system or system components which come with documentation, check that it is comprehensive, useful (with examples and clear procedures), clearly written, and complete. The documentation should include components such as a common errors list, clear installation and setup instructions, as well as equipment use, maintenance, and perhaps a troubleshooting guide. If it refers to other manuals that you have to buy separately, this should be made clear.

A number of different documentation standards exist, with varying degrees or rigor involved. Choosing what standard of documentation to use will depend on a range of factors, including:

- Organizational requirements; for example, your organization may mandate mil-spec or military standards documentation.
- The use to which the system will be put; for example, a temporary test system configuration used in a development lab will not require the degree of documentation that is appropriate for a system with a planned lifetime of a number of years.
- The intended end-user; for example, a test system designed to be supplied to a number of repair centers should have more complete and more self-contained documentation than a system designed for in-house use only, where you can refer to other sources of documentation that will be available within that organization.

The costs of different documentation standards will vary greatly, as will the documentation itself. Commercial documentation standards can vary greatly from vendor to vendor, although documentation from one vendor should ideally follow a consistent standard and layout.

Military standard documentation is extremely thorough and rigorous, but it has a correspondingly high overhead and will require some stringent practices to keep it up-to-date and in an auditable condition. Military standards allow different military users not familiar with your system, but familiar with the documentation standards, to quickly understand what your system does and how it does it, including what were the original design goals and how they were implemented. Familiarity with the mil-spec documentation standard allows these users to find the information they need about a system and start using the system much more quickly than if they were finding the same information in an unfamiliar format. This is an excellent example of how documentation standards can increase the speed and ease with which information can be transmitted.

You should also consider whether to contract out the writing of system documentation. The benefits include that of having an experienced technical writer to spot gaps in the material you have provided. An additional benefit is that an engineer is not tied down writing documents, but is instead actually delivering system work. Technical writers are also good at removing technical jargon and making documentation more readable.

14.1.1 Outsourcing the Development of Your Test System Documentation

To free up the time of your own staff or to gain access to expertise not held within your organization, you may choose to contract out the development of your documentation to a third party. Points to consider if you plan to outsource development of documentation include:

- The technical writer will need access to the subject matter expert (SME), as well as access to reviewers from your organization and time set aside for review meetings.
- You will still need to allow time for documentation preparation in your project schedule, preferably starting early in the project lifecycle.
- You will need to specify the type of documentation you will require as costs for different formats such as text only, screen shots, or step-by-step procedures will vary.
- Step-by-step procedures in particular can take longer to document thoroughly and can thus be more expensive.
- The document writer may need a work area at your site to complete the document, or equipment to work off-site.
- The technical writer (or the whole documentation team, which may include a separate editor, project lead, and more than one technical writer) should be familiar with the style and communication standards used in your organization.

You will need to start with a fairly clear view of the form in which you want the documentation, including whether you require components such as a quick-start manual, or a separate repair and maintenance manual. You may also wish to set a page or word limit to make sure that the most important information is presented in an appropriately concise form.

Remember that some documentation may be required even before the system is built. Such documentation may include a full system specification and perhaps even a first draft of operational documentation if this is to be specified at the start of the project. From these documents, system design documentation can be constructed detailing how all the requirements will be met.

These points also apply to an in-house documentation service if your organization has one.

14.2   Documentation and System Lifetime Costs

The quality of your documentation can affect your overall system lifetime costs. Poor documentation may cost less up-front, but means more effort in maintaining, repairing, upgrading, and duplicating your system.

Documentation, if written properly from the start, can save a lot of time and money if you need to investigate a problem in the test system. If you have poor documentation that is difficult to understand or incomplete, then you may have trouble tracking down the source of a problem in the test system. In the end, you may have to try to reverse-engineer the test system to get to the heart of your problem or even (worst of all) have to start again.

If the documentation is so poor you cannot understand it, then it may as well not exist at all, and the best approach is often to plan now to re-engineer your whole system rather than try to work out what was done in building the original test system.

If you need at some stage to upgrade your test system, then good documentation is vital to completing the upgrade successfully. The new system hardware and software must be able to be successfully combined with existing system components, while improving rather than degrading the system's overall performance. If you cannot establish exactly how the old system was interfaced or controlled, then you may have to use hardware or software workarounds to get new and old system components to work together. These workarounds may actually degrade the performance of the system because they introduce delays or are not the most effective ways of implementing the changes.

You will also find that you will have more problems selling the test system to potential customers if the documentation is not of a high standard. Your customer will want to be able to operate and support the test system easily and effectively, which is impossible without proper documentation.

Documentation is the alternative way to gain access to the designer's plans and thought processes in designing the test system, and allows you to transfer this knowledge to a customer who purchases the test system, or to maintain that knowledge in-house should key design staff move on to other jobs.

A well-documented project will have as its first document a request for tender or similar starting point. From this, a system specification document will be produced. Following this, a group of individual documents will be produced describing all the sub-systems that are required to complete the system specification. These individual documents may describe the instrument that is required to complete the task or may include an individual software module description. The software description will include interfaces, GUIs, and performance.

In this way, a history of the project is generated, such that any person can follow the project life from conception to delivered system. This type of approach is normally mandatory in defense projects, but is valuable when adapted to commercial projects as well. The important point to remember is not to write documents just to create paperwork alone, but rather to write enough documentation to adequately describe your project lifecycle, and to protect your company and the sponsor or client of the project.

14.3   Documentation and Intellectual Property

The importance of keeping access to IP, such as the system you have designed, is tied to the fact that this knowledge has value. Either you or your organization should maintain control of this in the same way that you would protect a physical asset.

The IP related to your test system can be sold in the form of a copy of the system itself. Even though the system components have been manufactured by other suppliers, the way that the system is designed and the way that it solves a particular problem has value over that of the individual components. This is the value of the IP. Your system may be so valuable that other groups or companies would be willing to buy a copy or multiple copies.

If your documentation is poor, the specific knowledge about this system – which is where the additional value resides – is too easily lost. Staff changes or even being busy with other projects can lead to the loss of information from the organization or from individuals if the information is not documented as part of the system design process.

The protection of IP is one more reason for documenting the test system properly.

14.4   Version Tracking

Version tracking refers to the tracking of updates and the evolution of documentation. Changes to documentation may occur because of an upgrade, an improvement in test procedures, or updated safety standards. It is important to document temporary changes, even if these are documented more briefly than permanent changes, because someone new working on the system must be assured that the state of the test system is fully known and that they can check details and find everything covered. Encountering undocumented changes opens up the potential that the individual may be at risk of injury from a change that they do not know about. This may not be the case, but having one undocumented change certainly means that others may also exist.

The test system documentation will typically have a master copy and one or more subordinate copies – particularly if multiple copies of the system exist. Any changes that occur to the master document must be then made to all the subordinate documents so that all sets of documentation are identical. A change made to just one test system if multiple copies of that system exist must be described in the documentation for that system, and a note should also be included in the master documentation specifying the change, whether it is permanent or temporary, and clearly identifying the particular system in question.

Most documents that have strict version control will have a tracking register so that changes can be logged and also audited. This is important to keep the documentation up-to-date. Should any of the documentation in the field fall behind the most up-to-date version, there is a risk that a problem will be encountered that has already been solved and the person with incorrect versions of documentation may not know about it. This leads to customer dissatisfaction at the very least, and can be costly to the supplier in terms of lost time and credibility.

14.5   Configuration Control

Configuration control is especially important if you want to build a copy of an existing test system. The support costs for two different versions of the same system are greater than supporting two identical systems. Having different extant versions of the system increases lifetime costs and decreases your ROI for the system.

Any upgrades or patches to a system to keep it current should be shared and integrated into any similar solutions out in the field.

Most large-scale or mission-critical systems will have a configuration and control board or use a similar configuration management process. This board or group controls the introduction of modifications into a system. Where this approach is used, a number of steps will need to be completed before the system can be modified. These steps will include proposal of modification and perceived benefits, testing modifications in-situ, documentation, and finally, the modification of all systems.

Smaller systems will not require a configuration and control board; however, the principles of controlling the system are still equally valid. The decision on configuration will be made from input provided by the engineering team, software team, operators of the equipment, and management of the system. This decision will normally be straightforward; however, sometimes the fallout of the decision may not be so straightforward. For example, stereotypes assume that engineers will always want to tinker with and modify systems even when they perform their task adequately, and that management will never want to spend any more money than absolutely necessary. Hence, the opposing views can sometimes clash. Always have a reason for the modification that is relevant to the project goals, and always document those reasons together with any actual changes to the system. Understanding why a modification was made is just as important as the description of the modification itself.

TIP:

If you have multiple copies of the same test system and you are making a change to one of those systems, then there is usually a good reason for this. Under these circumstances, it is a good idea to make the same change to all systems. This means that you only have one version of the test system to document and maintain – looking after different versions of a test system incurs almost the same costs as maintaining different systems; you lose the advantage of duplication.

14.6   Documentation and System Support

System support over the life of a system can far exceed the original manufacturer's expected support life. As discussed elsewhere, manufacturers obsolete and upgrade equipment for a variety of reasons, and it is a fact of life that no equipment will last forever.

Most systems are built for a support solution; however, sometimes the user will decide to extend the life of the system past the original timeframe. This may occur because often the cost of upgrading hardware is far outweighed by the cost of changes to the software in the system.

Your software in particular should be adequately supported by the system documentation, so that no matter how far down the track you are, obsolete or not, the principles of operation are known. This allows you a certain amount of isolation from the hardware, and thus allows you to be able to recover from any unforeseen changes in hardware based on the original measurement principles.

A system's supported lifetime will be driven by the industry in which it operates. A consumer market-driven product that is being continuously developed will likewise need a test system that is being continuously developed and keeps pace with the product. However, a military system that undergoes upgrades through a well-defined process will have its test system upgraded through the same process and in the same timeframe.

As a builder or supplier of a system, your system design philosophy and documentation must be relevant to the lifecycle and upgrade possibilities of the equipment it is to support. This may mean evaluating the likely obsolescence timeframes of equipment used in the system and planning support accordingly, or selecting equipment with an increased feature set to allow for short-term system upgrades.

The supplier of the system should ensure that the system documentation is applicable to the project lifecycle. If the system needs to be modified continuously, then the documentation should describe the system to the appropriate level required to allow for this. The documentation should describe how the major components are related, including interfaces, signal levels, and other parameters, as well as describing the functional block diagram. This will enable a new system component to be engineered into the system with minimal effort. The same reasoning applies to the software in that it too should be well-described and documented so that modifications can be easily engineered into the system.

Another area that can often be overlooked is to what level the test system is to be supported. If the system is to be repaired at the instrument level, then less documentation is required. If, however, you expect the test system to be supported down to replaceable modules within the instruments, then the appropriate level of documentation will need to be provided to make this possible. This documentation must include circuit diagrams descriptions of how the modules work and interrelate to each other, some fault-finding guide, the test equipment which is required to fault-find, and the expected signal levels on all lines connecting to the modules.

System support costs are a significant part of the total cost of ownership of a test system, and appropriate documentation can lower these costs considerably.

Operator Training

T his chapter deals with operator training, why it is important to both individuals and the organization, and how training can help you minimize certain classes of errors.

KEY POINTS:

- Training staff in equipment use and system test procedures will lower measurement errors and unnecessary equipment wear, and will increase the level of safety in the organization.
- The development and delivery of a training course should address the needs of the organization, the expectations of attendees, and past feedback in order to continue to improve the course.
- Training documentation should be managed and maintained to the same standards as the rest of the test system documentation.
- Updating training regularly and retaining skilled staff within an organization helps maintain an organization's advantage in its marketplace or field of operation.

15.1   Training Staff in Equipment Use

Training staff in the correct and proper use of test systems is critical. This not only increases the assurance you have that the test system will return the best possible results, but it also lowers lifetime system costs through less wear from incorrect handling, and increases the safety of staff through knowledge of correct safety operating procedures.

All operators should receive a hands-on training course. Depending on the system's complexity, the operators may need pre-study or even a refresher course after some time with the system to re-enforce the system to them. An appropriately trained operator will return increased value to an organization. Systems will only be used properly if the operators are comfortable with and knowledgeable about the system.

Training is a way to transfer knowledge within an organization, or from one organization to another (if you are delivering a test system to a client). Knowledge about the system can be gained not only from the system designers, but also from expert operators, or "super-users." Super-users are generally operators with a number of years of experience. They can often provide inestimable value to system designers in stretching the equipment, showing system designers what is possible with different test techniques and getting expert results. They can often make test equipment do things that amaze most theoretically-based design engineers.

Reasons for investing in training include:

- Safety of personnel, as safety within an organization is increased if all staff understand how to carry out their work correctly and thus safely.
- Greater accuracy and better results overall, as operators will be able to get the best possible performance from the test system.
- Less damage to equipment and components such as microwave cables, as operators will understand correct handling procedures.
- Lower maintenance and repair costs, as there will be less damage to the equipment with proper handling procedures.
- Higher efficiency and productivity, again since operators will be able to get the best possible performance from the test system.
- Maintenance, updating, and development of operator skills through regular update training.
- The ability to train new staff faster if existing staff know their jobs well.

Suitable equipment training can help to eliminate some classes of errors. The error in a measurement is the difference between the true value of a quantity and the measured value of the quantity. It is important to understand that the size or value of the error cannot be determined exactly, only estimated. To reduce this uncertainty requires well-trained operators using good measurement techniques.

There are two general types of errors: random and systematic. However, some engineers include gross errors as well. Gross errors are normally classified as mistakes by operators, which training should eliminate. A technique to determine if gross errors have occurred is to take three measurements and ensure that all have similar values. Some texts recommend averaging the three results; however, with good measurement techniques and well-trained operators, this should not be necessary.

Random errors or residual errors are simply what they are named: random or unpredictable events that add to the error on the measurement. These errors are traditionally handled by statistical methods. These errors account for the variations of measurement results after all the systematic errors have been accounted for.

Systematic errors can be divided into the following sub-groups:

- Instrumental errors due to shortcomings in the instrument and loading effects on the instruments.
- Errors caused by environmental conditions such as temperature.
- Observational errors.

Instrumental errors account for the fact that all instruments will have inaccuracies in their circuits; for example, a Wheatstone bridge may actually have a different ratio than the one that is marked. However, all measurements made with this device will have the same error, meaning that it is a systematic instrument error. This is the reason why it is so important to keep instruments calibrated.

Environmental errors relate to the surroundings in which the measurement is to take place. Temperature is normally considered; however, other factors will also need to be taken into account depending on circumstances. For example, if a receiver is being tested, then the environmental surroundings should be managed such that the external electric fields are minimized. This would typically require a screened room. If a test station has been designed for the test system, it should be used correctly, which includes making sure the door is closed on the screened room, the air-conditioning system is on, and that other operating conditions are met.

Observational errors exist because the user of the test equipment is human, and therefore will introduce a personal effect into the system. For example, if two operators use the same test system, one may always tend to read the meters high and the other may always tend to read the meters low.

To allow an operator to complete his or her role as accurately as possible, the training provided must ensure that all systematic errors are reduced. This may be through including training on calibration routines or other techniques. Remember, bad technique can render even the best equipment useless. The training of operational staff must reflect the complexity of the system and measurement. Poor results mean that you cannot charge as much for your system or services, that you could be returning products that are working correctly, and that the general efficiency of your system is reduced.

15.2 Training Staff in Test Procedures

Training operators thoroughly in test procedures will give you better results and greater repeatability in the use of a test system.

The training strategy of your organization may have a greater or lesser degree of formality, but overall, it should include the identification of knowledge gaps in the organization and how to address these.

Some aspects of system training will depend on the degree of intervention required by the operator, and thus on the degree of automation of the test system. For a manual test system, operators will be expected to understand the theory of the test system, not only because they will be manually carrying out each test, but also because they will at times need to troubleshoot the system itself. Your organization may use external sources of training for technology training or theoretical knowledge, or put together a plan of self study to cover the material required.

If the system is semi- or fully-automated, then less theory and more practical application may be appropriate in operator training. Some or all measurements in a semi- or fully-automated system are under computer control, so the point at which the operator is most likely to introduce errors is while handling the DUT and system fixtures. Hence, practical training in how to best handle the DUT and fixtures is more effective in increasing the quality of test system results. The ultimate choice here will depend on what the system designer expects of the operator.

When training staff, remember that the best way to remember something is to physically go through the process. If you are able to provide hands-on components as part of the training course, then much more of the training material will be remembered after the course. Wherever possible, allow enough systems so that people are actually driving the equipment and not just sitting around listening. Provide lots of examples that are relevant to their requirements to make the material more relevant.

If another company or organization has bought the system then the provider of the system will generally also be expected to provide a training course. If the system is intended for in-house use, then the tendency is to always leave training as an afterthought. This must be avoided at all costs. Training is what will get the system used by the operators and will assure the quality of the results obtained.

Training material and documentation are important parts of the completed test system. Documenting the training course well means that you will not be relying on one person to be available at all times to deliver training – they may easily change jobs or become busy with other projects. The material you leave with staff who go through the training is also a valuable resource, as it serves as a reference that can be used at later times. Training notes are an important reminder for operators and should be developed as part of the project process as the system is being developed.

Keep in mind that some organizations require training in a particular format or style. For example, formal training for defense systems may need to comply with defense standards. Commercial companies may also have a particular style that they require for their training materials. If you are delivering systems to a customer, then you will need to comply with these requests.

15.3   Training Development and Documentation

The primary purpose of developing and delivering a training course is to transfer knowledge about how to operate the system from the designer or the most skilled operator (or "super-user") to other operators. However, in addition, the training will need to address factors such as any relevant safety laws or other regulations, participants' expectations (for example, the mixture of theoretical versus hands-on time), whether it is an equipment technique or an application course, and any feedback from previous training courses.

The form and content of the training will depend on a number of factors. The operational needs of the organization, training system operators, will drive the content, and the culture and communication style of the organization will guide the format.

Evaluating each training course after it has been completed will allow you to gradually improve both the structure of the training and the format of the material covered, and allow examples to continue to be relevant and up-to-date.

Only allow trained operators to use your system unsupervised. Some systems are used by different departments, by different groups in an organization, or just by different staff members. You may need to control access to the system, particularly if there is potential risk to inexperienced or untrained operators. If there is a risk of damage to the equipment or invalidation of calibration if any setup parameter is changed, then restricting access for these reasons is also a valid option.

Training documentation should be relevant and up-to-date. The control of this documentation should be handled by the group or the office that manages the system design project, depending on the size of the organization. Whenever the system is upgraded, the training documentation should be updated as well. Try to be concise with the course materials, and not use too many overhead slides, unless you want attendees to fall asleep. Each student should get their own copy of the course so that they can continue to refer to it at later times. Ensure that any course notes handed out are correct so that students do not need to correct them as they go; this is frustrating for them and may also create doubts about the accuracy of the rest of the notes.

Training classes should be run as a professional course and not in an informal manner. Try to keep people away from their normal day-to-day routine as this disrupts the course. It is a good idea to get feedback from the course so that it can be improved on a continual basis.

The training documentation provides you with repeatability of processes and should be kept with other system documentation. Training instructors will always take a copy for their notes and to prepare for courses; however, if an instructor modifies his or her personal copy, the main copy should be modified to reflect these changes instead of asking the students to make the changes in their notes.

15.4   Maintaining Knowledge and Skills In-house

After some time, it may be that operators will become more relaxed about following the correct procedures and start to take shortcuts. This can be particularly dangerous if safety regulations are not being followed, hence a regular refresher courses may be appropriate. This will ensure that all skills are refreshed so that systematic errors (that can be introduced when procedures are informally modified) are minimized. In addition, this allows the introduction of new skills and updated procedures to the organization.

The refresher course may also be an opportunity to have your operators train other, newer operators, or to provide this training to other organizations. If any part of the training is applicable to a broader audience, for example if identical test systems are used in repair centers nationally, then providing the training to outside industry may become an additional source of revenue for your company. You may even be able to license the training course for delivery by a third party to earn revenue without tying up the time of your staff.

Hands-on time rather than pure operation description or a focus on theory is important for operators, whether new or experienced. Remember to ensure that there is adequate equipment for all trainees to work with when a training course is being run. Experienced operators may attempt to avoid refresher training courses and it will be up to the supervisor to ensure that even experienced operators attend. Guest speakers from instrument manufacturers can be included in the course to discuss new techniques or methods for getting the very best out of the equipment.

Knowledge is also portable in that trained staff may be moved to other projects or take new jobs. Expansion of a manufacturing facility or other organizational growth may also mean that you need to train new staff. Try not to get into the position where there is only one person in the organization who can operate the equipment correctly. If at all possible, ensure that before the individual leaves, a replacement is fully trained and is familiar with the system. After the new operator has completed all training courses, a hand-over period is recommended. This hand-over period should be long enough to ensure that the new operator is fully comfortable with his or her responsibilities.

Retaining skilled staff is the best approach for an organization. Those companies and organizations that value and invest in the expertise of their staff have an advantage over those with high turnover and the resultant loss of the skills of the individuals who leave.

CHAPTER 16

Support

T his chapter examines ongoing support of your system and common issues faced by system designers. Support costs form the major part of the test system lifetime cost of ownership, and an effective and appropriate support strategy (which may be in-house, contracted to a third party, or a mixture of the two) can save your organization money as well as providing other benefits.

KEY POINTS:

- Both software and hardware support are important for the test system. Software support costs can be unexpectedly high, particularly for a fully-automated test system.
- Configuration control can lower the overall support costs if you have multiple test systems by simplifying the support strategy required for multiple identical systems. For a single system, it is still important as a method of ensuring that you will be able to rebuild or "clone" a system easily if required.
- The choice between in-house support and third-party support is generally based on whether the costs to provide resources and staff for in-house system support (including opportunity cost) are lower than the cost of outsourcing the same level of support. Other factors such as confidentiality of data or methodology may also affect this decision.

16.1   Software vs. Hardware Support

Hardware and software support are two entirely different needs and are often supplied by totally different vendors.

Hardware support is generally at two levels: repair and calibration support. Calibration must be carried out at a registered facility that can provide traceable results to a national authority. The trail of calibration must be able to withstand an audit of any stage. The calibration services provider must be able to prove that the equipment used for the calibration is traceable to a higher standard, all the way back to nationally acceptable standards.

Hardware support tends to be at regular intervals for calibration or event-driven in the case of a failure – otherwise, there will be no need to ever contact the original manufacturer or a standards house. The requirement to upgrade equipment is normally event-driven – a failure beyond economic repair, or an upgrade due to new requirements that force you to upgrade to meet an accuracy or throughput specification not previously required.

Software support is constant and ongoing. There are several unavoidable issues, the first being that operating systems upgrade and vendors then gradually decrease support for previous versions. Assistance with software is essential. It is unusual to get all the software you need from one vendor, so it is important to stay up-to-date to remain in support with all your vendors. If you call a software house inquiring about old operating systems or interface products, then you may find that support is difficult to come by or is more expensive. New staff in software companies do not typically receive training on old products – they are required to support more recent products.

If you have lost your in-house expertise in a particular software system, you may have to start again. This is not as bad as it sounds, as you still have all your documentation (hopefully!) that the software was based on – the original test objectives. What you need to add then is the environment to get it all going. Many organizations are continually adding software to their system, as new products evolve. So you may have the same suite of hardware unchanged for many years but are constantly adding TPSs or software modules. Many large organizations have test engineering sections to do this work – they make the existing hardware compatible with new products by understanding the hardware capability very well and then adding the software TPS. This analysis and understanding is necessary to be assured that the equipment can meet the specifications.

16.2   Configuration Control and Multiple Test Systems

Configuration control and system version tracking are necessary even if you only have one test system, so that it can be cloned at any stage or even have a subsystem rebuilt if needed. There is a case for this as a disaster recovery procedure; for example, if you have a fire at a facility and the test system melts to a pool of metal, or is damaged through accident or (for a military deployed test system) hostile action.

The need to test generally does not go away and the test system will need to be reconstructed. If you have not kept your records and documentation in order you will have no chance of reconstructing your test system. You may have backups of the TPS, but they will be dependent on versions of operating systems, programming packages, graphics packages, and database programs for results, the Test Executive being among them. Having a list of the names of all of these is not enough, you must have the exact versions and revision numbers.

The main need for configuration control beyond the above situation is if you clone your system to get more throughput or to deploy a copy of the system in another location. If you write the programs at a central point then have to deploy them to other test systems in other locations, then the test system you deploy to must be consistent with the one on which the TPS was developed. This is actually all valid for hardware as well, but the situation is not as bad as test equipment tends to be more robust in the market. Versions do not change often, and vendors can generally support the equipment very well for a number of years.

If you send a new TPS to an outstation or even to a customer that you need to support, then you want it to work in that application without problems that can cost you time and money.

For multiple copies of the same test system, configuration control becomes vital. The support costs involved in maintaining and repairing a number of similar but not identical test systems are much higher than for supporting a number of identical systems. Two similar systems will almost have to be treated as two different test systems:

- The layout may be different, requiring different maintenance procedures for each system.

- Particular components may be different, requiring multiple sets of spare parts rather than just one set.

- The support engineer will have to check the documentation of each individual system to be sure of what differences exist rather than being able to use standard sets of documents.

Chapter 14, "Documentation," also discusses the value of version tracking and configuration control. Maintaining strict configuration control over a number of copies of a system will simplify your support processes and thus lower your lifetime support costs.

16.3   In-house Support vs. Third-Party Support

Many organizations will provide in-house support for both software and hardware. This typically involves a great deal of overhead. You need to decide whether you want to invest in the overhead of a support section for hardware and software

If it is a critical system, you can get 24 hour x 7-day-a-week support, however this is not for the faint-hearted. It is expensive – but this cost is all in proportion to what you are doing and trying to get done. If the design, build, and support of test systems is your company's core business, then you can probably do this faster and more efficiently than a company doing it for the first time. However, many companies building a test system for the first time do not understand the costs involved and normally believe that the hardware is the major cost of the system – it is not.

16.3.1 Software Support

The software and software support comprise the most expensive portion of the cost of owner-ship, particularly for a fully-automated test system and particularly as these costs may appear to be hidden from the user up-front. If you do not count all the hours for code development and design and then configuration control and support, then it appears that the cost of the software is just that of the packages you need to lay over the software.

Vendors of packages like operating systems tend to sell in very large quantities so their cost is proportionally low. When you hand-craft test programs and have to support them, partic-ularly to support them in terms of documentation, the cost can quickly escalate. Generally, the software will cost between five and twenty times what the hardware costs – a cost that is often overlooked.

As a rule of thumb, a good "code cutter" or software designer generally cuts ten lines of debugged, documented code per day. If your program is expected to be around one thousand lines of code, this will affect costs, the timeline for your project, and staff requirements if you need to set a number of programmers to work on the software to meet target dates in time.

Obsolescence of software products can be a major issue. Hardware vendors in most coun-tries provide support for equipment for at least five years after the obsolescence date, and gener-ally give one year's warranty. Software is very different; generally, ninety days is standard for warranty – and support may be difficult to obtain after obsolescence. If a product is obsoleted, it is important to consider for how long the manufacturer will provide support, spare parts (for hardware), and maintenance.

An organization will generally need to choose between in-house and third-party software support, both of which are discussed below.

16.3.2 Hardware Support

The builder of a test system can decide whether to support the system in a number of ways. As with software support, the choice is typically between in-house support and third-party support; however, under some circumstances, a mixture of the two may be appropriate.

Hardware support should include a regular maintenance program, particularly for mission critical-systems, as well as appropriate repair facilities which may range from component-level repair to module or card replacement.

REPAIR PHILOSOPHIES FOR COMMERCIAL AND DEPLOYED CUSTOMERS

Deployed organizations such as Search and Rescue, some scientific expeditions, the military, or some United Nations operations generally have three levels of support (see Figure 16.1).

   O level (Operational level). Modules that have failed are replaced, and the failed module is then sent to an I-level shop. BITE (built-in test equip0ment) is often used at this level, but can also be supported with test systems that can quickly help identify the source of failure down to a particular module. BITE comes in varying levels of complexity; some BITE works on a go/no-go level and some

---

> ### REPAIR PHILOSOPHIES FOR COMMERCIAL AND DEPLOYED CUSTOMERS (CONT.)
>
> is full parametric test traceable to a national standard. One potential problem is that if the assembly has failed, then the BITE may not work in that module, so the BITE has to cover this circumstance, for example by indicating whether the BITE is available or (depending how the BITE is implemented) what limited functionality is available.
>
> **I level (Intermediate level).** Modules are repaired by replacing CCT boards, etc. to get a module back into service at the O level. Failed CCT cards are then sent to the D level. BITE can also be used here, again depending on how extensive it is. Often it is a simple test to identify failed cards by swapping in known good cards until the fault goes away, in this case, the test system is just there to simulate the normal working environment (electrically) of the failed module.
>
> **D level (Depot level).** This is where circuit cards and modules can be repaired to component level. The repair solution at this level is normally built or designed by the manufacturer of the equipment, and usually has some sort of component-level test.
>
> Commercial philosophy on repair strategy is often one level of repair, "return to manufacturer," which means the manufacturer has to be able to test and repair the product quickly and cost-effectively. A manufacturer may even contract out repair to agents, as happens with many mobile cell phone brands, where agent repair shops will run manufacturer-recommended test equipment and also often the manufacturer's test software, sometimes guided by a manual procedure (see Section 3.2 on SOPS). Usually these repair centers allow a certain time to fix the phone or they replace it, as it is not cost-effective to spend too much time on any one device. What they lose on this repair they pick up from all the phones with simple, easy-to-fix faults.

If you use a mixture of in-house and third-party support, then it is important to clearly specify which party is responsible for what portions of the system support plan, and how to manage any overlaps in maintenance or repair requirements. If you need to stop to negotiate these once the system has broken down, then the time to getting it up and running again will stretch out far beyond normal. The choice of support strategy is normally made based on economic reasons, depending on whether your organization can provide support at a lower internal cost than that of contracting it out – including the opportunity cost of having those resources unavailable for other work. However, if hardware has been specifically designed by your company as opposed to general instruments, then you may have no choice but to maintain and repair it in-house.

16.3.3 In-house Support

Sensitivity of system information may prohibit the support of equipment from being outsourced. In-house support allows you to always be in control of the system and never have to rely on third parties. This requires, however, that appropriately trained staff be available on-site during the times for which you require system support. The expertise that makes good design engineers is typically different than the skills that make good system maintenance and repair engineers, so this involves building up a new set of skills within the organization if they do not exist already.

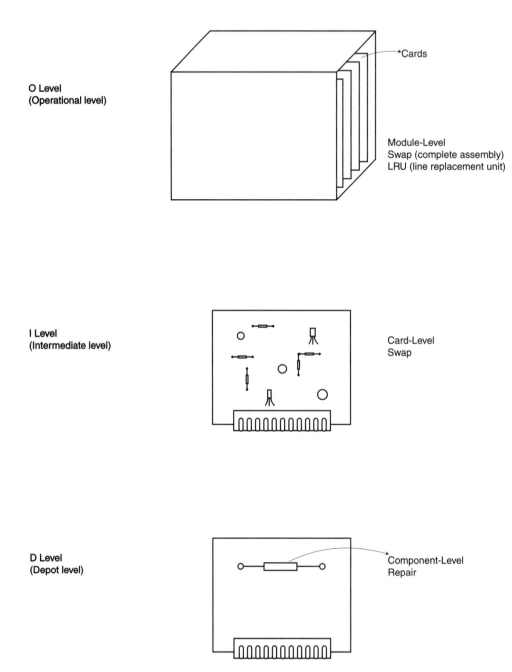

Figure 16.1   O, I, and D level repair setups.

One advantage is that no contracts need to be negotiated if you do support in-house; however, your organization's internal processes may require a service-level agreement or similar arrangement. In any case, a clear understanding of what is expected in test system support will prevent delays at a later stage.

In-house support can allow modifications to be handled within the organization or company without needing to change contracts or repair shops. Another reason for using it may be that you have developed a more or less unique method of performing a test that provides your organization with a competitive advantage and you do not want that information known to any other parties, hence you need to repair and maintain the system in-house. The system may also have unique qualities such as those of systems used in space testing that third parties do not have the facilities to maintain.

16.3.4 Third-Party Support

This is the outsourcing or out-tasking of your support requirements. Most companies do this because they perceive it to be the most cost-effective way of supporting a system. They believe that this will allow them to concentrate on their core business, which, for example, may be building test systems with other peoples' instruments. In this case, the instruments can be returned to the equipment manufacturer for repair using their own facilities.

Other reasons companies outsource support is to overcome resource limitations. The company may not have enough trained people to repair the equipment or does not have the demand to justify hiring trained people. Another factor to consider is that the life of the system may be many years. Instead of keeping old technology skills in your leading-edge company, you may wish to outsource this support requirement to a third party specializing in this technology.

Cost also plays an important part. Your people may cost more to run because they are highly trained engineers, whereas the equipment may require a less skilled maintenance level. Hence, to have your engineer repair the system is an expensive exercise to you and your customer. If this leads to increased costs for the system, this may eventually lead your customer to other test system manufacturers.

Outsourcing can also be a good way to make strategic alliances with other companies. This can benefit both you and the other company. That company may be the actual instrument manufacturer and this may allow you to get additional cost reductions in test equipment (for example). The arrangement may also be more beneficial in providing an additional workforce to your company in times of high workload by giving you an existing relationship with another company to which you can contract out some portions of your work. A mutually beneficial alliance can in some cases allow your organization to avoid having to invest in excess capacity that may not be required all the time.

Upgrading a Test System

At some point in its lifecycle your test system may become outdated; for example, as your test requirements change or as new test technology comes onto the market. Rather than losing the benefit and investment that has gone into designing the system in the first place, an upgrade can give your system an extended lifespan and thus a better return on investment.

A number of components in the existing version of the test system will be able to be reused in the upgraded system. Good documentation is an absolute necessity to retaining the value of the system and to complete the upgrade with minimum cost.

CHAPTER 17

Using Standard Software and Open Standards for Obsolescence Protection

T his chapter discusses how to improve the ROI of your system by planning for a longer useful lifetime. It describes how using standard software and open standards can make upgrades easier for your system and will help protect the investment you have made in designing and building your system.

KEY POINTS:

- Product capabilities and test requirements will certainly change over time, so planning the system design for flexibility in system upgrades will help increase the overall ROI of your system.
- Using a modular software design and avoiding equipment-specific code can increase the flexibility and re-usability of your software. Developments in software design have made that task easier over the years.
- Test methodology can also be planned for greater flexibility over the lifetime of the test system.

17.1 Longer System Lifetime and ROI

One of the certain aspects of designing a custom test system is that product capabilities or your test requirements will change over time; for example, if your company has started to manufacture a new product, or perhaps your organization has been given new technology requirements to test. This fact means that one of the test system designer's major aims should be to design a test solution where the test system can be upgraded easily and without excessive cost. System upgrades allow for extended life of systems, and thus protect the investment you initially made. If it is possible to design or upgrade a system in a way that makes future upgrades quicker and more easy to carry out, then you can further increase or extend the value and ROI of your test system.

Some key areas to consider in a system upgrade are: software and hardware. You may also decide to make changes to design aspects such as the test system's ergonomics, level of automation, number of systems fielded, safety features, or redundancy features.

17.1.1 Outline of the Development of Open Software Standards

Early in the history of automated test systems, application programs interfaced directly with specific pieces of test equipment and used commands specific to an instrument. With this approach, the measurement "process" occurred partly in the software and partly in the hardware. If the hardware was changed, the software also had to be changed.

Interchangeability is the ability to replace a given hardware asset or piece of test equipment with another one of different design but sufficient capability to make the measurement without having to change the TPS (or application software). Software changes are limited to replacing components directly associated with the test asset.

Open standards in hardware are a vital tool to allowing interchangeability of test equipment. However, new features, advances in test technology, or even differences in the internal design of substitute pieces of test equipment ("second order effects," that is, those effects not related to software command semantics) can still create test system challenges. Two different models of DVMs (digital voltmeters), for example, may have differences in their internal auto-range features which result in the instrument presenting different input impedances to the test circuit and thus requiring the engineer to establish which technology provides the correct answer and least error.

Using a four-channel oscilloscope as a replacement for a two-channel oscilloscope can involve updating your system's setup requirements, as well as allowing the possibility of streamlining some of the system's test procedures by using the other two channels for additional measurements. As changes in test and measurement technology allow the system designer a greater choice of solutions, decisions need to be made which could not have been made during the initial design of the system.

17.1.2 Structure

There are some general aspects of the test system software's structure that can be used to promote easy interchangeability of test equipment. The operating system that the software will run on is normally supplied with the computer. The computer hardware and operating system may or may not be from the same manufacturer; however, the system designer should choose hardware and operating systems that are industry-accepted and support the interfaces and have instrument drivers that support the instruments that you will be using.

After the operating system and computer hardware have been selected, the next task is to standardize the programming interface to instruments. The programming interface to instruments includes the instrument interconnect bus drivers and the instrument control drivers. The instrument interconnect bus drivers send the data and commands across the bus that connects the instruments to the computer, and the instrument control drivers control the instruments by sending data and commands to the instrument interconnect bus drivers.

The interface to instruments has taken two paths: one for ASCII-controlled test assets and another for driver-controlled test assets. The ASCII path started with the advent of the IEEE 488, or GP-IB bus. Messages to control test equipment over the IEEE 488 interface were in ASCII, but there were no standardized semantics, which meant that different companies used different commands to control the same equipment functionality. Hence, if a different manufacturer's box was used as a replacement, it required rewriting of portions of the software to allow the integration of the new instrument. The IEEE 488.2 standard provided some common commands and protocols, and then the SCPI language (standard commands for programmable instruments) provided an extensive set of standardized commands.

The history of driver development started about ten years later than that of ASCII but followed a similar path. Early driver-controlled test assets were created without common standards. Later, the VXI Consortium developed the VXI plug & play driver standard, which developed common commands, but there was still no semantic standard for instrument functionality. Even if all similar instruments could understand a single command language, actually connecting and talking to the various instruments was very complex given that certain test systems used RS-232, VXI, GP-IB, and even LAN/WAN-type connections. Again, using a standard such as SCPI & SICL, which provides a core set of I/O functions that are platform-independent, made any developed software more robust, transportable, and more easily maintained and enhanced.

Finally, the TPS is the control software written as part of the test system design process, and is the code that operates the individual test equipment when it is performing a specific task(s). This part of the software should be written in a modular structure, where one module can be a single test or possibly a group of related tests. Analyze your test methodology as completely as possible before code is started since a measurement can use multiple instruments for a single test, and the objective is to future-proof the software by removing the hardware dependencies.

The TPS would usually operate under the direction and control of the Test Executive (see Figure 17.1), which manages all the TPSs in a system. The Executive can be simple and just schedule tests one after the other, or incredibly complex and even include a learning AI computer system. An AI system learns over time what fault symptoms relate to in the diagnostic process and can analyze faults and problems very quickly, having seen them before and knowing what components that were replaced led to the solution. This type of Test Executive fits very well into the environment where component-level repair is required.

To summarize, the challenge for the designer is to develop software TPSs that interface with the system's test equipment in a way that does not tie the system design to a particular set of instruments and other test assets. Interchangeability is increasingly important to users, especially with the increasing speed of technological change in many industries. There have been some very good attempts at producing a robust test system environment, one of which was ATLAS a test system environment which even dictated the operating system. ATLAS, which had

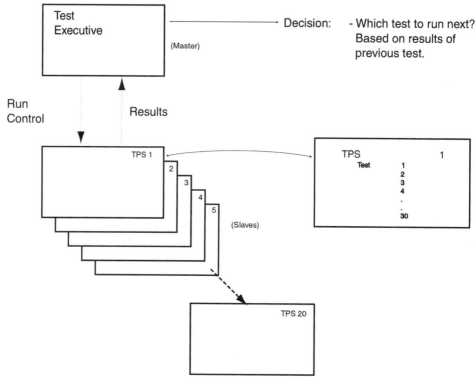

Figure 17.1 The Test Executive and TPS.

its origins in the commercial aircraft industry of the mid-1960s, was a commonly used signal interface. A basic principle of ATLAS as a programming language was that programs written in it would not make any direct reference to test instrumentation, to support equipment inter- changeability as well as interoperability of the TPS software. A well-designed ATLAS imple- mentation fully abstracted test equipment functionality and would then not be tied down to a specific set of test system assets. However, complete semantic standards did not exist for all aspects of evolving test technology and there were cases where TPS developers had to use direct calls to test equipment in the system. Non-ATLAS modules (called NAMs) achieved this, but at the cost of linking the software to specific test equipment. Future trends in the design of test sys- tem environments next took a sub-system approach, where standardized programming interfaces were used, particularly for driver-controlled test system assets; one example was the use of IVI (interchangeable virtual instruments) drivers.

Semantic standardization is now being developed through the work of the IVI Foundation, through their creation of standards for the software interfaces of common instrument types. IVI drivers provide standardized application programming interface (API) functions for test equip- ment. As long as there are no "second order effects" such as those mentioned above (unrelated to software command semantics), the use of an IVI driver will provide a good degree of interchangeability. Partly to respond to some of these other test interchangeability challenges, the IVI Foundation also has a sub-group called the IVI-MSS, which works on the specifications for building measurement sub-system solutions, where two or more test assets are used together to deliver specific test and measurement functionality.

The only really guaranteed way to verify interchangeability is to test the system. This depends, however, on knowing which interface features were actually used in the application and on the number and complexity of the TPSs used by the test system. Large, automated test systems existing today can operate many TPSs, which makes fully testing for interchangeability a mammoth task. If the system's TPS software interacts directly with test equipment, then the only way to verify that the "same answers" are obtained after an interchange is to collect all the DUTs along with their associated TPSs and check every one. Designing the test system software with interchangeability in mind can greatly simplify this task.

17.2   Planning for Future Requirements

There are some basic design points to keep in mind either when you design a new test system or upgrade an existing one. The main points are to avoid test-specific code, equipment-specific code, and exotic or unusual test equipment.

The rationale behind upgrading an existing test system is to keep it going for a longer period of time. That time is dependent on how well you design your upgrade to extend the test system's life as long as possible before the next upgrade or total replacement. This is also a good time to consider how you can make the next system upgrade easier as well.

One of the dangers of writing test equipment-specific code is that if you ever need to change your equipment or a test procedure, you can run into problems that are instrument-specific.

Do not use exotic equipment; remember all electrical quantities can be derived several ways, so do not get caught up in the thought that there is only one way or piece of equipment to do your job. Similarly, some salespeople can get caught up in their own company's training material about a particular new feature; however, you will need to evaluate these features against the criteria on which you will be judged. There may be, or may not be, other ways to achieve the same results. Using exotic equipment may tie you down to exotic test methods that will mean that your software will not work with other equipment.

You will have some interesting problems if you need to upgrade the system and there is nothing on the market that immediately meets your needs. In this case, you have to fall back on fundamentals. Measurement is an art form – talk to a metrologist and you will soon see there are different ways to measure any quantity. Your system software design may be able to get the most out of the test equipment in the system.

As a test system evolves, it is easy to accept the development without really watching the overhead, until something happens. If your key test system design specialist or the software designer who wrote all the code leaves, that is the point when you usually find out how badly exposed you are to industry problems. If your code is documented, then you can check to see if

---

"WAR STORY"

One of the authors once worked on a test system that was timed to a 36-pin digital output connector on a voltmeter, which was obsolete. The voltmeter could not be replaced as the 36-pin bus was unique. The military agencies who used the system scoured the world for second-hand units to buy up as spares. As each component became unavailable, the military would retrieve from the voltmeter manufacturer the exact characteristics of the current part being hunted and would test thousands of items to get one with the right characteristics. On the surface, this appears to be an unbelievable waste of time – however, the cost of rewriting the software for the tests on new equipment and delivering that solution worldwide was prohibitive, even when compared with the cost of tracking down replacement parts.

Worse still, the original test system vendor had gone out of business, and all records of why they wrote a test in a particular way were lost. The military organization's best way to support the test systems they used was to somehow keep the test system going – which for some time they managed to do.

This story highlights the need for very good documentation of system software in particular. Documentation that is designed to describe the entire system, from system requirements all the way down to software design documents (so that the system can be traced as to why things were designed and implemented the way they were all the way back to the original system requirements), is essential. These documents should exist for both the hardware and the software.

---

the operating system and specific language the programmer used is still supported, and if it is, for how long. You now have a finite life for your test system, and you may not be able to upgrade it easily. The risk you run is that you may spend more time trying to reverse-engineer your existing test system than you would designing and a building a new one with all the new ideas you have learned.

Never approach problems with ad-hoc fixes: Think hard about what the costs are to your company and plan your approach like any other engineering task. Ad-hoc fixes have the regrettable habit of coming apart at critical times. It always helps in these cases to have a support plan in place for your systems, and some budget money allocated to the continual upgrading of your test systems. You need to institutionalize early in your work area procedures to keep the solution alive over a long time, and to ensure that the solution is a long-term one, not just a build-and-ship exercise. And for people to document the work they do, you need to incorporate all the add-ons and fixes that keep a system alive. If you remove all these and your system no longer functions, then you are in real trouble – you cannot reliably replicate your work or tests. Apart from this, the above situation is normally viewed as a quality control process or documentation control problem. Many organizations will not accept work without the appropriate quality control in place because of the problems of dealing with companies that allow the above to occur.

Do not select equipment on the sole basis of new technologies standards promoted by single vendors. Unless you are driven by a requirement for a specific test capability that is otherwise unavailable, try to remain with mature standards, open standards, and not the latest flash-in-the-pan "standard." If large test houses are not supporting it, ask why? It may be that it is an emerging standard that will eventually be widely accepted, but even then, the standard may change and evolve as it is taken up and accepted by standards bodies. The standard itself may be fantastic, but if its sellers cannot support you, then it is no good to you.

When you do your initial requirement study on your current test system, which will involve a support analysis, the projected length of time that each manufacturer will produce their equipment for should be approximately determined. From this analysis, you can predicate when to upgrade based on the availability of spares. If nothing else changes, most companies will, after removing an item from their product list, guarantee support for a period of time – this may be five to ten years. If you leave things to the last minute, you will be disappointed. Some company personnel believe this to be a ploy by test instrument manufacturers to sell more equipment; however, this is not the case. Test equipment manufacturers face the same trials as every other company building systems, including their suppliers ceasing production of critical parts. Before the stage when the equipment becomes endangered, you should know what test equipment will be problematic to find and duplicate, and should make alternative plans – if you have already compromised your design to fit in critical test equipment, then you are already heading for doom. Stay with fundamentals in your design – focus on the end application and what you are trying to achieve – that way, you will not get sidetracked into instrument-specific measurements.

Some key points that help with planning for future requirements include:

- Make your software modular and equipment manufacturer independent wherever possible. Software should be an industry standard where possible, and should be designed with equipment interoperability in mind. Software development and upgrade costs are generally greater than system hardware costs, so building as much future flexibility into your system software as possible will pay dividends in the future.

- Ensure your measurement ranges do not approach too high a performance level as you may get locked into a single supplier. If you need a particular piece of test equipment, try to isolate it from the rest of the system to negate future problems. For example, a small second switch that is used to direct I/O to the specific instrument and a switch that has extra capacity in the main design means that if the specific instrument becomes obsolete, you have the extra capacity in the main system switch to fit a new piece of test equipment. If a new (preferably open standard) product comes onto the market that has caught up to the performance of the previously used equipment, you will be able to integrate it into the system with a minimum of problems.

- Design your test system racks with expansion in mind. Try to understand the product you are testing and the future implications of that product's lifecycle. Where does this product plan to be in three to five years, because where the product goes, your test equipment has to go. There are usually available sources of literature and experience to help predict where the product will be in five years' time. Armed with this information, you can start to plan the evolution of your test system from now into the future. When you gather functional groups of test equipment together in a rack for a test system, you can leave room for expansion then. A few blank panels are not a big problem, perhaps space for an extra rack, etc. Remember, if the industry you service is fast-moving, then your systems need to be quickly and easily adapted.

• Use higher frequency connectors where you can without adding excessive cost. The same applies to cables. If you can get better cables and connectors at a slight cost premium, then it may be better to invest straight away rather than waiting for the next system upgrade. However, if you know that your system has a limited life, or you are already planning to abandon the current system and build a new test system, then any investment in capability or accessories beyond your immediate needs would not be indicated.

If you realize up-front that your system will evolve and have additional test or analysis capability added, along with additional DUTs as your organization takes on extra work and writes more TPSs, then time spent planning at the beginning is rarely wasted. Do not treat your test systems as an afterthought or necessary evil, but as fully integrated engineering systems. When planning for the future, remember to take into account things such as changing floor space requirements, power, cooling, and other factors that are relevant to your system and industry.

17.3   Open Standards and Obsolescence Protection

It is good practice to design any systems, as well as plan for upgrades to any systems, using open system standards wherever possible. This gives you the best protection against obsolescence as well as giving you the largest selection of equipment from different manufacturers to choose from.

Open systems are a comparatively recent concept for the test and measurement industry; for some observers, the idea of manufacturers working together is an interesting one. The bottom line is that there are standards at different levels, and you can subscribe to them fully or partially. For example, if you use RS-232, you can accomplish communication with as little as 3 wires or use all 25 pins available, or take a compromise of just 9 pins. The different levels of security and data integrity diminish as you reduce overhead. If you make full use of standards like VXI, then you can be assured that you can be integrated into other vendors' solutions. It reduces risk and increases your available market.

If you design using unique equipment, even if it is better than anything else on the market, it will still easily succumb to a less technically advanced product that is easier, and thus less risky, to integrate. It is tempting to build your own test equipment occasionally, but you must consider the full cycle to understand the costs involved. When you have to upgrade because of accuracy or speed requirements, chances are that it will be an expensive upgrade as you will have to start from ground zero, since you have nothing to build on.

Extensive reports have been done many times by various users of test systems, particularly major users such as military organizations. The costs involved in being restricted to equipment using a proprietary standard, or in trying to make different standards work successfully together, have been the major driving force behind the development of open standards. The U.S. Air Force has managed to mandate on industry an open standard that has been adopted as the VXI standard – it is one of the most successful open test equipment standards being used in the market today. Better and more advanced tools are being developed for using such standards. Many tools can generate faster underlying code than software engineers can when finally assembled into run-time versions.

> **TIP:**
>
> Although familiarity with and skill in using a particular standard will pre-dispose an engineer toward using that standard, it is important to keep up-to-date with emerging industry trends, particularly when new standards offer technological advantage. The best way to move ahead is with standards. One way to keep up-to-date with possible industry directions is to observe and watch what the big users of test equipment are demanding, because they will be the ones who are listened to by the test equipment suppliers.

Finally, never give your test projects to the least experienced staff member, simply because you view the test system as an afterthought. Ideally, a test system design project can be seen as an opportunity for less experienced engineers to learn from senior staff. In the short term, it may save money to throw together a system in a hurry; however, in the long term, you will incur additional costs and labor to keep your test capability up-to-date.

CHAPTER 18

Dealing with Obsolete Items

T his chapter examines what happens if you want to upgrade or replace any of the equipment in your system – only to find that the equipment you originally used has since become obsolete. The key to minimizing problems is the use of open standards wherever possible, or upgrading to open standards if they were not part of your original design.

KEY POINTS:

- Equipment may become obsolete for a number of reasons, and replacing it with a new model will most likely involve procedural and software changes for the test system.
- Evaluate your long-term support requirements.
- Evaluating the current computer, control system, and software in the system will allow you to gauge to what extent these will need to be upgraded along with the new hardware. In some limited cases, the existing software may still work with new equipment.
- Calibration and certification will need to be updated with a system upgrade or replacement of equipment or software. More frequent calibration cycles may be necessary at first to verify that the system still performs as required.
- Under some conditions, it will be better to consider a complete rebuild rather than a system upgrade.

18.1   Selecting Replacement Equipment

A test system designer faced with a system upgrade requirement will face some of the same issues as a designer starting on a plan for a completely new system. Planning for the length of time the system will be required in its current configuration and workload as well as planning for future requirements are just as important as for a new test system.

One of the major difficulties faced by the system engineer is when equipment they want to source (to provide drop-in replacement for an existing piece of test equipment that has failed) has become obsolete and is no longer available. Test equipment and other test system components can become obsolete or unavailable for a number of possible reasons. They include:

- A shortage of the materials required to make the device – microprocessors in particular date very quickly and come to be in short supply, as do other components. Some organizations will buy second-hand equipment to keep a test system running, or make a lifetime spares purchase from the manufacturer. This is not a permanent solution. Eventually supplies will run out; however, it saves you from having to upgrade the test system software at that stage, which is often more expensive than sourcing second-hand equipment. The test equipment vendors may have relatively little control over the supply of the components they need for their own manufacturing. The component manufacturers themselves will introduce new products to keep pace with changing markets, new technology, or a need to lower their own production costs.

- The test equipment manufacturer releasing a new generation of products, which has more features and gives the manufacturer a market lead for their new products. Many test equipment manufacturers aim to have at least 50% of their product sales revenue each year come from products introduced in the past three years. Test equipment manufacturers need to turn over their products to keep up with market needs and technical improvements, and the demands of their customers.

- A declining market for that equipment, which may force the equipment supplier to end production for business reasons.

- The end of support life for that equipment. Obsolescence is not the end of the support period for that product; most manufacturers of test equipment will guarantee post-obsolescence support for a minimum period, commonly five years. You may be able to buy extended support after this, if the manufacturer has sold a large quantity of this item, as it may be viable for them to continue support.

If the equipment you need is no longer available and you need to find a replacement product, it is unlikely you will find a direct drop-in replacement for your device on the market, unless it is very simple. In addition to finding products with suitable specifications, an additional problem exists in procedural or software changes, both of which require a re-think of the way you do things now.

18.1.1 Procedural Changes

These changes examine the measurements done by the current item of test equipment and compare them to the new device, or devices for specification fit. At the same time, you will want to keep your form factor the same if possible, or you will have to change your rack layout. If the new device is smaller or larger, it presents an engineering issue. You will have to decide whether to move things in the rack to make room, or expand the rack if the item is larger than the one it is replacing. Consider the effects of heating or airflow turbulence in the rack if the new item is deeper than the old one. If the new item is smaller, it is somewhat easier, but you do need to block any gaps sufficiently so as not to disturb your airflow.

18.1.2 Software Changes

These changes are not to be underestimated, as they are a serious and time-consuming task (also see Section 19.5, "Updating Software Modules"). If you have the most modern test equipment with an open standard driver system such as plug & play or IVI, then your task may be reduced. Chances are that you will have a completely new set of control instructions to deal with. Your Test Executive, if designed properly, will allow for changes, but how extensive they are depends on what you need to do with the tests. This may lead to modifying the Test Executive as well. Try to avoid this, as the implications are significant. A well-designed Test Executive is the manager of all the TPS and other software tasks performed.

Some test equipment vendors may not maintain complete compatibility between their control codes, meaning that there may not be conformity between different models. Sometimes the control instructions will relate to something specific to that particular model, such as the layout of the buttons on the front panel. For example, the first function button on the top left of the front panel (which might be AC volts) will be referred to as F1 in that instrument's command code; the next button, regardless of its function or relation to the first function, will be F2, and so on. If the next model that comes out has a different front panel, the same labeling convention will mean that the code used for the first model will not be compatible with the next model of the same instrument. Many vendors are avoiding these problems in their newer designs; however, you may still encounter products where these or similar issues cause problems with code compatibility.

The changes to your test system code will be extensive, as software control of test equipment can be very complex. A system tuned for maximum throughput is constantly polling equipment and working at its most effective speed. To integrate your new item into this will require a thorough understanding of how it fits into the program. Your documentation is critical to how well (if at all) you can integrate your new equipment. If you cannot get into the code because you do not understand it for lack of documentation, then you may have to have the code rewritten from the start. This is very expensive and time-consuming – more so if it stops your production work or whatever task your test system is doing.

18.2 Revising the Test Parameters Matrix

The original test parameters matrix for the test system (assuming that one was used and that it was kept as part of the test system documentation) can be used to simplify the system upgrade process. The method for developing the test parameters matrix was discussed in Chapter 4, "Choosing Test Equipment."

If you plan to add new tests to the system's capability as well as upgrade the equipment required for existing tests, then you can use the test parameters matrix to see how new tests will fit in. This is when your quality of documentation comes into play. If you can bring up your original design and then add the new tests, you may find that your existing equipment may well have sufficient capability to satisfy your test requirements. This situation will then allow you to design your software through the switch or patch panel with little difficulty. The software will have to be modified and possibly new modules added to the Test Executive's control. The new TPS will have additional capability not seen before by the Executive nor by the analysis routines. Not only do you have to write new tests, but you also have to rewrite the way the system displays and conducts the testing.

If you discover during your analysis of the matrix and new tests that you need to add new routines to your system, then the test parameters matrix will give you a process to establish what new equipment you will need.

When analyzing the matrix, you should see if any of the new tests are redundant, for example, if they were already covered by the system. Additionally, you should determine if any of the tests can be derived from data already present in the results database of the Executive.

Once you have established what new tests you will include to uncover additional information, then you will need to plan your programming such that there are no unnecessary range changes or other parameter changes that will affect your original design.

18.2.1 Upgrading the Test Parameters Matrix

Steps to upgrading your original requirements matrix are:

- Establish what new tests are required.
- Enter the tests into the test parameters matrix table.
- Compare the test to what the existing test equipment can accomplish.
- Establish where the gaps are.
- Upgrade the test list to include the new tests.
- Determine if there are any tests that the test equipment cannot do.
- Decide what possible new test equipment you need.
- Survey the industry to procure new equipment – then purchase.
- Decide how you will order the new tests into the existing test flow.
- Build any new fixtures required, or add to the matrix or patch panel.
- Add any new cabling to the system.
- Document the procedures into your documentation.
- Continue testing.

18.3   Evaluating Your Long-term Support Requirements

Long-term support usually means support for the life of a project, whatever your original plans. It can often happen that you will have to support your test system beyond the support life offered by the manufacturer (most manufacturers will support their equipment for a minimum period such as five years after obsolescence). It is not often possible to get the end of product sales life data out of a manufacturer, as they may be planning to produce the item until external circumstances such as non-availability of key components or a sharp decline in the market lead them to stop. As these factors are out of the manufacturer's control, they will not be able to tell you when they may have to obsolete a product. If the company plans to replace an existing product with a new model, they are also unlikely to release that information ahead of time as it will affect sales of the current model until the newer model is released.

Most equipment manufacturers will give a period of notice such as one year or six months before obsoleting a product, and an annual check with suppliers of key equipment can ensure that you do not miss out on this news. Some products, however, are phased out very quickly, so do not rely on receiving notice if you are relying on one particular piece of equipment. If you plan to make a lifetime buy of spares to maintain your test system in a particular state (as opposed to upgrading it), you may want to consider making the purchase at some time prior to product obsolescence.

An alternative to making a lifetime buy of the test equipment itself may be to purchase kits of spare parts from the manufacturer. You may need to negotiate this as part of an ongoing support contract. The kits may give a percentage of assurance of fixing faults, or a fault coverage percentage – for example, that the kit will repair 80% of faults in the manufacturer's opinion based on warranty failures and analysis of components used in the manufacturing process.

Obsolescence is not the end of support for a product. There is also a minimum period that the manufacturer guarantees to support the equipment fully. End of support is the time at which the manufacturer stops guaranteeing support and moves to a best-effort program of repair. This generally means that most repair work will be billed on a time-and-materials basis rather than fixed-price repair (if that was previously available). If the manufacturer is unable to repair the device due to lack of parts, you may still be billed for the time and work done to reach that point. Best-effort refers in part to the possibility that certain components may not be available – if you require a microprocessor that is no longer made and has been out of production for a year or more, then you may have no chance whatsoever to get that component.

Another option to extending the life of equipment is to buy spares, possibly after obsolescence, on the open market from auctions or from second-hand equipment vendors – of which there are many. Looking for them is not difficult; for example, the web or Internet are good places to start.

18.4   Upgrading the Computer and Control System

The computer system that you originally start out with is unlikely to last more than a year or so without being replaced by a newer model. If you decide to go through a test system upgrade, this means that you have several choices:

1. Support the existing configuration until your test requirements change and you no longer need that system. This may mean that you will have to forego any advantages offered by factors such as increased clock speeds or software processing advantages.

2. Upgrade the system so that you are not dependent on the particular microprocessor in the system. This involves a potential risk in that it may be a short-term fix, and may need to be addressed again with the next change.

3. Upgrade your system to be totally independent of microprocessor problems. This involves moving to an architecture that allows independence from these devices.

4. Move to a system that is more robust and will not give you problems from version to version – many experienced programmers prefer rich operating systems like UNIX for this purpose. Whatever system you run, you will run it on the latest engine regardless of how it was originally written.

5. Make sure that the control software run on the computer is also independent of the computer type used – otherwise, you have to lock to a particular microprocessor, operating system, and control language yourself. The risk is that you may be on your own supporting this configuration, since as years go by and the rest of industry updates equipment, you may find you are the only one supporting this configuration. Certainly not a good story to tell your prospective customers that your support is unique, not standard, and requires a lot of resource overhead.

When you do decide to upgrade, always do this as part of a complete plan. Do not allow a single vendor or datasheet to dictate the upgrade without evaluating the alternatives available on the market. You need to change a number of things other than the software, so you should be going back to your original test matrix and looking at that in conjunction with your software control decisions. It may be that you can retain your existing Test Executive – this would certainly be a bonus, and at the least, your measurement analysis will still be valid. It is very much a matter of how the changes are implemented.

Deciding whether to upgrade the control method of your test system from manual to semi- or fully-automated or from semi- to fully-automated control will be based on whether the costs of the upgrade will be outweighed by the benefits gained from a greater degree of automation. Increasing production volumes may warrant an increased degree of automation to cut test time, or you may want to move experienced operators to more valuable work and automate the system to increase the accuracy and reliability of results with inexperienced operators. Speed, reliability, and freeing up the time of experienced staff are all factors that may guide you toward investing in a test system upgrade.

With increased automation and shorter test times, it may also become warranted to upgrade the DUT handling for your system. The benefits of cutting test time to a few seconds or milliseconds are negated if the DUT handling process takes five seconds for each connection. Chapter 6, "Interfacing to the Device Under Test," discusses methods of handling the DUT in more detail.

To introduce automation to your system or to increase the degree of automation, the test equipment involved will require bus control. Equipment for the original system may have been bought with bus control for future automation, but if it was not, then you will have to upgrade it with bus capability (many vendors have retrofit kits available for this) or purchase new test equipment if an upgrade to bus control is not available. You will also need to write or expand the control software for the test system – typically a larger and more expensive task than sourcing the right test equipment and accessories.

Some questions to ask when you are considering upgrading the test system's computer and control system are:

- What are the advantages to be gained from upgrading the computer? Increased speed? Additional capability? Access to a new operating system?
- Can you upgrade your software to be independent of links to a particular processor?
- Will changing the computer affect any of the test equipment or test routines in the system (for example, if the old software is linked to clock cycles at a particular speed)?
- Will test system hardware require upgrades such as retrofitting bus capability?
- Will the cost of upgrading both hardware and software be offset by productivity gains?
- Can the whole test process be upgraded to match the speed of the upgraded test system? For example, DUT handling may need to be automated so that it does not slow down test time out of proportion to productivity gains in the system itself.

As with any system upgrade decision, you should go ahead with the upgrade only if the benefits outweigh all the costs involved. Some systems perform very well as they are and for these, the costs of an upgrade would not be matched by the overall productivity gain in the test process.

18.5   Evaluating the Current Software

Evaluating how much of your software is re-usable is an important step in the system upgrade process, as software development is generally a major component of the system development or upgrade cost. If thorough development procedures were followed when the system was originally designed, then the software will be well-documented.

If the software for your system is modular, then it may retain a lot of value in its existing form. You need to look at how modular it is: Are the measurements modular or are the entire test routines modular, as there are various definitions of modularity. The measurements themselves should be self-contained and include the setup time for test equipment as well as the measurement itself and the process of returning data to the central computer and storing it somewhere – such as a spreadsheet or database. If the test routines are modular, you may have problems; the test routines generally contain all the measurements to make up the tests for a DUT. Any new DUT will have to have the measurements written again. It would be easier if the test routine called the measurement routines when needed, that way, the test routines would then manage a number of tests, then deliver all those results to the Test Executive.

The test routines can be easily added to by adding new measurements or existing measurements to them. Generally, the further you break down measurements, the easier it is to build them up to a test routine – however, the opposite is not true.

Evaluating whether the existing software will work with new equipment also needs to be done thoroughly. In some circumstances, trying out the equipment will be your only source of complete certainty that the software will still work as intended. Even then, any new code will still need to be tested to make sure that it will work as well. See also Section 18.6, "Old Software and New Equipment."

Chapter 17, "Using Standard Software and Open Standards for Obsolescence Protection," discusses interoperability and the re-use of software in more detail.

If little or no documentation exists for the test system software, then the time and costs involved in working out how the software is structured so that you can evaluate whether it can be upgraded will be immense. Under these conditions, it will often be more effective to rewrite the software from scratch – documenting it properly this time, of course. In general, try to keep the system as simple as possible, and have all the measurements as sub-routines that can be added together to form a test routine for a particular DUT. This way, the objective of each measurement is more easily understood, and building new routines is a matter of putting measurements together to get the desired results.

18.6   Old Software and New Equipment

Under some circumstances, such as a new model of a piece of test equipment with a superset of functionality of the previous model, one could expect that the old software should still work with the new equipment. Small changes in functionality, however, can cause problems with software execution, and it is important to test the old software with the new hardware before relying on the upgrade.

It may happen that an equipment vendor makes equipment upgrades to new models without completely analyzing the implications of any changes. One upgrade encountered by the authors involved a model that was described as having an unchanged instruction set and that it was a direct drop-in replacement for the previous model. However, it caused problems in the test system because the manufacturer of the test equipment did not check to see whether the new model took the same time to transact each instruction. This led to problems for the test system contractor, and the vendor was mystified by the whole problem for some time as well.

The vendor may not be able to test the new equipment under the full range of conditions that the contractor will subject it to. The combinations of conditions are so vast that it is unkind to expect the vendor to fully implement all the conditions of the previous range of equipment.

Chapter 17, "Using Standard Software and Open Standards for Obsolescence Protection," discusses test system lifetime, planning for future requirements, and obsolescence protection.

18.7   Calibration and Certification

Obsolescence of equipment by the original manufacturer does not make it unsupportable, nor does it stop it from being calibrated. Indeed, devices that are decades old can be calibrated if their original specifications are known. The ability of a piece of test equipment to be calibrated does not have any relation to obsolescence at all.

Certification of equipment normally refers to the calibration documentation. However, you will need to have all your documentation intact. If the original equipment supplier cannot supply a description of the calibration procedures used, then you will have to rely on your original manuals for procedures or have them rewritten to an industry-acceptable standard. This is expensive and time-consuming if your record-keeping is not up-to-date.

If you have the original specifications and no procedures, then a good calibration laboratory can generate new procedures easily. If you have no original specifications, then you have to make some assumptions about the equipment's ability and then test these against physical tests. In the short term, you will have to have very short calibration cycles (possibly six months) to assure yourself or your testing house that the assumptions are valid and the equipment actually can perform the measurements asked of it. Some devices as they get older will have components that decay, such as the movement jewel in the axle of a moving pointer device. It may not be able to respond with the same accuracy, as the jewel bearing for the axle wears and gives greater variation to the movement of the pointer. This does not make it useless, rather it degrades the usefulness of the device.

Calibration refers to the recording of the difference between a standard and the device being calibrated. The differences are recorded and are judged to be within the accepted parameters or outside of them. The certification certificate comes from the body doing the calibration for you; they must be able to withstand an audit of their calibration traceability. The devices they use to calibrate your equipment must have their calibration results recorded against calibrated instruments better than yours, which in turn are always calibrated against instruments which are better still – all the way back to national standards. Should one of your measurements be questioned while you are within the time limit of your calibration, you should assume there is no failure electrically. You must then be able to challenge your certification authority to prove they have indeed calibrated to a national standard. Most calibration facilities have their ultimate standards, called transfer standards, calibrated by the national authority, who uses what are called artifacts. Artifacts are natural devices that produce a standard quantity. Most standards are derived from a limited number of quantities, derived from physical laws. For example, frequency is derived from time, which is derived from so many oscillations of electrons at a certain level of the Cesium 134 atom – it is absolute and does not change.

Calibration is essential to measurement; you cannot design a test system that will be producing devices that if measured somewhere else will yield a different result.

18.8   When to Consider a Complete Rebuild

If you reach the stage with your system where there are a number of issues with obsolete equipment, particularly if you cannot get it repaired any longer, then you should evaluate the complete system to decide if it needs to be upgraded or completely rebuilt. Rebuilding the system from the ground up may also be quicker and thus cheaper than an upgrade if you have no documentation. New technology may also allow rebuilding to give you a more valuable outcome. A complete rebuild will generally be necessary if the following conditions are met:

- You cannot test to desired speeds.
- Test equipment is costing more to maintain and calibrate than new equipment.
- Software platforms are no longer available – there may be newer and better ones.
- Software upgrades are becoming costly to perform in both time and money.
- You can no longer get access to people who have the skills for your older software platform.
- You have all the original design data for your measurements.
- You want to add more equipment and you do not have the room.
- You want to automate a system that was not built for it; for example, a manual system that was not designed with future automation upgrades in mind.
- You want to move from a bench manual system to a fully-automated one.
- You want to make your system transportable, and it was not in your original design.
- Newer test equipment will save you time and money by upgrading.

CHAPTER 19

Interface, Rack Layout, and Software Revision for an Upgraded Test System

$\mathbf{T}$his final chapter considers some aspects of the system upgrade strategy, and goes through the process of designing the layout and racking a system upgrade, including tips on how to make the upgrade as simple as possible.

KEY POINTS:

- Equipment may become obsolete for a number of reasons – some of which may be difficult to predict – but you can plan a system upgrade strategy that will help you manage any necessary transitions more easily.
- Your upgrade strategy may have to consider measurement techniques, documentation, rack layout, hardware and software upgrades, and training and support.

19.1   Replacing Equipment

During the working life of a test system, you will often reach the end of life of one or more items of test equipment or other test system components. It may be that improved models of particular test equipment have become available, and if the benefits offered by the equipment outweigh the cost of purchasing it and upgrading the test system, then a system upgrade to take advantage of the new features makes sense. Test equipment improvements may come in the form of increased speed or new measurement features that allow users to obtain more useful results. An equipment breakdown may also be an appropriate time to evaluate whether an upgrade rather than a replacement would be most suitable. Alternatively, the manufacturers may have obsoleted a piece of test equipment. This can occur for several reasons, which may include:

- Shortage of components required to build that equipment.
- Release of improved models.
- End of the guaranteed support life for that model.
- Declining market for that product.

Chapter 18, "Dealing with Obsolete Items," discusses strategies for selecting replacement equipment or stocking spares, as well as evaluating existing software for upgrading or replacement. Here, the process of integrating that new equipment into an existing system is discussed.

Upgrading a test system differs from designing a completely new system in that there will be a number of existing parameters for the engineer to deal with. Equipment placement, racking, and interface decisions made for the first system design may or may not be appropriate for the upgraded system.

The approach to use when re-racking a system will depend on the reasons for upgrading it in the first place. If the upgrade was done to gain performance enhancements (either the primary reason for the upgrade, or as a result of another reason such as unavailability of spare parts for the system's current equipment), then you will either be integrating new test equipment, or the same test equipment but a newer model. If the replacement equipment is a model enhancement, then it should simply slide into the existing rack arrangement (although any control software should be properly checked – see the discussion of interoperability in Chapter 17). If the replacement is new equipment entirely (a different brand or a different type of equipment), then the implications on control software, training, and method of measurement need to be determined.

Factors to consider include:

- The measurement method used may need to change to take advantage of new technology, better performance, or updated practices – this will result in benefits such as speed enhancement in taking the measurement or more accurate measurements.
- Training will need to be updated to ensure operators are familiar with any new equipment and any new test methodology.
- Control software may need to be modified to take advantage of the speed increase (if the timing of tests can be modified to shorten the overall test time), any commands that are different (if the new equipment uses different command terminology), or new test methodology (if the equipment has additional features or capabilities that will be used). This is one of the advantages of TPSs that allow separate programs to control individual tests, thus allowing a modular software upgrade path.
- If it is the computer you are upgrading, then speed of commands and operation may affect the use of other devices.
- Finally, the documentation will need to be modified to reflect the new system. This is not a trivial task and should be carried out at the same time as the system upgrade – not delayed to a later time.

If you have more than one test system of the same design, it is a good practice, if possible, to run the old and new versions (i.e., one original version system and one upgraded test system) against each other for a while to compare results, before fully committing to the new system.

If the test system is being upgraded because required equipment is no longer available or no longer supported by the manufacturer, then this could be a good time to consider alternative form factors such as VXI if the system does not take full advantage of open standards. Transition to an open standard such as VXI can typically take place while still largely running the test system as it is. For example, if the current model voltmeter in a system is no longer available, then a VXI one that will allow the rest of the existing test system hardware to run could be set up; however, the VXI voltmeter will function when required. If the system's counter then fails at a later time, a replacement could be purchased in VXI form factor and added to the VXI voltmeter in the VXI cardcage. This method allows continuous improvement over time, while not requiring the designer or operator to replace the whole system because of some unavailable equipment. The additional benefit from this method is a reduced racking size. Once again, all documentation will need to be updated to reflect the changes.

One of the advantages to keeping the existing rack is that test system users feel comfortable with its operation and "look and feel." As a designer of test systems, never underestimate the thoughts of the operator. Keeping to the existing rack allows users to upgrade gradually as new functionally equivalent sections are added. Remember that test systems should have a whole-of-life support plan and an upgrade plan. All too often, these are left as afterthoughts, causing problems when test instruments are no longer supported by manufacturers. The other advantage of a gradual increase in capability is that training is more gradual, allowing operators time to settle in with the new equipment while still enjoying the familiarity of a known environment. There is also less chance of downtime with a gradual improvement process rather than one global overhaul.

If the initial test system design was carried out with the possibility of future upgrades in mind, then there will be a number of advantages during the upgrade process. Good documentation of the original test system design is the most important factor that will allow an easy test system upgrade. Other advantages that will come from a well-designed system rack-up include: well-labeled cables with spares for future additions, good grouping of equipment with functional similarities, and a well-balanced rack, as it will be less likely to topple if just one piece of equipment is removed if the whole rack was well-balanced in the first place.

An existing racked system that is well-designed will mean that the advantages of keeping much of the existing rack arrangements are greater. A poorly designed system may require a full dismantling of the test system and re-racking from scratch. Essentially, poor work requires a total redesign.

Section 19.2 discusses evaluating the existing switch interface based on an updated test parameters matrix (the process for updating the matrix is described in Chapter 18). Section 19.3 deals with how to redesign the rack layout to allow for updated switching and any new test equipment or other test system components. Sections 19.4 and 19.5 cover aspects of updating software for a semi-automated or fully-automated test system. Section 19.6, "Updating Documentation," is just as important for a test system upgrade as good documentation is important to an initial test system design.

19.2   Evaluating the Existing Switch Interface

When your organization's production outputs or test requirements become more complex and new DUTs are added, the test system may need additional leads and connections to them as a function of new test requirements or of the tested equipment. As this occurs, you will need to evaluate whether your switch matrix can handle the additional connections at the present time. The current configuration may not be capable of supporting additional signal paths. There may also be upgrade needs for much higher frequency or higher voltages or currents.

TIP:

The more switches you add, the less signal you eventually have to work with – don't add switches to a system unless they are necessary.

To evaluate the existing switch interface:

• Develop a new test parameters matrix, as the capabilities of the test system equipment may have changed (this is described in Chapter 18). When determining the new test parameters matrix, be careful not to ignore the switching matrix. The switching is one of the most important components of a test system, but it is too often overlooked. If the new equipment or test matrix calls for additional switching or modified switching, this must be accomplished first. If the ATE is fully-automated, the switch control will need to be verified first that it can actually achieve the new requirements. Modular switches that can be expanded within "modules" are ideal for systems that need continual upgrading, since they can be expanded to meet future requirements instead of buying a new switch or adding on additional independent switches. Remember that each switch degrades the measurement by a small margin. Because of this, the designer should pay careful attention when modifying switches.

• Compare the interface to the original (back to the importance of configuration control and documentation). After the new switch is chosen, the drivers must be written for it if they do not already exist.

• Redesign your switching to add new signals to the DUT as required. Group all the additional switched lines into their functional classes, create the driver, and then test. Always ensure that the paths are fully tested – you may also want to check the isolation by measuring on parallel paths while injecting signal into the main path.

> TIP:
>
> Avoid building the switch matrix and supporting it yourself. It may seem an apparently easy task, but it is probably the worst support task on a test system.

19.3   Redesigning the Rack Layout

When redesigning the rack layout to allow for updated switching and new test equipment, some or much of the existing system layout can be kept for the upgrade – depending how well the original test system was designed with a view to future upgrades.

A number of components will hopefully be worth keeping. If the equipment is still functional and meeting specifications, then it can generally remain as part of the upgraded system. If it is failing to meet your test environment's evolving standards (which may be increased speed, higher performance, or system up-time), then replacement of the equipment should be part of the system upgrade plan. Key components in the system or components that have long mean time to repair (MTTR) should have backup designed into the test system as part of the upgrade if it does not already exist. For example, you may become aware of key equipment that has a long MTTR during the life of the original system.

Hence, these areas should be designed for easy upgrade or modification. The software interface should be maintained during upgrades so that operators are not continually learning new interfaces. The equipment behind the interface can change, but control of the look and feel of the system should be maintained as much as possible.

The cabling should remain unless it absolutely needs to be replaced or modified, since this may require large amounts of engineering time. Generally, the racks can stay unless they have suffered an unusual degree of wear or damage.

Some test system components are a logical choice for replacement with any system upgrade. The computer can typically be replaced for an upgraded model; however, it should be capable of running the existing software without modification, as the software designer's aim should have been to allow modular updating of the system software. Low-maintenance components such as power supplies are easily obtained and as such would probably not be on the replacement list. Any equipment that will still be supported by the manufacturer for the life of the system and that is still meeting performance can stay in the system. However, if improved models become available that give good cost benefit in terms of price or performance, then they should be considered as replacements.

The new system should meet any improved or updated requirements without the need to change the operator interface. The look and feel of the test system should remain as close as possible to what the operator is used to. The work area should remain constant so that established efficiency is at least retained and hopefully improved as a result of the upgrade. There is no value in upgrading the test system if any advantages are lost; for example, through poor repositioning of the work surface so the operator takes longer to position and connect the DUT. All connections and patch panels should stay as close as possible to maintain established operation patterns.

Power to the rack and the environmental condition of the rack must also be checked during a system upgrade. The power supply to the test system may need to be upgraded to take new equipment into account. Remember that power strips may need an additional GPO connected (do not ignore relevant safety standards), and new equipment may require a different heating and cooling profile. This should be dealt with as part of your system redesign. Additional fans may be required because more equipment is running in the rack. The physical stability of the racks will need to be re-examined also, particularly if test equipment is replaced or moved to a new position within the rack.

During the physical upgrade installation process, always have a diagram to work from with rack units clearly shown. Use cardboard cutouts with labels as "stand-ins" for new equipment if any positioning for the new system needs to be checked. Place these over the existing equipment for a trial run. Have a plan for the upgrade that includes tests which can verify the operation of the system. Do not remove everything and then replace it all and expect it to work immediately. After you replace a piece of test equipment or other system component, verify it in the system. This will allow the old inputs and outputs to be connected to ensure operation.

Start from the top of the rack when you dismantle it – or remove any equipment – it's good practice not to leave heavy items high in the rack; remove them then re-install later, as it seriously affects the safety of the ATE.

The switch or any other components that have a number of cables attached to them should be labeled as they are disconnected. There are lots of labels that can be attached for short-term application with rubber bands. This will re-inforce the labels that should already be on the cables, and can back up that information with any extra notes that will help keep track of equipment and connections during the re-racking process.

The cable labeling system that was used when the original test system was designed and built may use a positional labeling system, for example "RUB34-C2" for the cable that connects to the instrument positioned at rack unit B, position 34, to the unit in rack unit C position 2. Many organizations have their own in-house codes that work very well. The cabling reference diagram and table in the system documentation should make all these details clear. However, while dismantling the old and re-racking the newly upgraded system, it will probably be more helpful to add a temporary label that includes functional information as well, such as "rack 1 spectrum analyzer –RF output". This, however, is a personal choice that is left to the designer or the engineer carrying out the upgrade. However, if the existing labeling system is cumbersome or has already been replaced with a new one in your organization, then the system upgrade is an ideal point at which to update the labeling and documentation as well as the test system itself. The same applies if new or spare cables are being used in the system.

When the new component is secured in the rack, begin by reconnecting each cable, and if possible, test immediately to make sure that the component is functioning. Then, mark this section off on your plan and diagram with a highlighter. If you no longer need a particular cable, remove it if possible, as it will only end up confusing someone at a later date –spare cables should already be built in and labeled as such.

Continue to work through the upgrades in this manner. If you have an original system, run the two systems side by side for a while to ensure there are no problems. Have your training and documentation for the new system prepared ahead of the system upgrade so that operators are not left to try to run the system based on their own knowledge of the old version of the test system. Some sample DUTs that are known to be working and some known not to be working (preferably with the specific faults known as well) will help out enormously here to verify whether the test system as a whole still functions properly.

Completing the process by carefully updating all documentation is vital. Once you are satisfied that everything is in order, remove all outdated documentation, instructions, posters, and other material, and replace with the new ones for that test system.

Always take note of and follow any local or organizational regulations for the proper disposal or recycling of any components no longer required for the test system.

19.4　Adding New Software Drivers

Updating software drivers will be part of the upgrade process if new equipment is installed, new functionality of existing equipment (that may not have been included in the original driver) is accessed in the new system, or if a new model of the same test equipment comes with a different software driver.

Adding new drivers to the software suite should be done in accordance with logical checks before the process is begun:

- Check versions of the operating system (if it is NT™ or Linux®, etc.) and the revision levels. Ensure that your driver is compatible; for example, if it is for Windows 3.1, it may not be compatible with Windows 95.
- Ensure that you understand the linkages that need to be performed to link to the operating software (the software that runs the TPS); for example, there may be internal memory settings required and polling request addresses to set.
- Check all addressing information so the driver can link to the item of test equipment.

Run a beta test version first (beta testing is done with an outside party to the software design team, who carry out alpha test) – ensuring that the operators are aware that it is a beta version – so that a log can be kept of any problems encountered with the code. Again, compare known results from good and bad DUTs with results from the new code to ensure that all is well.

If you use a UNIX environment, then shared libraries are convenient to use, as new code can be included without the need to recompile the whole code. Windows has a similar concept with DLLs (dynamic linked libraries). Try to keep the code modular so that it can be easily understood. Have printouts of what the code is doing and what version it is during testing phases so that its progress can be followed.

Please note that use should be made of software-specific references and expertise, as this volume focuses on test system hardware rather than software.

One of the easiest ways for engineers to add code is via an existing "plug-and-play" driver. However, full documentation on the driver is required to be certain that it will control all the functions you need. You can use a high-level development environment such as HP VEE™ to quickly prototype the program, and then reduce it to a language. Once this is done, the module can be added into the program. The services of a software engineer are recommended whenever code is being developed, as this is a non-trivial task.

If you write your own drivers, then you only need to write in the functionality that you need to meet your test requirements. When you get drivers from shareware Web sites and even equipment vendors, do not assume complete functionality in the driver. The person who wrote it may have only written the functions they required; for example, the driver for a complex oscilloscope that only controls five functions of a possible sixty. The only way to assess the driver is to test it for your application. This can be tedious and you have to have a lot of equipment at your disposal if your item of test equipment is complex.

TIP:

If you contract a third party to write a software driver, be careful to specify exactly what functionality you require in the driver. If you don't need full functionality, then the cost will be much lower if you contract just for a partial driver.

19.5   Updating Software Modules

Adding new measurements to a test system as the products you test become more advanced and/ or as you take advantages of new features in test equipment is a normal process in the lifetime support of a test system. It is likely that you will add new equipment and software capability at the same time, so a careful planning process is important to make the upgrade as straightforward as possible. Software modules are normally installed under the control of the Test Executive. The new TPS module may also include new drivers for devices, or more extensive versions of existing drivers to get more capability out of current test equipment.

The new software modules may carry out other tasks, such as data backups over remote connections or networking of the test system into a site management system. There are a number of advantages to be gained from this level of added capability, particularly from features that will improve the data management capability of your organization.

Tasks of this type work at a higher level than a driver, which is test equipment-specific. This deals with the level of software that calls the drivers of test equipment to carry out various tasks. There may be existing routines in the system already that the new module can make use of – check your documentation to determine how best to map in the new module. It has to seamlessly link into the system so that results from the module's activity can be added to the required output, stored, and processed.

Sometimes modules can be added by a call to another module outside the TPS suite. This may then perform a set function and return the results to the Test Executive. However, this would be an isolated process as you would have trouble trying to control two items of test equipment from two different sources – so when you use calls to remote modules, the test equipment you are calling is usually not integrated into the system.

Try to re-use modules of code if possible. Few test engineers completely enjoy cutting code, so where appropriate, cut and paste as much as possible without degrading your new module. When you do cut and paste, however (as well as when you cut code from scratch), make sure that the test is run in a logical manner, and takes advantage of the speed and throughput available in the system and the test equipment used. You may want to "tune" the module at a later stage for even better throughput, such as a minimum of range changes or other techniques that take advantage of your knowledge of the test technology involved. For example, a signal generator when set to a new frequency has a finite time before that new frequency is stable – you may find that your accuracy requirement is met even before the device has fully settled. Many vendors will even specify such features; for example, full accuracy of the specification in 100 ms, and 90% of the specification in 20 ms. The other 80 ms are being held by the vendor to get the best publishable specification for their datasheet while still allowing equipment users as much flexibility as possible in their use of the equipment. If your requirement is only for 90% of the available specification (the specification of the signal generator may exceed your needs by a long way), then you can elect under your software module to terminate the test when you are satisfied that the required accuracy has been met.

19.6 Updating Documentation

Any time that changes are made to your system, the documentation must be updated – if this is not done immediately, then undocumented changes can cause problems for operators as well as maintenance and repair staff who need to work on the system. Even minor changes must be documented. If they are not, and someone working on the system encounters the discrepancy, then the status of the rest of the system may be in doubt. It can also be dangerous to put people in a position where they are asked to work on unknown configurations. In addition, any further changes – even if documented – will bury the undocumented changes until a time comes when engineers will have to reverse-engineer the test system to determine its current status and condition.

Its impossible to understand what the designers were trying to do or how they did it if no documentation is provided. Reverse-engineering to establish exactly what test process is being used in a system can take months. Good documentation should lead to relatively easy changes to your systems when needed. Any organization should have a rigid process to ensure that the quality of the documentation is upheld, and does not become sloppy over time. Military standards (Mil Std), evolved from the U.S. Space program and U.S. military due to their need to have items coming in from thousands of vendors work smoothly together. When everyone has to use the same process, and when the individual documentation of each item is added together, it all adds in seamlessly. Otherwise, your manuals will be a mixture of styles and formats, some good, some bad, where the biggest problem is consistency.

As people cycle through system areas, there will be an ongoing need for updating or replacing items, even as simple as a cable or connector. If all the changes over the years are done to the same documentation standard, then the system's life is likely to be extended as long as components are available. Eventually, every system retires, as it cannot keep up with all the changes needed and it becomes a simpler job to build a new test system than to completely refurbish an old one. Generally, the new one should be being built while the old one is running down.

When you build your new system, you can retain all the base of measurement of your old system. What you need to redesign is the way you will control your test equipment and interfaces. Your documentation of measurements will serve you well here as they will retain all the parameters and how and why they are being tested.

Bibliography

Abid, Mohamed and Ahmed Jerraya. 1997. Towards Hardware-Software Co-Design: A Case of Robot Arm Controller. *Journal of Microelectronic Systems Integration.* Vol. 5, No. 3, p167.

Alderson, Norton W. 1997. Switching Considerations When Testing High-Speed Digital Devices. *Evaluation Engineering.* July 1997, p50.

Anderson, Dwight. 1998. Accelerated Design Verification and VXI Maker a Perfect Match. *Electronic Design.* September 14, 1998, p94.

Beane, Mike. 1998. VXI Platform Reduces Compatibility Concerns in System Design. *Evaluation Engineering.* June 1998, p35.

Bennett, Paul. 1996. What Test-Management Software Can Do For You. *Evaluation Engineering.* May 1996.

Buetow, Mike. 1997. Dual-Use Specifications: Mission Impossible? *Circuits Assembly.* January 1997, p30.

Cashar, E. Elaine. 1997. Development of a TPS Reuse Library Using COTS Tools. *IEEE AES Systems Magazine.* October 1997, pp12-16.

Colton, Glen. 1998. Uncovering Hidden Costs: The Challenge of Test System Development Programmes for Automotive Electronics Manufacturers. *Environmental Engineering.* December 1998, p11.

Degan, Ken and Doug Perkins. 1998. An Integrated Approach to VXI Test. *Evaluation Engineering.* May 1998, p24.

De Maine, Paul A. D., K. D. Bradley, W. H. Carlisle and W. B. Dress. 1995. Integrated Systems I: Design Principles. *Journal of Systems Integration.* Vol. 5, pp187-199.

De Maine, Paul A. D. 1995. Integrated Systems II: Multi-tier Interfaces for Integrating Families of Systems. *Journal of Systems Integration.* Vol. 5, pp201-217, 1995.

Doherty, Brian J. 1996. A Guide to Selecting ATE Power Supplies. *Evaluation Engineering.* November 1996, p140.

Drenkow, Grant. 1998. 10 Years of Development Bring Cost Savings to VXI. *Evaluation Engineering.* February 1998, p37.

Elder, William and Paul Dhillon. 1997. VXI-Based Simulator Designed for International Space Station. *Evaluation Engineering.* December 1997.

Feng, Shaw C. and Yuhwei Yang. 1995. A dimension and Tolerance Data Model for Concurrent Design and Systems Integration. *Journal of Manufacturing Systems.* Vol. 14, No. 6, 1995, p406.

Fluke Corporation. *Calibration: Philosophy in Practice* (2nd ed.). 1994.

Frank, Allan. 1995. Standards Key to System Integration. *Data Management Review.* Vol. 5, No. 10, p22.

Guentner, Steve and Jerrold V. Birbal. 1996. How VXI is Impacting Mil-Std-1533 Testing. *Evaluation Engineering.* December 1996, p22.

Haas, Jim. 1998. Design a Reusable Test Executive. *Test & Measurement World.* August 1998, p37.

Haworth, David. 1996. VXIplug&play Provides Programming Benefits. *Evaluation Engineering.* July 1996, p40.

Hiller, Paul and Joseph McDonough. 1996. Managing Turnkey Test-System Development, Part 1. *Evaluation Engineering.* April 1996, p90.

Hiller, Paul and Joseph McDonough. 1996. Managing Test-System Development, Part 2. *Evaluation Engineering.* July 1996, p136.

Hubbard, G. Scott, Alan B. Binder and William Feldman. 1998. The Lunar Prospector Discovery Mission: Mission and Measurement Description. *IEEE Transactions on Nuclear Science.* Vol. 45, No. 3, June 1998, p880.

Jacob, Gerald. 1998. Successful Systems Integration Requires Multiple Commitments. *Evaluation Engineering.* July 1998.

Kelly, Leslie (Ed). *The ASTD Technical and Skills Training Handbook.* New York: McGraw Hill, 1995.

Kochut, Krys J., Amit P. Sheth and John A. Miller. 1999. *Component Strategies.* March 1999, p45.

Krasovec, George and Steven Howell. 1995. *Journal of Systems Integration.* Vol. 5, pp309-339.

Maher, Michael C. 1994. The DOD COTS Directive—What About Radiation Hardness? *Defense Electronics.* October 1994, p29.

McConnell, Ed. 1997. The Future of Virtual Instrumentation. *Sensors.* July 1997, p22.Elder, William and Paul Dhillon. 1997. VXY-Based Simulator Designed for International Space Station. *Evaluation Engineering.* December 1997.

Mead, Jay. 1998. Measuring the Value Added by Technical Documentation: A Review of Research and Practice. *Technical Communication.* Vol. 45, No. 3, p353.

Miller, Ted and Thomas J. Gallagher. 1998. VXI-Based Functional ATE Shortens Test Times. *Evaluation Engineering.* July 1998.

Oblad, Roger P. 1997. Applying New Software Technologies to Solve Key System Integration Issues. *AUTOTESTCON-1997 Proceedings.* Piscataway, NJ, IEEE, p181-189.

Oblad, Roger P. 1999. Achieving Robust Interchangeability of Test Assets in ATE Systems. *AUTOTESTCON-1999 Proceedings.* Piscataway, NJ, IEEE, p687-698.

Rowe, Martin. 1997. Lunar Prospector Tester Simulates Moon and Sun. *Test & Measurement World.* August 1997, p12.

Rothwell, William J. and Peter S. Cookson. 1997. *Beyond Instruction.* San Francisco: Jossey-Bass.

Sacher, Eric. 1997. A system View of VXI ATE Design. *Evaluation Engineering.* January 1997, p42

Stout, Melville B. 1960. *Basic Electrical Measurements* (2nd ed.). Englewood Cliffs, NJ: Prentice-Hall.

Thibeault, C. 1995. Using Fourier Analyses to Enhance IC Testability. *Journal of Microelectronic Systems Integration.* Vol. 3, No. 2, p83.

Wang, Huaiqing. 1997. Intelligent Agent-Assisted Decision Support Systems: Integration of Knowledge Discovery, Knowledge Analysis, and Group Decision Support. *Expert Systems With Applications.* Vol. 12, No. 3, pp323-335.

Zimmermann, Charles H. 1999. Project Management Techniques for Effective Systems Integration. *Journal NEWWA.* March 1999, p30.

Index

U

V

W